The Practical Science of
PLANTING
TREES

The Practical Science of
PLANTING
TREES

Gary W. Watson,
The Morton Arboretum

E. B. Himelick,
University of Illinois and
Illinois Natural History Survey (Emeritus)

International Society of **Arboriculture**

International Society of Arboriculture
Champaign, Illinois, U.S.
217.355.9411
permissions@isa-arbor.com
www.isa-arbor.com

Editing: Edward Hargrove
Book Design and Layout: Diane Rigoli / RigoliCreative.com
Editorial and Production Manager: Amy Theobald
Illustrations: Bryan Kotwica
Cover Photographs: Gary W. Watson
Photographs on pages vi, viii, and x: Aaron H. Bynum

The majority of the photographs in this publication are by the authors. The contributions of additional photographers and illustrators are most appreciated and credit acknowledging their work is given near the image.

Printed by Premier Print Group

10 9 8 7 6 5 4 3 2

RF/10-15/1000

ISBN: 978-1-881956-73-0

Preface

Appropriately planted city streets, parks, industrial grounds, and residential areas provide a landscape that increases in value over the years and provides many benefits. To create a functional and beautiful landscape that will thrive and increase in value, one must have knowledge of plant materials with training and experience in their use. Careful selection and placement of plants, correct planting practices, and adequate maintenance to assure establishment and growth through maturity are all essential.

To acquire training in this field, students need a reference that describes transplanting procedures and the research behind them. This publication focuses on the research science supporting tree planting in order to go beyond instructions and help the reader understand why.

Every effort has been made to include all research published, even when studies seem to conflict. The inconsistency can sometimes be explained by narrow circumstances of each study, or it may be just that more research is needed to further clarify. This does point out the need for caution in extrapolating results of any single study. Sometimes, studies that only include a particular species, or in a specific climate, may establish principles, but those principles may not apply to every situation.

Acknowledgments

A 1943 publication entitled *Transplanting of Trees and Shrubs in the Northeastern and North Central United States* was published by the National Shade Tree Conference. It was prepared by a committee of several nationally recognized arborists and horticulturists. A second committee prepared a revision published in 1958.

In 1981, the publication was rewritten by E.B. Himelick and entitled *Tree and Shrub Transplanting Manual*. It was published by the same organization, now known as the International Society of Arboriculture. Revisions published in 1988 and 1991 were reviewed by several plant professionals throughout the United States.

Gary Watson joined Gene Himelick in updating the publication once again in 1997. The title was changed to *Principles and Practice of Planting Trees and Shrubs* to reflect the more extensive inclusion of a research supporting practices. Reviewers came from both academia and industry.

Many plant professionals throughout the United States provided constructive review comments at many stages during the preparation of this book. The authors are grateful to the following reviewers for their contributions:

Complete Manuscript Reviewers

Thomas Green, Western Illinois University
Angela Hewitt, The Morton Arboretum

Chapter Reviewers

Michael Arnold, Texas A&M University
Kris Bachtell, The Morton Arboretum
Julia Bartens, University of California–Davis
Nina Bassuk, Cornell University
Donita Bryan, University of Wisconsin–Platteville
Laurence Costello, University of California–Davis
Susan Day, Virginia Tech
Francesco Ferrini, University of Florence
Alessio Fini, University of Florence
Edward Gilman, University of Florida
Roger Harris, Virginia Tech
Roger Kjelgren, Utah State University
James Klett, Colorado State University
Andrew Koeser, University of Illinois at Urbana-Champaign
Peter May, University of Melbourne
Bryant Scharenbroch, The Morton Arboretum
Thomas Smiley, Bartlett Tree Research Laboratories
Daniel Struve, The Ohio State University
James Urban, Urban Trees + Soils
Keith Warren, J. Frank Schmidt & Son Co.

Table of Contents

Introduction

Six revisions of the original 1943 publication written in response to a request from the U.S. Army Camouflage Branch Engineer Board have documented changes in tree-planting practices. Equipment has improved. Trees are now grown in containers as well as in the field. Education of the workforce has improved. The biological and horticultural science that controls the response of trees to transplanting has not changed, though we have a greater understanding of it today. The 1997 publication was expanded to include more research support for planting practices. Much additional research has been published since then and is included in the extensive reference list for further reading by serious students.

This book is intended to help landscape professionals and gardeners alike to successfully plant trees. Information on the biology of the plant response during digging, planting, and establishment at the new site constitute the science of planting. Information is included that will help the reader to develop a basic understanding of how the transition to a new environment affects the trees. An understanding of the basic principles involved will be useful when encountering new situations. As much information as possible is presented, even if some of the cited research is unconfirmed or controversial.

It is recognized that at least 80% of landscape plant problems may originate below ground in the soil and root system. Most of them could be minimized or avoided completely through proper site preparation, selection, and planting. Improper planting has a profound effect on tree survival, health, and longevity. Up to 50% loss of trees within the five years of planting is not uncommon. The half-life of street trees in general ranged from 13–19 years, but for inner city trees on even more difficult sites was only 10–15 years (196, 474, 509). Lack of tree establishment leading to drought stress was found to be the most frequent cause of death (196, 556).

The focus is naturally on trees because they are larger, more difficult to move, and take longer to establish. The same principles apply to smaller plants. Chapters are organized by logical steps in the planting process.

CHAPTER 1

Understand the Challenges of Planting on Urban Sites

Evaluate site quality thoroughly. On this site, much of the construction debris was just covered with a thin layer of topsoil.

The first step in evaluating a potential planting site is to carefully and systematically observe and gather information. Is the site a high or low area? Just a few of inches of depression without a way for the water to drain away can create poorly drained soils during wet periods. A slightly elevated area or a gentle slope will probably drain better. Are there other trees and structures nearby that will create shade? What part of the day? Is it near pavement where the use of de-icing salt may be high? As you walk on the soil, does it feel soft or hard? Finally, what other plants are growing on the site, and how well are they growing? Simple observations can reveal a great deal about site conditions and help to select trees that will create a sustainable planting.

Elements of Nature in Urban Soils

Tree species are adapted to the environment in which they are found in nature. Few urban sites match any natural site or provide optimum conditions for tree growth. Natural soil profiles that took thousands of years to develop can be destroyed by heavy equipment in minutes (Figure 1-1). Nutrient cycling is disrupted by the removal of leaves and woody debris. Restricted soil volumes often limit root development. Aboveground environmental conditions can be extremely stressful when trees are exposed to heat and light reflected from surfaces. There may be exposure to soil and air pollutants not found in natural environments.

The differences between natural and urban sites were demonstrated when sugar maples (*Acer saccharum*) growing in a woodland were compared with trees planted on a college campus only 1 mile (1.6 km) away. Soil moisture, air temperature, leaf temperature, relative humidity, vapor pressure deficit, bulk density, pH, leaf nitrogen (N), potassium (K), and other nutrients were all less optimal in the built campus environment. Water stress was greater in campus trees and correlated with low soil moisture and high atmospheric demands. As a result, the campus trees had less growth and exhibited earlier fall color and leaf drop (108, 109).

Site characteristics can affect tree growth and longevity. Trees tend to have the shortest life spans in highly disturbed transportation corridors and commercial/industrial zones, followed by high-density residential areas. Low-density residential areas and parks generally have longer-lived trees (178, 179, 304, 324, 418).

Few urban planting sites are ideal, but some tree species can tolerate more severe site conditions than others. Species that require a narrow range of site conditions generally do not make the best urban trees. Early successional (pioneer) and bottomland (Figure 1-3) species are often the most adaptable to urban conditions. Unfortunately, some tree species that were most tolerant of adverse urban site conditions can no longer be planted because of introduced diseases

Figure 1-1 Natural soil profiles that took thousands of years to develop can be destroyed in minutes.

and pests (e.g., Dutch elm disease of *Ulmus* sp. and Emerald ash borer of *Fraxinus* sp.). Some have fallen out of favor because of undesirable characteristics (weak branch structure of *Ulmus pumila* and *Acer saccharinum*). Understanding and improving site conditions is becoming more important in order to support a greater diversity of species more difficult to grow in the urban environment. The first step in any successful tree planting project is to properly assess the conditions on the planting site. Only then will it be possible to make necessary site improvements and select appropriate species.

Figure 1-2 Poor quality urban sites may limit success of planting projects. Twenty years after this highway was built, the trees are still very small.

Soils and Plant Growth

Poor soil conditions frequently limit planting success. Poorly drained, clay soils, typical of many modern urban developments, require special planting procedures to improve survival and initial establishment. Trees may never be vigorous, or long-lived, when planted on highly disturbed sites. In contrast, trees can often be planted successfully with minimal effort in well-drained, friable (crumbly) soil found in undeveloped areas and in some older neighborhoods. Basic soil properties such as texture and structure have a great influence on the soil resources that support plant growth, such as water, aeration, and nutrient availability. Thorough discussions of urban soils are available (92, 127, 488).

Topsoil and Subsoil

The terms *topsoil* and *subsoil* are commonly used, but often not well-defined. It is usually assumed that topsoil is of higher quality than the subsoil, but the characteristics are often not adequately specified. Topsoil and subsoil properties are highly dependent on the soil characteristics described in this chapter. According to one report (66), quality topsoil should have:

- Loam texture (maximum 40% clay)
- Granular (crumb) structure
- High organic matter (approximately 5% by weight; 10% by volume)
- Good water percolation and aeration
- Moderately high water-holding capacity
- High nutrient content
- No herbicides or other contaminants.

Figure 1-3 Species that grow on floodplains in nature are often the most adaptable to urban conditions.

Subsoil, by default, is of lesser quality, and the transition between topsoil and subsoil can be very abrupt, particularly in a modified urban soil where a thin layer of topsoil has been spread after the land was developed. The subsoil should have structure to permit good drainage, but this is not always the case after site development.

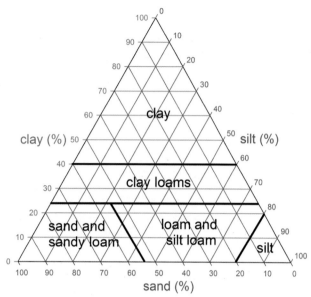

	Clay	Silt	Sand & Sandy Loam	Clay Loam	Loam & Silt Loam
Air space	low	low	high	moderate	moderate
Drainage	very slow	slow	rapid	moderate	moderately slow
Infiltration	very slow	moderately slow	rapid	moderately rapid	moderately slow
Compactability	high	very high	low	moderate	moderately high
Nutrient capacity	very high	high	low	moderate	moderate
Tilth	poor	poor	good	very good	good

Figure 1-4 The soil texture triangle (Modified USDA Classification, Bryant Scharenbroch).

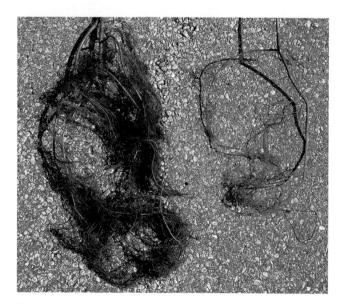

Figure 1-5 When moisture and nutrients are adequate, root development can be quite extensive in sandy soil (left) when compared to a compacted clay soil (right).

Soil Texture

Soil *texture* is the ratio of particle sizes (sand, silt, and clay) in a soil (Figure 1-4). Sandy textured soils are composed mostly of larger particles (0.05–2.0 mm). They are loose, easy to work, and readily permit water and air percolation, but they have low nutrient and water-holding capacity. These characteristics can result in a rapid breakdown of organic matter and the loss of some plant nutrients through leaching. Slow growth of urban trees has been linked to underlying sand and gravel (324), but when moisture and nutrients are adequate, root development can be quite extensive in sandy soils (Figure 1-5).

Clay soils are composed of many microscopic particles (<0.002 mm) and have characteristics opposite of sandy soils. Water is held tenaciously, resulting in slow drainage. Air exchange is slow, resulting in reduced root growth and slow decomposition of organic matter and release of nutrients. Some plant nutrients may be tightly bound to the clay particles. Clay soil is easily compacted, which can severely inhibit root penetration.

Silt particle sizes are intermediate between those of sand and clay (0.002–0.05 mm). Silty soils can also be compacted and poorly drained.

When the particles of sand, silt, and clay are in such proportions that the properties of no one group predominates, the soil is called a loam. In these soils, the excessive porosity of sand and the undesirable compactability of clay are favorably modified. Figure 1-6 illustrates how to determine soil texture by feel.

Soil Structure

The term *structure* refers to the manner in which the sand, silt, and clay particles are arranged or grouped together. These groups are called aggregates and can be of many sizes and shapes. Well-structured soils have spaces between aggregates that provide optimum air and water movement through the soil and provide space for root growth (Figure 1-7). Organic compounds hold the soil particles together in the aggregates, even when wet (Figure 1-8). Poorly structured soils are common in developed landscapes after the soil has been moved and trafficked by heavy equipment, or pulverized intentionally. Incorporating organic materials—such as compost—into soils with high clay content, along with proper cultivation, can help to encourage aggregate formation, making them more suitable for root growth.

Soil structure is important for root growth. Figure 1-9 illustrates how soil structure influences the amount of plant growth. In soil with the original structure preserved, tree growth in the topsoil layer (0–12 inches, 0–30 cm) and the first clayey subsoil layer (12–20 inches, 30–50 cm) is vigorous.

Soil Texture by Feel Method

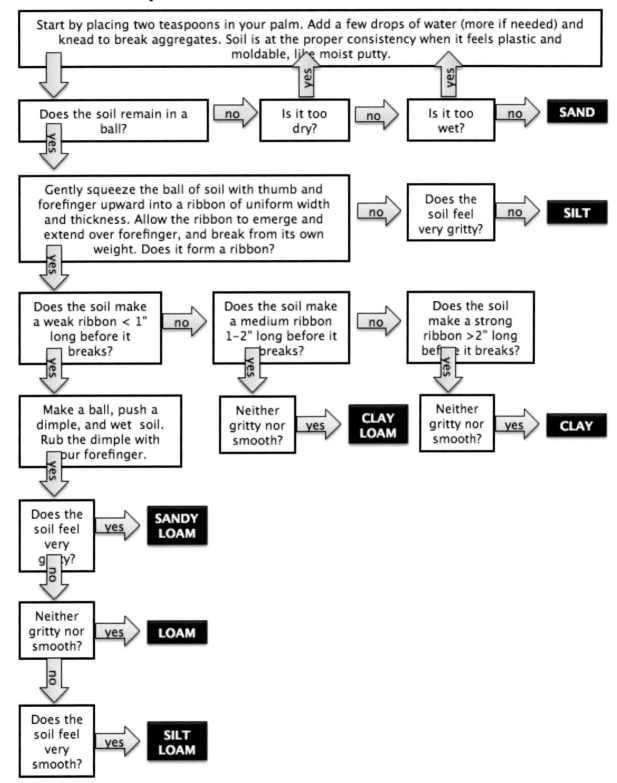

Figure 1-6 Determining soil texture by feel (Modified from: S.J. Thien, 1979).

A root is emerging
from a natural crack.

Figure 1-7 Soil structure creates cracks that may be the only place that roots can grow, especially in dense, clayey soils.

Figure 1-9 Soil structure is important. When destroyed (right), plant growth in soil from all three layers is reduced dramatically. Note that growth in the deepest subsoil with structure maintained is as good as—or better than—any of the soil layers without structure.

Figure 1-8 When dry, both well aggregated (A) and poorly aggregated (C) soils may look similar after cultivation. When wetted, the well aggregated soil "crumbs" hold together (B), while "crumbs" of the poorly aggregated soil do not (D).

Only in the deepest subsoil layer (>20 inches, 50–80 cm) is growth reduced. When soil structure is destroyed, growth in the same topsoil is reduced by more than half. Plants struggle to survive in both of the clayey subsoil layers. The poor growth above ground reflects poor root growth in the soil without structure. Subsoil with poor structure is often what remains to grow trees in after a site is regraded by heavy equipment.

Soil Factors Limiting Plant Growth

The factor that is the most limited in supply will limit plant growth (Figure 1-10). Soil texture and structure play an important role in a soil's ability to provide basic growth factors for trees. Water is most often the limiting factor during the growing season. If water is adequate, a nutrient deficiency can limit growth. In the dormant season, temperature limits growth. A shortage of carbohydrates produced by photosynthesis in the leaves can also limit growth. When all physical and chemical factors are non-limiting, growth may be limited by genetic potential.

Compaction

Compaction is common in urban soils. Once a soil is compacted, it may take decades for natural weathering processes to reverse it. Compaction by heavy equipment is commonly recognized, but foot traffic can also cause serious compaction. Soil compaction commonly occurs in parks and public places. Bulk density (mass divided by volume) of soil on the National Mall in Washington, D.C. was measured at 2.2 g/cc, the same as concrete (426). Bulk densities as low as 1.5 g/cc have been associated with reduced tree growth (310). The

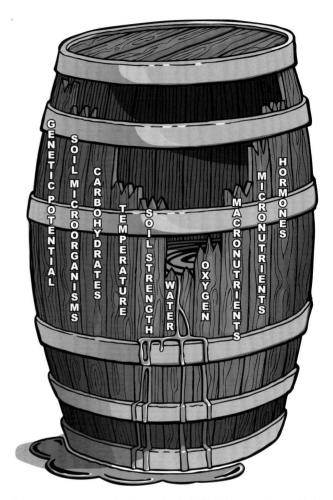

Figure 1-10 Any growth factor that is in limiting supply can limit growth, just as the height of water in a barrel is limited by the shortest stave.

Table 1-1 General relationship of soil bulk density to root growth based on soil texture (420).

Soil texture	Ideal bulk densities (g/cm³)	Bulk densities that may affect root growth (g/cm³)	Bulk densities that restrict root growth (g/cm³)
Sands, loamy sands	<1.60	1.69	>1.80
Sandy loams, loams	<1.40	1.63	>1.80
Sandy clay loams, loams, clay loams	<1.40	1.60	>1.75
Silts, silt loams	<1.30	1.60	>1.75
Silt loams, silty clay loams	<1.10	1.55	>1.65
Sandy clays, silty clays, some clay loams (35%–45% clay)	<1.10	1.49	>1.58
Clays (>45% clay)	<1.10	1.39	>1.47

Figure 1-11 Compaction can alter soil structure (left) and limit the movement of water and oxygen into the soil for root growth.

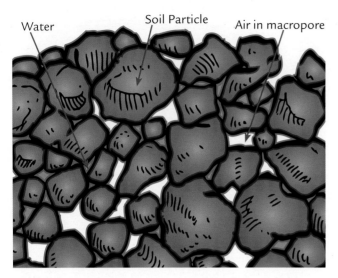

Water   Soil Particle   Air in macropore

Figure 1-12 Water drains quickly from the larger pore spaces. Water held in the micropores by capillary action is held tightly enough to be present in the root zone for extended periods, yet loosely enough for the plant to extract it. Some water is bound so tightly by soil particles that the roots cannot extract it.

bulk density at which root penetration is inhibited varies by soil texture (Table 1-1).

Compaction alters soil structure (Figure 1-11), inhibiting movement of water and soil gasses. If carbon dioxide builds up to toxic levels in the soil, the excess carbon dioxide can be more damaging than reduction of oxygen (352). A compacted soil can be very wet at times because of the lack of macropores and poor percolation. The same compacted soil can be very dry at other times from reduced infiltration and high runoff. The more moderate soil conditions in between these extremes may be very short-lived.

Compaction can reduce the root and shoot growth of newly planted trees by 50%, but incorporation of organic matter can partially reverse the effect of soil compaction on shoot growth (306). Tree species vary in their ability to penetrate compacted soils. Silver maple (*Acer saccharinum*) roots can grow in moderately compacted soil when high soil moisture content decreases penetration resistance of the soil but reduces oxygen. Flowering dogwood (*Cornus florida*) is less tolerant of the wet, low-oxygen conditions, and so cannot produce new root growth when soil penetration resistance is reduced by high moisture. As a result, overall dogwood root development is reduced in compacted soil (145).

Soil Water and Aeration

Water absorbed from the soil has several functions in plants. Most of the water absorbed by the roots is translocated through the plant and is released into the atmosphere as vapor through the leaf stomata. In the process, dissolved nutrients are transported within the plant and evaporation helps to cool the leaves. Small amounts of water are used in the biochemical processes within plant cells. Trees that transpire less water to avoid drought, such as little-leaf linden (*Tilia cordata*) (615), may be more suitable for certain urban environments.

A good soil contains about 50% pore space divided equally between small pores (micropores) and large pores (macropores). Water is held in the small pores by capillary action, where it is available to plant roots. Gravity drains water from

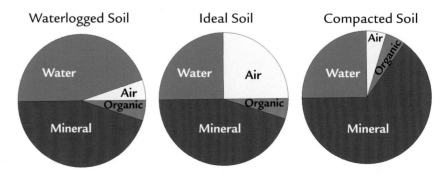

Figure 1-13 Ideally, soil should be half pore space for air and water. When soil is compacted, macropores are reduced, and aeration can be insufficient. When drainage is inadequate, macropores also fill with water, leaving no space for air.

the large pores, providing aeration for roots (Figure 1-12). A sandy soil may have too many large pores and few small ones. Thus, it has a low waterholding capacity, a high air capacity, and a high percolation rate. A clay soil can have many small pores and too few large ones, resulting in a high waterholding capacity, but low air capacity, and low percolation rate. The 50% of the soil that is solid particles should include about 5% organic matter by weight (Figure 1-13). Such a soil would have sufficient waterholding capacity, adequate drainage, and good aeration.

Not all water in the soil is available to plants. Gravitational water drains to a lower level in the soil and is gone from the root zone so quickly that it is of limited importance to plant growth. Some water that is bound hygroscopically to soil particles is held so tightly that the roots cannot extract it. Water held in the micropores by capillary action is held tightly enough to be present in the root zone for extended periods, yet loosely enough for the roots to extract it. The proportion of hygroscopic, capillary, and gravitational water depends on soil texture and structure.

The maximum amount of capillary water a soil can hold after the gravitational water has percolated through is called field capacity. Field capacity is when water available to plants is at its maximum. When only hygroscopic water remains, the soil has reached the permanent wilting point. The difference in water content between field capacity and permanent wilting point is considered plant-available water. Loam soils tend to have the greatest amount of plant-available water (Figure 1-14).

The importance of soil aeration should not be underestimated. Plant roots require both water and oxygen for normal development. Soil water and oxygen availability are interrelated. Too much of one may mean too little of the other. Urban planting sites are often excessively wet (53, 195). Overwatering and poor

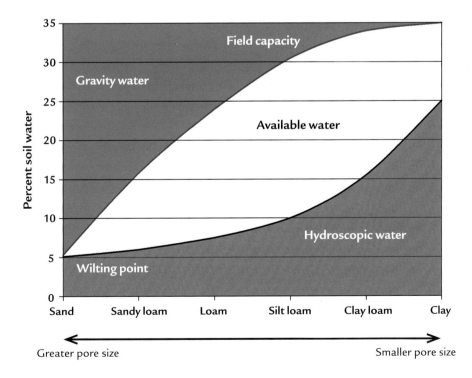

Figure 1-14 Relationship of soil texture to available water-holding capacity of soils. Water is available to plants between field capacity and permanent wilting point.

Figure 1-15 Root growth of several tree species has been correlated with rusting of steel rods placed in the soil. The steel turns gray when the soil is too wet for rust formation or root development.

drainage create waterlogged conditions with poor aeration. Compaction reduces macropores and compounds the problem (Figure 1-13). When soils do not drain properly, nearly all the pore spaces fill with water, and there is insufficient oxygen available for the living roots (Figure 1-13). With the exclusion of soil air, enough roots can be killed to reduce water uptake, causing desiccation of foliage. Excessive soil moisture can also decrease the permeability of roots to water (347). As a result, excess soil water can produce the same leaf symptoms caused by drought. Trees killed by too much water are found most frequently in compacted clay soils.

Plant roots and soil microflora continually use oxygen and give off carbon dioxide, which can be toxic at elevated levels. Thus, a continued exchange of gases between soil and air must take place if carbon dioxide is to be replaced by oxygen.

Soil aeration is difficult to measure without specialized equipment. A measurement at any single point in time may be misleading. Since soil aeration is directly affected by the amount of soil moisture, a heavy rainfall can fill all of the soil pores with water for a short time and greatly reduce aeration temporarily until gravitational water drains away. Assessing soil aeration over several weeks or months may be more valuable. This can be done with a little-used technique, where steel rods are inserted into the ground for an extended period of time and the corrosion pattern is evaluated (Figure 1-15). Oxygen is needed for rust to form. The steel turns gray when the soil is too wet for rust to form or black under more extreme conditions. Root growth of several species has been correlated with the rust on the rod (578).

Figure 1-16 Trees grow better on the slope (left) with better drainage than trees planted in the low, flat area where water accumulates.

Table 1-2 Approximate water infiltration rate based on soil texture (283).

Soil texture	Infiltration rate in inches (mm) per hour
Sand	>0.8 (>20)
Silt	0.4–0.8 (10–20)
Loam	0.2–0.4 (5–10)
Clay	0.04–0.2 (1–5)

Drainage is affected by a number of factors including: soil texture and structure, precipitation, permeability, infiltration characteristics, and landscape position. Soils are poorly drained if water ponds on the surface or saturates the topsoil for extended period of time during rainy or wet periods. This is especially prevalent in topographically low, flat, or depressed sites that receive runoff from surrounding areas (Figure 1-16). Situations like these often cause decline in plants not adapted to wet conditions. Poorly drained soils may require artificial drainage, careful species selection, and special planting techniques (see Chapter 2).

There is a very effective way to determine if there is adequate drainage. After digging the planting hole, fill it half full of water. If the soil is quite dry, the water may soak in rapidly at first, but it will soon begin to pool in all but the most well-drained soils. If the water that fills the bottom of the hole has not dropped appreciably after an hour or two, drainage will be problematic, especially during wet seasons (Figure 1-17). A more accurate measurement can be made by refilling the hole the following day and measuring the drop in water level; a drop of 0.1 inch (3 mm) per hour is slow, and 5 inches (120 mm) per hour is very rapid. Table 1-2 lists infiltration rates for different soil textures. A preliminary test of drainage can be performed in advance of planting by using a small hole made with a soil profile tube (Figure 1-18) and a wooden dowel as a dipstick. It may not be as accurate since the volume of water is so small, but can still be a good indicator of severe drainage problems.

Temperature

Favorable soil temperature is needed for root growth, movement and absorption of water and nutrients, and microbial activity. The extent of soil warming depends on the average daily air temperature, the intensity of the sun's rays, and the ability of the soil to absorb heat. The degree to which the soil will change depends upon the moisture content of the soil. Therefore, in early spring, well-drained soils tend to warm more readily than soils saturated with water. Thick mulch can insulate the soil beneath and delay warming of the soil in spring and cooling in fall by a few days. Mulch can be effective in reducing daily temperature peaks in summer.

Nutrients and Reaction (pH)

Trees should be fertilized based on a demonstrated need. Growth of newly planted trees is more likely to be limited by water than by nutrients (438, 585, 562). Deficiency symptoms occur when there is an imbalance between absorption by the roots and use by the crown. Recently transplanted trees may be able to overcome a temporary deficiency without addition of nutrients, as balance is restored by roots exploring a larger soil volume and top growth rate adjusting to available supply. The availability of nutrients can be determined by a soil test. Foliage analysis or visible symptoms can indicate a deficiency (Figure 1-19).

Levels of one nutrient can affect the availability of another. The application of high nitrogen during plant establishment has caused magnesium deficiency in areca palm (*Dypsis lutescens*) and Chinese hibiscus (*Hibiscus rosa-sinensis* 'President') (85). High N:K ratio fertilizers applied to adjacent turfgrass can exacerbate potassium and magnesium deficiencies of palms (82).

Figure 1-17 If water does not drain readily from the planting hole, excess water may kill the roots of a tree planted in the hole.

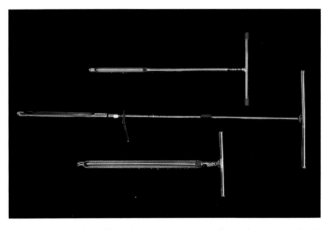

Figure 1-18 Soil profile tubes remove a core from the upper 10–18 inches (25–45 cm) of soil. Many soil properties can be observed by examining such cores.

Figure 1-19 Visible nutrient deficiency symptoms demonstrate the need for fertilization. Soil tests may also reveal low availability even without visible deficiency symptoms.

The nine essential elements needed in relatively large quantities are oxygen, carbon, and hydrogen plus the following macronutrients:

- Nitrogen
- Phosphorus
- Potassium
- Calcium
- Magnesium
- Sulfur

Carbon, hydrogen, and oxygen come from the atmosphere or from soil water. Three macronutrients—nitrogen (N), phosphorus (P), and potassium (K)—are available in most soils, but not always in sufficient quantity to permit optimum growth. Calcium, magnesium, sulfur, and most micronutrients are readily available in most soils and do not often limit plant growth.

The following seven essential elements needed in small quantities are called micronutrients:

- Iron
- Manganese
- Copper
- Chlorine
- Zinc
- Boron
- Molybdenum

Of all the nutrients, deficiency in nitrogen most often limits plant growth. Most soil nitrogen comes from decomposed plant material broken down by soil microorganisms. Mulch decomposition can supply nutrients at rates similar to natural litter decomposition in the forest (0.5–1.5 lb N/1000ft²/yr [0.27–0.72 kg N/100m²/yr]) (605, 354, 607) though considerably lower than the rates called for by arboricultural best management practices (2–6 lb N/1000ft²/yr [0.96–2.88 kg N/100m²/yr]) (517).

Nitrate is the form of nitrogen most readily absorbed by trees. It leaches through the soil easily and may be in short supply at times when soil conditions are not right for conversion from other forms of nitrogen. An unusually cool, wet, or dry spring can cause some species to produce pale, green foliage initially. This condition is usually alleviated when the soil becomes more favorable for nitrogen conversion by soil bacteria.

A sufficient amount of phosphorus is often available, but in some soils, additional quantities may be needed for optimum growth. Both phosphorus and potassium move very slowly in the soil, phosphorus more slowly than potassium.

Soils differ in their ability to store nutrients. Many nutrients exist in the form of ions in the soil. These ions can be held by soil particles, where they are available for absorption by plant roots. The Cation-Exchange Capacity (CEC) is the measure of soil's ability to store nutrients in this way. Sandy soils have almost no ability to store nutrients. These soils will not be able to hold nutrients applied. CEC is higher in finer textured soils. Organic soils have the highest CEC of all.

Availability of nutrients is dependent on the acidity or alkalinity of the soil. This is commonly is referred to as soil reaction, or pH. A pH of 7.0 is neutral. The pH numbers below 7.0 indicate acid reactions with increasing acidity as the number decreases. Numbers above 7.0 indicate alkaline reactions with increasing

Table 1-3 Amount of lime needed per 1,000 ft^2 (93 m^2) to raise the pH of three soil types.

From pH	To pH	Sandy loam pounds (kg) lime	Silt loam pounds (kg) lime	Silt-clay loam pounds (kg) lime
6.0	6.5	23 (10.5)	41 (18.6)	58 (26.4)
5.5	6.0	23 (10.5)	41 (18.6)	55 (25.0)
5.5	6.5	46 (21.0)	83 (37.7)	115 (52.3)
5.0	6.0	46 (21.0)	83 (37.7)	115 (52.3)
5.0	6.5	69 (31.4)	124 (56.4)	173 (78.6)

alkalinity as the number increases. The pH scale is a logarithmic scale with a 10-fold difference between units. A pH of 9.0 is 10 times more alkaline than a pH of 8.0 and 100 times more alkaline than a pH of 7.0.

Soil pH is important because it is a general indicator of nutrient availability. In slightly acid to neutral soils (pH between 5.5 and 7.2), most nutrients are available at optimal levels. Some nutrients, such as iron and manganese, become less available in alkaline soils (pH above 7.2) because of chemical changes caused by the alkalinity. Other nutrients become less available in highly acid soils (pH less than 5.5).

Tree species vary in their ability to grow well in alkaline soils. Many plants that require acid soil also require well-drained soil. In areas of high rainfall, acid soils are usually well-drained. Selecting a tree species adapted to existing soil conditions is preferable. Permanently changing the pH of field soil is usually not practical and is frequently impossible. However, some short-term adjustments in pH can be achieved. Changing the pH will take time, but the pH can be raised more quickly than it can be lowered. Lowering the pH of fine-textured clay and clay loam soils and high lime soils may not be practical.

Applications of lime are used to raise soil pH. Aluminum sulfate and sulfur can help to lower pH. Aluminum sulfate may cause injury to some plants when high rates are used, particularly in broadleaf evergreens. The injury is believed to be caused by excessive aluminum. Ammonium sulfate may be as effective as aluminum sulfate, but neither is as effective as granular sulfur (393). Ammonium sulfate can also be used if nitrogen application is needed along with pH reduction. Tables 1-3 and 1-4 provide recommended levels of lime and sulfur to add to the soil to change pH.

Table 1-4 Amount of sulfur needed per 1,000 ft^2 (93 m^2) to increase the acidity of silt loam soil. Soils high in calcium carbonate may require higher rates.

From pH	To pH	Pounds (kg) Sulfur
8.0	7.0	20 (9.1)
8.0	6.5	30 (13.6)
8.0	6.0	40 (18.2)
7.5	7.0	18 (8.2)
7.5	6.5	20 (9.1)
7.5	6.0	35 (15.9)
7.5	5.5	50 (22.7)
7.0	6.5	15 (6.8)
7.0	6.0	20 (9.1)
7.0	5.5	35 (15.9)
6.5	5.5	25 (11.3)
6.5	5.0	40 (18.2)
6.0	5.5	15 (6.8)
6.0	5.0	30 (13.6)

Soil Ecology

Healthy soil is teeming with life. Biological components of the soil environment are critical for healthy plants. Microbial processes are directly impacted by soil organic matter.

The total soil organic matter is composed of a labile fraction and stable fraction. The labile fraction consists of readily decomposed plant, microbial, and animal products. Even though it is a minor amount of the total soil organic matter, labile organic matter is very important in nutrient cycling. The stable organic matter is humus, a relatively stable form of carbon sequestered in soils for decades or even centuries. Humus contributes to Cation-Exchange Capacity, water adsorption, and soil structure stability. Stable organic matter decomposes very slowly, and as a result, releases nutrients very slowly.

Disturbance triggers activity among bacteria and other organisms that consume organic matter (convert it to carbon dioxide), depleting the labile fraction first.

Figure 1-20 All three trees were planted at the same size and at the same time. The more restricted root spaces slowed the growth of the tree.

Practices that build soil organic matter (reduced disturbance and regular additions of organic material) will raise the proportion of labile organic matter long before increases in total organic matter can be measured. As soil organic matter levels rise, soil organisms play a role in its conversion to humus.

Higher plants are the major producers of organic matter in the soil. The microorganisms (bacteria and fungi) are the major decomposers and are mainly responsible for the cycling of nutrients and energy in soil ecosystems. Nutrients are efficiently recycled in natural ecosystems. Interference of the cycle in urban landscapes by removal of litter results in lower organic matter content and reduced soil fertility. Soil animals play a minor role in cycling of nutrients and energy, but play an important role in earth-moving activities.

Bacteria tend to use simpler organic compounds, such as root exudates or fresh plant residue. Fungi are common decomposers of more complex compounds, such as fibrous plant residues, wood, and soil humus because these have large amounts of complex, hard-to-decompose carbon. Only fungi produce some of the enzymes needed to degrade the complex compounds in humus.

Forests tend to have fungal-dominated food webs. The ratio of fungal to bacterial biomass may be 5:1 to 10:1 in a deciduous forest and 100:1 to 1000:1 in a coniferous forest. Grass and agricultural soil ecosystems are usually bacteria-dominated, and the ratio of fungal to bacterial biomass is often near 1:1 (Table 1-5). With reduced disturbance, the ratio of fungi to bacteria increases over time, and arthropods become more plentiful (521).

This zone of soil adjacent to plant roots with a high population of microorganisms is the rhizosphere. Bacteria feed on sloughed-off plant cells and the proteins and sugars released by roots. The protozoa and nematodes that "graze" on bacteria are also concentrated near roots. Thus, much of the nutrient cycling and disease suppression needed by plants occurs immediately adjacent to roots (521). Rhizosphere pH can be up to two pH units different than the rest of the soil (373).

Compost teas are liquids containing soluble nutrients and species of bacteria, fungi, protozoa, and nematodes extracted from compost. Compost teas are being used to enhance soil biology and provide nutrients, sometimes as an alternative to fertilization, but research support for their effectiveness is lacking (486). Healthy soils with favorable physical and chemical characteristics will support active soil biology naturally. Improving soil conditions is preferred over addition of compost teas, biostimulants, mycorrhizal fungi, etc.

Mycorrhizae are symbiotic relationships that form between common soil fungi and plants. The fungi colonize the root system of a host plant, providing increased water and nutrient absorption capabilities while the plant provides the fungus with carbohydrates formed from photosynthesis. Mycorrhizae also offer the host plant increased protection against certain pathogens. All trees have mycorrhizae. The fungal spores are usually present and will form mycorrhizae if the soil environment is favorable. Both root growth and mycorrhizae formation can be reduced in unfavorable urban soils (624).

Root Space Limitations

Pavement surrounding trees has been shown to limit tree growth (235, 309). The soil compaction required to support a stable pavement surface and the impervious nature of the pavement itself effectively create a limited space for the tree roots. Just as a potted plant can grow too large for the volume of soil in the pot, so can a landscape tree reach a size where its growth becomes limited by the available root space. When the root system cannot increase in size anymore because the rooting space is filled to capacity, the crown growth will slow but not stop (64, 620). Gradually, the size of the restricted root system becomes proportionally smaller relative to the size of the slowly expanding crown. Water stress becomes more frequent and severe, which can make plants more susceptible to secondary disease and insect problems. Because of a restricted root system, trees in small planting spaces grow more slowly and have a shortened life expectancy (Figure 1-20). For more information on designing root space into urban environments, see Chapter 2.

How can very large trees growing in seemingly small spaces be explained (Figure 1-21)? The most likely explanation is that a few roots have "broken out" of the confined space and have obtained a source of water and nutrients somewhere else. Roots sometimes grow through narrow spaces, up to 100 feet (30 m) or more with very little branching until they reach an area of quality soil. Often, the roots are found growing in nearby sewer or water drainage pipes, which have an ample supply of nutrients and water.

Figure 1-21 Trees growing in seemingly impossible places may have roots in a sewer pipe as a source of water and nutrients.

Aboveground Limitations

Urban Microclimates

The average summer temperatures in the city can be 2°F to 12°F (1°C to 6°C) warmer than those in the surrounding suburbs—a phenomenon called a heat island (483). City centers can be an especially warm environment. The buildings, asphalt, and concrete, which absorb and store heat, comprise 70%–90% of the spaces around plants. Such large-scale aspects of the urban environment are only part of the aboveground site evaluation process.

Environmental conditions in urban landscapes can differ widely over short distances. The amount of sunlight a plant receives and the time of day the sunlight is received can limit the kind of plant that can be used. An area with morning sun and afternoon shade often produces adequate sunlight early with shade in the afternoon. A location like this will warm quickly early in the morning but minimize stress during the hottest part of the day, and may be suitable for species sensitive to drought stress or growing at the edge of their range (632). An area with morning shade and direct sun during the hot afternoon hours may be more suitable for plants that are tolerant to heat or drought stress.

The amount of potential radiation received on a street is influenced by: street aspect (e.g., north-south vs. east-west), planting location (side of street), height and number of buildings (length of shadow cast), street width, and building setback. Downtown streets generally receive only a fraction of the total radiation found at more open areas, perhaps only 4–6 hours of direct sun per day (616). Inner city sites with taller buildings often do not reach the 80% daily sunlight threshold needed for optimal growth (324). Shade-tolerant species are the best choices for these areas (104).

Locations on the south side of buildings (north side in the southern hemisphere) surrounded by pavements are more exposed to sweeping winds, full reflected sunlight from building surfaces, and reflected heat from surrounding pavements. In contrast, on the north side (south side in the southern hemisphere) of the same building, the plants may never receive direct sunlight and the associated heat. If this difference is not recognized, irrigation timers may be set so that both locations receive the same amount of water, subjecting the south side plants to drought stress, or the north side plants to waterlogging. Proper plant selection and good management practices are both important for vigorous, healthy plants.

Table 1-5 The number and type of microorganisms and animals in the soil is characteristic to the type of system. There are more fungi and soil animals in forests. Turfgrass inhibits the natural development of soil ecology that is more natural for trees (521).

FOREST : GRASS RATIO	
Bacteria	1:1
Fungi	10:1*
F:B ratio	up to 10:1
Protozoa	1,000:1
Nematodes	up to 10:1
Arthropods	up to 50:1
Earthworms	1:1
* Much greater in coniferous forests	

Figure 1-22 De-icing salt can accumulate on surfaces near major roads and be washed into the soil near heavily used pavements.

Airborne Pollutants

Airborne pollutants cause injury primarily to foliage. Conifers are generally more affected than deciduous plants. In northern cities, the most serious airborne pollutant is usually de-icing salt used on roadways (Figure 1-22). In the northern United States, de-icing salts are applied at up to 19.4 U.S. T/lane mile (11 MT/lane km) 0.6 lb/ft², 2.9 kg/m² annually (Figure 1-23) (406). Both saltwater mist and dry salt dust particles are dispersed into the air by high-speed traffic. Salts cause plant damage by drawing moisture out of the tissues. Salt deposited on twigs can cause dieback and witch's brooming (Figure 1-24) (152). Sensitive plants can be damaged up to 1,240 feet (378 m) away from a high-speed highway (331). Highly susceptible species should not be planted near major roads that are frequently salted. Ocean salt spray can also cause tree damage in coastal areas.

Buildings close to the pedestrian sidewalk on the south side of an east-west street often shade the pavement and prevent the sun from helping to melt the snow and ice on the sidewalk. As a result, trees planted on the south side of the street may be subject to higher levels of de-icing salt than those on the north side of the street, where sun exposure can help to melt snow and ice (330). Higher de-icing salt concentrations in tree cutouts close to the curb, and on wider streets, was also linked to poorer tree performance (324). A small raised curb around planting pits (Figure 1-25) can help prevent salty runoff from entering the planting pit (330).

De-icing salts from airborne deposits and runoff from melting snow on pavements can accumulate in the soil over winter. Excess sodium leads to poor soil structure. Clay particles are dispersed from aggregates and plug soil pores, resulting in reduced soil permeability and poor aeration. When soil is repeatedly wetted and dried and clay dispersion occurs, soil becomes almost cement-like with little or no structure.

Salt in the soil decreases osmotic water potential and reduces the rate of water uptake by roots. An increase in soil salinity produces the same net effect on water uptake as that produced by soil drying (180). High levels of soil salts can dehydrate and damage plant roots (250) and cause desiccation of the entire plant. Soil salts can be translocated to the shoots during the growing season where it can cause twig dieback, witch's brooming, and marginal leaf scorch similar to aerially deposited salt. Trunk lesions have also been associated with root absorption of soil salt (195, 152).

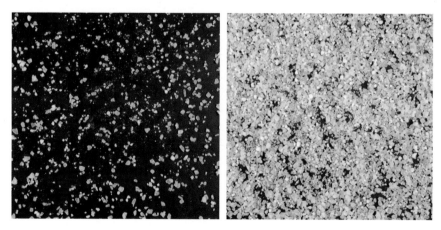

Figure 1-23 De-icing salts applied to road surfaces at rates of 1 oz/ft² (290 g/m²) per snow event (left) and 0.6 lb/ft² (2.9 kg/m²) per winter season (right) can have a severe impact on nearby trees.

Even moderate levels of soil salt (750 g/m) can result in reduced shoot growth (66). Unless drainage is inadequate, salt that accumulates in the soil will usually be diluted and flushed away with the spring rains.

Site Evaluation Checklist

It is important to understand how all of the physical, chemical, and biological aspects of the soil environment function and interrelate. Evaluating the attributes and limitations of each planting site is imperative. This information is used to make site improvements before planting, and to choose tree species that will survive and thrive on the site.

Carefully evaluating a site in advance is critical for successful tree planting. Many plantings fail because site characteristics are either improperly evaluated or even ignored.

Above Ground

- Light exposure (hours of sunlight, reflected light, and heat load)
- Wind
- Salt usage
- Pollution
- Slope exposure
- Overhead wires
- Street and security lights
- Proximity to buildings, structures, and signs
- Visual assessment of existing plants
- Vandalism
- Irrigation levels

Below Ground

- Soil pH
- Soil texture
- Soil compaction
- Drainage
- Soil salinity
- Other soil contaminants
- Soil depth
- Root space restrictions
- Underground utilities

Figure 1-24 De-icing aerial salt spray can cause twig dieback and witch's brooming.

Figure 1-25 A small raised curb can be very effective in preventing salty runoff from entering the planting pit.

CHAPTER 2

Design for Tree Health and Longevity

Few city trees will live for 100 years, but even challenging sites can be designed so that trees can be healthy and live many years.

W|hen planting a single tree in an older neighborhood, where the soil profile was never disturbed by heavy equipment, the job may be as simple as digging a hole large enough for the root ball. This would be an uncommon site in urban areas. Most situations will require extensive site preparation before planting.

Providing a high-quality site is the investment with the best return if you want long-lived, healthy trees. It is often necessary to spend more on preparing the planting site than on purchasing the tree, but in the long run, it may cost more to replace trees prematurely and repair damage to infrastructure caused as a result of inadequate site preparation. A tree is only as good as its root system, and urban planting sites that have poor soil conditions will severely restrict root growth. A tree planted with space for the root system to spread will outperform a tree planted without sufficient preparation and planning. If you want the tree to grow 100 feet tall and live for 100 years, you must provide a site that will support it. This lofty objective will be very difficult to achieve on most urban and suburban sites, but limitations of every site should be managed to provide for the longest lived trees possible.

Figure 2-1 Some landscape sites offer sufficient root space to support adequate growth of a tree for many years.

Information obtained from a site evaluation is very important in determining the best way to prepare the site for planting. Site preparation must be most intensive on disturbed sites, or on sites with naturally poor quality soils. On such sites, even a properly prepared planting hole can only provide an optimum environment for root growth for a limited time—usually just a year or two. Tress will benefit greatly by improving soils over a larger area.

Figure 2-2 Three feet (1 m) of root growth is typical for trees in northern climates in two years.

Large Spaces

Undisturbed Sites

Some landscape sites offer sufficient root space to support adequate growth of a tree for many years (Figure 2-1). If soil quality is good, site preparation should focus on speeding tree establishment by providing the highest quality environment possible for initial root growth during the first year or two after transplanting, possibly longer for trees over 4-inch (10 cm) caliper. Even in cool northern climates, roots may extend about 3 feet (1 m) from the root ball after two years (Figure 2-2) (596, 577). To avoid damage when planting within the drip line of an existing tree, plant in between the large tree roots and dig a smaller hole (Figure 2-3).

Disturbed Sites

On newly developed sites, soil quality may be poor. Compaction and resulting poor drainage account for high losses of new trees. Research supports improving conditions beyond the planting hole to improve tree growth and survival.

A survey of 3,600 street trees showed that trees in shrub beds grew better and also sustained less damage than trees planted in other parts of the landscape (294). Several studies have shown that incorporation of organic matter—such as pine bark, peat, or compost—into planting beds increased the growth of shrubs (36, 58, 57, 50, 365). Incorporation of compost is more beneficial than tilling alone (365).

Subsoiling large areas with an excavator before planting has been used to improve soil properties and increase tree growth on compacted sites. It can reduce soil bulk density and penetration resistance, and increase porosity at

Figure 2-3 Digging a planting hole under an established tree can result in loss of a large portion of the root system. Avoid digging near the trunk, dig a smaller-than-normal planting hole, and take care not to cut any major roots.

field capacity. Tree growth was increased in sandy soil, but not in the clay soil (471). Building on this early study, more recent research is showing that profile rebuilding (rototilling topsoil and subsoiling with an excavator) can improve soil physical properties and tree growth. Early results indicate that the profile rebuilding treatment is accelerating the process of soil structure formation (102).

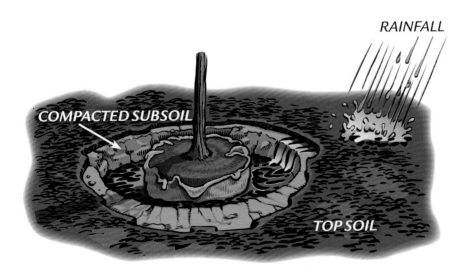

Figure 2-4 Water that cannot penetrate compacted subsoil flows laterally to the lowest point. Planting holes can fill up with water and damage the root system.

Figure 2-5 Gravel in the bottom of the planting hole can make drainage worse. Moisture will accumulate in fine textured soil above a coarse textured gravel layer until the soil is completely saturated.

Figure 2-6 A drainpipe can be installed between the bottom of the planting hole and a lower point on a slope to improve drainage. In this case, trenches with pipes from several trees are connected and outflow is located away from the evergreens down slope to avoid adding more water to them.

Figure 2-7 On very poorly drained sites, the only way for trees to survive may be to plant with a portion of the root ball above grade. There should be a gradual slope between the top of the root ball and the original grade.

Drainage

Even when surface soils are improved, water can flow into the planting hole from the surrounding landscape when the subsoil does not drain well. The lower portions of backfill and root ball soil can become saturated, driving out oxygen and killing roots (Figure 2-4). This may occur naturally from rainfall only intermittently or at certain times of the year, but even short periods of saturation can cause death of roots of many species. Irrigation systems can create the same situation throughout the growing season. Irrigation systems designed for lawns often overirrigate woody plants in the same area. Excess irrigation water will accumulate in planting holes even during severe droughts.

Solving drainage problems may be expensive but worth the investment because it is essential for acceptable tree performance. The need for correcting drainage should be investigated before planting (see Chapter 1). Before plans for new developments are approved, proper surface drainage is required by building codes, but drainage may later be altered by changes made to the landscape. Something as subtle as adding soil to a planting bed can disrupt surface drainage and create a wet area. Providing adequate drainage to individual trees is often difficult. On many sites, improving the drainage on the entire site may be a better approach. If drainage of a large area requires improvement, regrading to increase surface slopes or installation of underground drain tiles may be required.

A layer of gravel in the bottom of the planting hole can make drainage worse, not better (Figure 2-5). Water accumulates in the finer textured soil above the layer of coarse gravel until the soil is completely saturated. This is known as a perched water table.

Drainage for individual trees can be improved in several ways. A ring of perforated plastic tubing around the root ball in the bottom of the hole connected to a pipe discharging the water at a lower level can be effective (Figure 2-6). A 3-inch (8 cm) fall per 100 feet (30 m) of pipe is a minimal slope to obtain adequate water flow. This approach works well for trees planted on slopes. If the planting area is too level, sometimes permission can be obtained to drain the pipe into a nearby storm sewer.

If a well-drained layer of soil exists underneath a poorly drained layer, then a vertical hole several inches in diameter can be drilled through the poorly drained layers and filled with gravel to allow the water to drain.

Another approach to providing improved drainage is to plant the top of the root ball partially above grade. No more than one-quarter of the root ball should be above grade, and the soil should be gradually sloped between the top of the root ball and the original grade (Figure 2-7). This method may utilize excess soil from the planting hole if it is of sufficient quality, or additional soil of good quality may have to be added. An important drawback of this method is that the soil in the upper part of the root ball and backfill may dry out more quickly during dry periods. Supplemental irrigation may be required until the roots can spread beyond the raised soil.

Confined Spaces

Traditional sidewalk planting spaces have been small cutouts in the pavement, often covered with an open grate for pedestrian safety. Average tree life expectancy in one of these small sidewalk cutouts can be as little as 10 years (418). Grates designed with large center holes sections are less likely to cause trunk constriction (Figure 2-8). Tree grates are expensive and easily damaged. In one assessment, 80% of all tree grates in the city needed repair due to tree constriction and traffic breakage (186).

The more the quantity of root space is limited, the more important the quality of the soil will be. High-quality soil and intensive maintenance can compensate for limited root space soil volume to some extent. It may help to reduce stress, but it will not allow a tree to grow large in a very small space. Incorporating expanded root space into the site design before planting is a better approach.

Figure 2-8 Tree grate maintenance can be costly. Modifications are required as tree trunks enlarge. Grates with larger holes (bottom) provide more space for trunk growth, but filling it with rigid material defeats the purpose.

Root Space Requirement (Soil Volume)

When trees are planted in paved areas, the limited root space available in planting pits will ultimately limit the size of the tree. Crown spread and trunk diameter of trees growing in parking lots is reduced as nonpaved surface is reduced (140, 235). The need for larger root spaces is now more widely recognized, and better designs have been developed. The variables to be considered when determining how large a tree a root space can support are:

- The quality (water and nutrient storage capacity) of the soil present
- How much evaporation and transpiration is expected
- How often the tree will receive rainfall or irrigation

Figure 2-9 Trees with limited soil volume will decline prematurely. This parking lot island had approximately 400 cubic feet (5.6 m³) of quality soil if the soil was 3 feet (1 meter) deep. The tree outgrew its space and failed at approximately 7 inches (17 cm) dbh as predicted by Urban (559).

As a general guideline, if aboveground and belowground environmental extremes are not severe, the root space should be approximately 1–2 ft³ of soil for each square foot (0.3–0.6 m³ for each square meter) of crown projection area of the expected mature size of the tree (343, 361, 558, 559). The shape of the root space can be adapted to the site and does not have to be the same on all sides. Urban (559) describes a case history of a tree failing after 16 years with only 400 cubic feet of soil, which would be considered generous in many sidewalk cutout situations.

Trees growing in light soils and very hot or dry climates will require greater soil volume. Cool, moist climates may permit the use of smaller soil volume to get the same results. Watering will be required more often for trees in a confined root space than it would be for trees with root systems in a larger soil volume, especially during dry periods.

A computer model has been developed that uses climatological data to estimate the soil volume necessary to provide moisture during the driest growing conditions likely to be encountered for an area. The example used is New York City using a 20-foot (6 m) crown diameter tree with 600 ft³ (17 m³) of soil, as recommended by Lindsey and Bassuk (361). Without irrigation, the tree would face a water deficit every other year. If the soil volume is increased to 967 ft³ (27.4 m³), the tree would face a deficit only once in 10 years. With only 152 ft³ (4.3 m³) of root space soil, the tree would need irrigation every fifth day to face a deficit only once in 10 years, similar to the larger soil volume (146). Using a different method, Blunt (61) calculated that under British weather conditions, a mature tree would require at least 1,765 ft³ (50 m³) of high-quality soil with soil moisture recharged by rainfall or irrigation 10 times during the growing season to avoid drought stress. This soil volume is larger and supplemental irrigation requirement more frequent than the results of the field research and computer model from New York. The difference may be related to the size and species of tree, which was not specified.

Figure 2-10 Trees with shared root space in the center of the planter grow larger than those on the ends and larger than single trees in a small pavement opening (far right). (Photo: J. Patterson)

Soil Specifications (Soil Quality)

When soil volume is restricted, soil quality becomes very important. Too often, trees are planted in whatever soil is present on the site. When soil was amended with organic matter to a 2-foot (60 cm) depth, root development was greater than when just the upper foot (15 cm) was amended (520).

The soil is often of very poor quality in pavement opening and should be completely replaced. Soils for restricted spaces should contain (measured by weight) less than 27% clay, at least 50% medium (1 mm) sand, and 5% compost (10% compost by volume) (Patrick Kelsey and Phillip Craul, personal communications). Deeper soils—especially those under the root ball—should contain less compost to avoid excessive settling.

Shared Root Space

When cutouts are combined and shared by several trees, the performance of the trees seems to be better than when trees are in several smaller individual planting spaces of the same total volume (Figure 2-10). The closely spaced canopies of the trees help shield each other and the soil from sun and wind. Below ground, roots can spread over a larger area. Though not much additional soil is available for each tree, the larger shared root space provides a more consistent environment for the roots.

Expanding Root Spaces

Soil Conditions Under Pavement

In many urban landscapes, the only place to expand root space is under pavement. The soil compaction necessary to support stable pavement restricts root growth. The pavement itself can have mixed effects on the root environment beneath it. Soil moisture can be greater under pavement than surrounding unpaved areas because it reduces evaporation (296, 26). Maximum summer soil temperatures under pavement in the northern United States were 90°F to 94°F (32°C to 34°C), and up to 18°F (10°C) warmer than nearby unpaved areas (241, 248). In Texas, summer soil temperatures under pavement exceeded 118°F (48°C), were 18°F (10°C) hotter than unpaved areas, and remained above 95°F (35°C) for all but a short time at night (26). Temperatures are highest under dark pavements, as would be expected.

Root zone temperatures of 77°F to 95°F (25°C to 35°C) can reduce tree root growth, depending on species (26, 237, 240, 242, 243), and the longer the soil temperature remains at high levels each day, the more root growth is reduced (243, 245). Direct heat injury of roots can occur when the soil remains above 90°F (32°C) for extended periods of time (239). Honeylocust (*Gleditsia triacanthos*) appears more resistant to elevated soil temperatures than most of the limited number of other species studied to date (245).

Figure 2-11 Constructed root paths use aeration or drainage strips to give roots a way to grow under pavement in order to share root spaces among pavement cutouts and access a greater volume of soil in adjacent green spaces. (Photo: D. Miles Barnard)

Pervious Paving

Several approaches have been used to provide suitable conditions for root growth under pavements without compromising stability of the pavement. It has been suggested that pervious paving materials could improve the soil environment beneath pavements for better tree growth, but research has not yet shown this to be consistently true. Soil oxygen was insufficient for root growth (less than 12% oxygen) for prolonged periods beneath two of five pervious paving products tested on park footpaths (125). Differences in soil oxygen and moisture between impervious and pervious concrete pavements are inconsistent (399, 566). Pervious concrete plots had greater soil moisture in deeper layers in some seasons, but not in summer, when it would be most beneficial, and there was no difference in tree growth rates,

Figure 2-12 Suspended pavements (left) can provide high quality root space and dense root development underneath pavements. Structural soil mixes (right) are 80% stone, allowing roots to spread between the stones, but limiting fine (absorbing) root development.

Figure 2-13 Precast concrete structures can be filled with quality soil to expand the planting space under pavements. Larger soil volume would be better.

leaf water potential, or gas exchange (567). The narrow width of pavements used in these studies—less than 5 feet (1.5 m) wide—may have allowed water and oxygen to diffuse under the pavement from the edges of the solid pavement just as easily as through the pores of the pervious pavement. To function correctly, pervious concrete pavement systems must have underlying soil that percolates well, which would also be beneficial for roots. If soil beneath the porous pavement is too compacted, the resulting poor soil aeration and penetration resistance itself are likely to be factors limiting tree performance rather than the pavement (566).

Root Paths

Root paths provide a path for roots to grow from restricted planting spaces to open spaces on the other side of the pavement. They are narrow trenches approximately 4 inches (10 cm) wide and 12 inches (30 cm) deep installed in a compacted subgrade under pavement (Figure 2-11). Paths can also connect individual planting spaces to gain some of the benefits of a shared root space. Commercially available strip drain material is usually installed in the trench and then backfilled with loam soil (118, 559). It could take several years for roots to grow through the root path and access the soil beyond. There is not yet any research to confirm that roots are able to take advantage of the paths to access the soil beyond the pavement and improve tree growth and longevity.

Suspended Pavement

If the pavement is engineered to be suspended above the soil, the soil does not have to be compacted to support it. The larger the soil volume provided, the better the tree will perform. Drainage and irrigation systems are usually installed as well. Suspended pavements range from elaborate designs constructed on site to simpler and smaller precast concrete structures (Figure 2-13). More recently, several specially designed plastic cells have become available in the United States and Europe. These interlock and stack to form a rigid structure to support pavement while providing over 90% noncompacted soil space within the cell structure. Time has proven that though suspended pavements are better than a small cutout, trees will grow better in a larger volume of open soil (Figure 2-14).

Structural Soils

Soils designed to support pavement without settling are often called load-bearing, skeletal, or structural soils. To expand root space under pavement in this way, the soil must provide a favorable environment for root growth while supporting the pavement. No structural soil can support as much root development as the same volume of a high-quality loam soil, so they should be used only when there is no better option.

The first soil of this type was developed in Amsterdam, Netherlands. Amsterdam Tree Soil specifications call for 91%–94% medium coarse sand, 4%–5% organic matter, and 2%–4% clay (by weight). Phosphorous and potassium are added as necessary. The compost provides a source of nitrogen (124). The soil mix is carefully compacted to a specific density (70%–80% Proctor density) when installed, and aeration is provided through spaces in the pavers placed over the soil (Figure 2-15). This system has been shown to be effective in supporting vigorous trees

Figure 2-14 Tree growth is limited to the amount and quality of root space. The trees on the left have about 300 cubic feet of available soil under the suspended pavement in a shared root space. Though they have survived longer than if they were planted in small pavement cutouts, they are much smaller than the trees to the right of the sidewalk planted in a large green space. (Photo: The Urban Horticulture Institute, Cornell University, Ithaca, New York, USA)

Figure 2-15 When structural soil is used to provide root space under pavement, it is best to use a paver design that provides aeration for the roots through spaces in the pavers placed over the soil (above).

and stable pavements for many years. *Pyrus calleryana* trees grew almost twice as rapidly in Amsterdam Tree Soil compared to standard pavement construction and 50% faster than those grown in grass (454).

More recently, other load-bearing soil types have been developed. Most are a stone-soil mix (Figure 2-16). Usually, gap-graded (limited to a certain size range) stones are used to create a network of interconnected spaces that can be filled with soil for root growth (Figure 2-17). Systems developed in Europe are often created on site by first putting down stone and then working the loam soil into the spaces between the stones with a vibrator (Figure 2-18).

The stone-soil mix type of structural soil in widest use in the United States, CU-Structural Soil™, is premixed and then transported to the installation site (Figure 2-19). Considerable research is available on soil conditions and root growth response of this mix. Premixing the stone and soil provides assurance that it contains the correct proportions to ensure that the soil is not compacted in the spaces between the stones. When mixed and installed properly, structural stone-soil mixes compacted to 1.85g/cc and greater did not reduce macropore space or restrict root penetration in the soil between the stones (231, 236). In a container study, structural soil held 7%–11% moisture by volume, similar to a loamy sand, and had high infiltration, good drainage, and good aeration (236), but no field measurements have been reported.

Tree Performance in Structural Soils

Early tests of structural soil mixes in containers showed that stone-soil mixes could support better root and top growth than compacted soils or road base materials (349).

Figure 2-16 The stone-soil mix type of structural soils are composed of primarily gap-graded stone with about 20% soil.

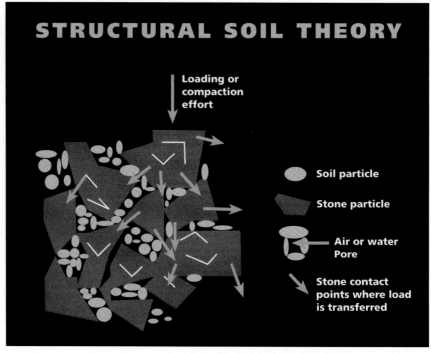

Figure 2-17 Structural soils can consist of stones to create a network of interconnected spaces that can be filled with soil for root growth. (Illustration courtesy of: The Urban Horticulture Institute, Cornell University, Ithaca, New York, USA)

Figure 2-18 Structural soils can be created on site by first putting down gap-graded stone of preferred size, and then working the loam soil into the spaces between the stones with a vibrator.

Figure 2-19 Some structural soils are transported to the site ready to be installed. Installing in 6-inch lifts ensures that the proper level of compaction is attained.

Growth was limited by net soil volume rather than the total volume of the stone-soil mix (364). The root-crown ratio was greater in stone-soil mixes than topsoil alone (same size pots), indicating a larger root system was needed for absorption of water and nutrients when the soil was spread out in the mix (349).

Results of field studies have been mixed. At 3 and 10 years after installation, growth (dbh, height, and canopy width) of trees planted in structural soil under pavement was not different than trees planted at the same time in a lawn adjacent to the sidewalk (231, 234). However, the trees planted in structural soil were within a few feet of an adjacent open lawn area, and their roots had probably grown into that soil. Other reports show that trees planted in noncompacted soils in open planters (Figure 2-20) (91) or covered by suspended pavement (514) will outperform all structural soil mixes. Structural soil can be a useful compromise in

Figure 2-20 Though methods to provide root space under pavement are an improvement over small pavement cutouts, they are not an equal substitute for large open planters.

Figure 2-21 When using structural soils, the planting pit should be as large as possible and filled with quality soil (top). In this optimal installation, the planting pits were not covered with pavement. Fourteen years later, the trees are growing well in the generous planting pit plus the additional space under the pavement (bottom).

situations where high-quality noncompacted soils cannot be used, but it will not produce the same results as the same volume of quality soil.

Structural soils may increase tree anchorage. Trees were more stable in structural soils than traditional tree pits due to greater root length in stone-based skeletal soil (41). This finding is supported by a computer model in which a 20% soil, 80% granite chip mix was optimum for withstanding wind forces required to uproot trees (453).

Stormwater Storage Beneath Pavements

Soil conditions suitable for root growth under pavements also provide some level of stormwater storage (142). If significant, this could be additional justification for the higher cost of the expanded root space. The effectiveness will vary with the soil type used.

Infrastructure Conflicts

Pavement Damage

When pavements are laid on a compacted soil base, roots are often able to grow in the favorable environment in the gap between the pavement and the compacted soil under it. Moisture is high because the pavement prevents evaporation, and condensation can form on the underside as the pavement cools (344, 571). Aeration can also be adequate under narrow pedestrian sidewalks (130, 344). As roots enlarge in diameter, they can eventually lift and crack the pavement.

Potential for conflicts between trees and pavement is high when one or more of the following factors are present (456, 629):

- Tree species that are large at maturity
- Fast-growing trees
- Shallow rooting habit
- Trees planted in restricted soil volumes
- Shallow topsoil (hard-pan underneath topsoil)
- Limited or no base materials underneath the sidewalk
- Shallow irrigation
- Distances between the tree and sidewalk of less than 6–10 feet (2–3 m)
- Trees greater than 15 to 20 years old

Pavement damage is most commonly associated with large trees in restricted planting spaces (131, 390, 459, 629). The larger the tree and the closer to the pavement, the more likely infrastructure damage will occur. Eighty percent of *Swietenia* sp. (Puerto Rico) trees were causing damage to the pavement if the pavement was only 3 feet (1.0 m) from a 12-inch (30 cm) dbh tree. When the pavement was 6 feet (2 m) from the tree, only 25% of the trees were causing pavement damage (183). While damage is greatly reduced with increasing distance, the amount of damage is still quite high, and greater distances may be impractical in the built environment.

Sidewalk pavement cracks near roots are usually assumed to be caused by the roots, but recent research has challenged this. Sidewalk damage has been shown to be more related to soil type and age of pavement. Older sidewalks failed more often. Sidewalks did not fail at higher rates where trees were present (545). With no roots present, 61% of all pavement expansion joints were cracked (130). Roots were more likely to be found under a cracked expansion joint in the sidewalk than under an uncracked joint, but the cracks may actually be contributing to roots growing under sidewalk pavements. Once sidewalks fail, more root growth may occur beneath the cracks due to increased oxygen in the soil (130, 545).

Preventing Pavement Damage

Barriers are sometimes installed to prevent root growth under the pavement. Barriers have been constructed from plastic, metal screening, and geotextile impregnated with herbicide. Most of these barriers are effective at blocking roots between the surface and the bottom of the barrier. Differences in effectiveness of products have sometimes been reported in the first few years, but may not persist with time (519).

Installation of root barriers reduces the number of roots and causes them to grow deeper for a limited distance on the far side. This has been reported consistently in both poorly drained soils (569) and well-drained and well-aerated soils

Figure 2-22 After roots grow under the barrier, they often grow back toward the surface within a short distance. (Photo: E. Gilman)

(120, 201, 431, 441, 512, 519). After they grow under the barrier, they grow back toward the surface within a short distance from the barrier (Figure 2-22), but may remain deeper long enough to lessen pavement damage. The effectiveness of barriers may not be permanent since pavement damage by *Prunus* trees was associated with large roots as deep as 16 inches (40 cm) below the pavement (414, 415).

Depth and installation of the barrier is important. An 18-inch (45 cm) deep barrier reduced roots under the pavement (513), while a 12-inch (30 cm) barrier of similar design did not (204). Barriers need to be installed with the uppermost edge above grade. Roots are often able to grow over the top of barriers because of incorrect installation, deterioration of the exposed barrier material, or mulching over the barrier, and significant damage to pavements can occur (513).

Barriers can reduce overall root development of trees (37, 201, 519, 570), but in most studies, no effect on trunk diameter growth is reported (37, 38, 120, 204, 431, 513).

Certain root barrier products that are impregnated with herbicides to reduce root growth raise concerns that mycorrhizae could be affected. Sweetgum (*Liquidambar styraciflua*) (endomycorrhizal) and pin oak (*Quercus palustris*) (ectomycorrhizal) root mycorrhizae collected from within 0.5 inches (1 cm) were unaffected in the only reported study (318). For an extensive review of root barrier research, see Morgenroth (398).

There is no evidence that root barriers will decrease stability. Slightly more force was required to pull over trees with root barriers. The increased stability was attributed to deeper roots (515). The situation may be different if roots are not able to grow under the barrier, such as on sites with very poor aeration or very deep barriers. In such a situation, the limited root system on one or more sides could result in increased instability.

Other alternatives to root barriers have proven to be effective in preventing roots from growing beneath pavements and causing cracking and lifting. Extruded polystyrene foam 4 inches (10 cm) thick installed directly under poured concrete forced roots to grow under the foam. The expanding roots crushed the foam instead of heaving the pavement (513).

When pavements were laid on a base of coarse gravel or brick rubble, roots did not grow directly beneath the pavement (204, 344, 513). The coarse material was apparently not a suitable environment for root growth between the stones, and the roots grew in the deeper soil underneath it. Thicknesses of 6 inches (15 cm) and 12 inches (30 cm) were somewhat more effective than 4 inches (10 cm).

A 4-inch (10 cm) thick layer of structural soil beneath the pavement is not the intended use of structural soil, but has been used in place of gravel in practice. Whereas the use of gravel discouraged root growth, a similar 4-inch (10 cm) deep layer of structural soil allowed vigorous root growth in the soil between the coarse stones, as it is designed to do (513). Roots in the stone layer resulted in extensive pavement cracking and lifting. When structural soils are used with a minimum depth of 24 inches (60 cm), or a preferred depth of 36 inches (90 cm), roots grew to the full depth of the soil and were not found exclusively at the surface (233).

Just as disease resistance is the best way to control a tree disease, developing trees with deeper root systems would be the best way to reduce pavement damage. Unfortunately, developing root stocks with deeper roots may be very difficult. Research has shown that individual trees of certain tree species with root systems that often cause sidewalk damage—shamel ash (*Fraxinus uhdei*), zelkova (*Zelkova serrata*), Chinese pistache (*Pistacia chinensis*)—can be selected for deep rooting patterns. Unfortunately, when these trees were propagated by rooting cuttings, all of the propagated trees had shallower root systems (96).

Sewer Pipe Intrusion

Tree root intrusion into sewer systems can be a substantial problem, especially in smaller and older pipes (472). Most species of trees and some shrubs are capable of causing root intrusion, and not only poplar (*Populus* sp.) and willow (*Salix* sp.) that are often seen as most likely (424). Tree roots rarely damage pipes, but take

Figure 2-23 Though tree roots commonly enter sewer pipes through breaks and loose joints and can restrict flow, they rarely are the cause of damage to pipes. (Photo: M. Streckenbach)

advantage of breaks and loose joints in pipes and then proliferate rapidly once inside the moist, nutrient-rich environment (Figure 2-23). Planting distance from infrastructure is important to minimize conflicts. Tree roots are less likely to grow into sewer pipes if planted 20 feet (6 m) or more from existing pipes (455), but this may not be practical in small urban sites.

Foundation Damage

Tree roots have been associated with building foundation damage, but rarely are they the direct cause. Roots in the vicinity of shallow foundations on soils with a high shrink-swell capacity can contribute to soil-moisture depletion during drought, causing the soil to shrink and the building foundation to settle and crack. Tree genera (roots cannot consistently be identified to species) vary in the amount their root systems can spread and contribute to building subsidence. The distance between damaged foundations and the tree with roots contributing to the damage was recorded for over 11,000 trees in the Kew Tree Root Survey. The average distance at which foundation damage was recorded varied from 8 feet (2.5 m) for cypress (*Cupressus*) to 36 feet (11 m) for poplar (*Populus*), with damage from most species occurring between 16 and 23 feet (5 and 7 m) (129).

British National House Building Council guidelines provide recommendations based on shrinkability of the soils, the depth of the foundation, and the water demand and mature height of the tree. On a highly shrinkable soil, if a high-water demanding tree is located a distance equal to its height away from the foundation, the foundation would need to be 4.9 feet (1.5 m) deep. At half of that distance, an 8.2-foot (2.5 m) deep foundation is recommended (Figure 2-24) (55).

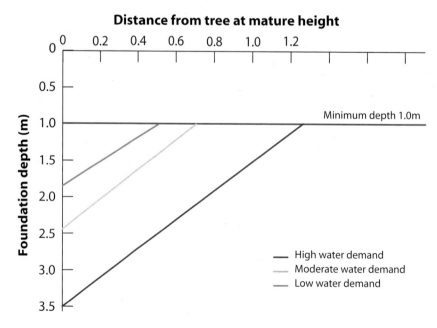

Figure 2-24 The foundation depth required to avoid roots contributing to subsidence is related to shrinkability of the soils, the depth of the foundation, and the water demand and mature height of the tree (after 55).

Figure 2-25 An aboveground planter with small trees was the only option for this downtown Chicago street. Irrigation and drainage must be included in the design.

Aboveground Planters

In downtown areas, sidewalks and courtyards may be built over basements, underground parking, or subway systems. In situations like these, the only choice is to plant trees in aboveground planters (Figure 2-25). The decision to plant a tree in a planter must include the realization that their lifespan will be shorter, even with intensive maintenance. The limited amount of moisture held in the extremely small soil volume can be depleted very quickly. Frequent, but monitored, irrigation is required. If the drainage system becomes clogged, excess water will cause damage to roots. Extremes in temperature, especially extremely low temperatures in winter, can cause root injury and death of the tree. The use of larger planters can help reduce these problems.

Planting success depends on good root growth. Good root growth depends on a good quality soil environment. Without adequate site preparation, the tree will not grow vigorously and reach its full potential in the landscape.

CHAPTER 3

Choose the Best Tree for the Site

Once it is determined that a species can tolerate the existing site conditions, there may be several cultivars to choose from. Both of these trees are European beech (Fagus sylvatica).

The first criterion for species selection is that the tree must be able to survive on the site where it is planted. Narrow the choices to species and cultivars that have proven survivability. Then, focus on appearance. Showy flowers, brilliant fall color, and other aesthetic features will have little value if the tree does not survive and thrive. It is important to consider future maintenance when selecting a tree. Fast growth may be desirable as a young tree, but weak wood and poor branching habit may become a liability as the tree matures. With time, tree crowns and roots may interfere with overhead and underground utilities. The majority of problems associated with landscape trees can be anticipated and prevented with proper planning. In some locations, the choice is not what tree to plant, but whether a tree should be planted at all.

The tree you plant will be part of a large plant community: the urban forest. Street trees, trees on private properties or in parks, forest preserves, and undeveloped wooded areas all influence the urban environment. The tree you plant can have lasting positive or negative influence on its surroundings.

Figure 3-1 Urban landscape design often calls for large numbers of the same species to be planted. A single disease or insect pest could kill every tree on a site like this.

Species Diversity

Diversity is often lacking in urban landscapes. It is not unusual to have large numbers of popular species planted in cities. The 10 most dominant species account for 45.7% of the urban tree population in Chicago (419), 47.8% in England (69), and 55.7% in Hong Kong. One species, *Aleurites moluccana*, constitutes 12.9% of all urban trees in Hong Kong (321). In Nordic cities, a single species can comprise up to 90% of all trees planted (479, 508). In other European cities, only three to five genera usually account for 50%–70% of all street trees planted (427).

Although a few popular species are often overplanted, urban areas can be repositories for a wide range of different kinds of trees. Many cities may have upwards of 100 or more tree species planted on the streets. In milder climates, some cities have a greater number of diverse species (43, 69, 321). Unfortunately, most of the species are planted in very small numbers.

Guidelines for maintaining species diversity in the urban forest were proposed as the "10-20-30 rule," where no more than 10% of all trees could be from one species, no more than 20% from one genus, and no more than 30% from one family (482). While this guideline is intended to prevent devastating losses from diseases or insects attacking a single widely planted species, such as when Dutch elm disease decimated the urban American elm monocultures, a single invasive pest with a wider host range would still be devastating.

Positive attitudes toward increasing diversity may not always be reflected in practice. In California, most municipal arborists indicated that species diversity was an objective of tree selection, but less than half actually included this in their management plans. Approved species on planting lists were much narrower than the species mix listed in the current inventory (400).

Invasiveness

Concern over invasive species is growing. The United States Department of Agriculture defines invasive plants as "a species that is non-native to the ecosystem under consideration and whose introduction causes or is likely to cause economic or environmental harm or harm to human health" (405). These species can thrive in areas beyond their natural range of dispersal, are adaptable and aggressive, and have a high reproductive capacity. Their vigor combined with a lack of natural enemies often leads to outbreak populations that can dominate natural plant communities (Figure 3-2).

Invasiveness of any species can vary by region. A certain tree species may be invasive in some regions, but not in others even though it is not native in either area. Climate change may alter invasive characteristics of species in any region over time.

Many of these invasive characteristics can also make these species the kind of "tough trees" needed for some urban sites. As a result, many municipal planting lists include some moderately invasive species. Protecting against invasive species was not a concern of most arborists in California (400).

Figure 3-2 Species such as European buckthorn (*Rhamnus cathartica*) can become invasive when introduced, and it can dominate the understory of woodlands and be a nuisance in developed landscapes.

Native Species

Planting tree species native to the area is sometimes desirable, but urban sites can be too challenging because the environment is not similar to their native growing conditions. Some indigenous species will do well in urban parks, campuses, and other open areas, but not in more highly developed areas, where "tough" trees are required for the "tough" planting places (574). Some exotic tree species can add important diversity on difficult urban sites. Exotic crabapple (*Malus*) cultivars are a good example of trees with attractive fruit characteristics and disease resistance. Native crabapples have large, messy fruit and are prone to serious diseases.

When planning to use native species, consider that the best performing trees are often trees from nearby seed sources (provenances). These trees may be the better adapted to the region. In a study of green ash (*Fraxinus pennsylvanica*) trees in Kansas, USA, the fastest growing trees originated within 150 miles north or south of the site. Sources from more arid regions to the west did not perform as well (68).

Cultivars of native species are available. Some cultivars are of known provenance. For example, among sugar maple (*Acer saccharum*) cultivars, Flashfire® is from a Caddo County, Oklahoma, native seed source, and Northern Flare® is from northeastern South Dakota. Both perform well in their native region. Legacy® is of

Plant Hardiness Zones in 1990

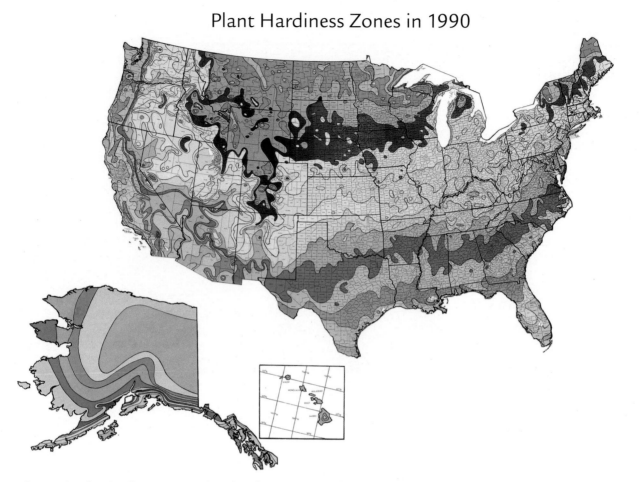

Figure 3-3A Plant hardiness zones are based on the average annual minimum winter temperature over an extended period and is the standard used to determine which plants are most likely to thrive at a location (560).

AVERAGE ANNUAL MINIMUM TEMPERATURE

Temperature (°C)	Zone	Temperature (°F)
-45.6 and Below	1	Below -50
-42.8 to -45.5	2a	-45 to -50
-40.0 to -42.7	2b	-40 to -45
-37.3 to -40.0	3a	-35 to -40
-34.5 to -37.2	3b	-30 to -35
-31.7 to -34.4	4a	-25 to -30
-28.9 to -31.6	4b	-20 to -25
-26.2 to -28.8	5a	-15 to -20
-23.4 to -26.1	5b	-10 to -15
-20.6 to -23.3	6a	-5 to -10
-17.8 to -20.5	6b	0 to -5
-15.0 to -17.7	7a	5 to 0
-12.3 to -15.0	7b	10 to 5
-9.5 to -12.2	8a	15 to 10
-6.7 to -9.4	8b	20 to 15
-3.9 to -6.6	9a	25 to 20
-1.2 to -3.8	9b	30 to 25
1.6 to -1.1	10a	35 to 30
4.4 to 1.7	10b	40 to 35
4.5 and Above	11	40 and Above

unknown provenance, but it has proven to be a superior performer in the Southeastern United States.

Given the uncertainties of climate change, however, it may prove beneficial to favor seed sources that will do well in your region now, as well as a region where current climate conditions are similar to those predicted for your location in the future.

Climate Change

Climate change is predicted to affect trees through rising average temperatures and changes in the amount and seasonal distribution of precipitation. Though the effects will differ somewhat from region to region, we can expect lengthening of growing seasons and changes in the range and distribution of plants and animals everywhere. Trees will be affected not only by overall temperature increases, but also by periods of extreme hot and cold temperatures and by frequency and severity of storm events.

Changes in plant hardiness zones have been documented in the United States (Figure 3-3A and 3-3B). Average minimum temperatures are generally one half-zone warmer throughout much of the United States, as a result of a more recent averaging period (1974–1986 vs. 1976–2005) (560, 561). The trend is expected to continue, so should we be adjusting our plant palette? To some extent, less hardy

Plant Hardiness Zones in 2012

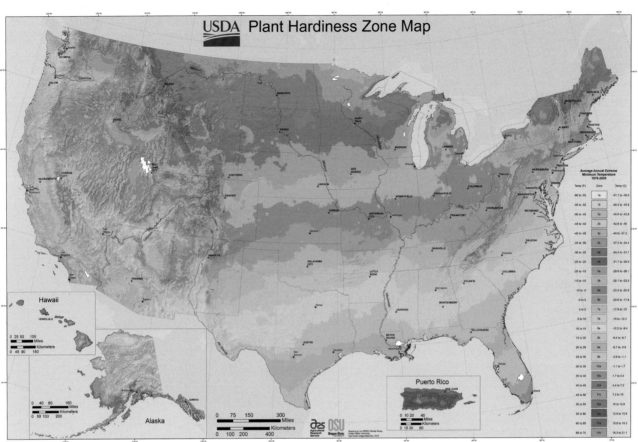

Figure 3-3B The Plant Hardiness Zone map was revised in 2012. Hardiness zones have shifted north (561).

plants can be used farther north than in the past. However, caution is advised. Change is slow, and a single extreme cold weather event can damage or kill trees after growing successfully for many years. We must also ask how far into the future we should be planning. Trees in urban areas are not as long-lived as their counterparts in the natural forest. Mortality rates of trees in developed areas vary by land use. The average life expectancy of trees planted in commercial and industrial areas may be as little as 10 years, while trees may live an average of nearly 50 years in low-density residential areas (418). The shorter the average life expectancy of a tree is, the less need there is to consider climate change in tree selection.

What Makes a Tree Tough?

Ecological amplitude is the term used to describe the range of tolerance of a species to environmental conditions. Trees with wide ecological amplitude can tolerate diverse conditions and often perform the best on urban sites.

Evidence from Nature

Some of the best landscape trees come from difficult sites in nature. In floodplains and swamps, prolonged flooding in springtime, and excessively dry soils in

Figure 3-4 Bottomland species tolerant to flooding in springtime and excessively dry soils in summer have proven very successful as street trees.

summer, permit survival of only those trees evolutionarily adapted to a broad range of soil-moisture conditions. Many disturbed urban soils are also excessively wet in the spring and very dry in the summer. Bottomland species such as American elm (*Ulmus americana*), plane trees (*Platanus* sp. and hybrids), pin oak (*Quercus palustris*), willow oak (*Quercus phellos*), water oak (*Quercus nigra*), and green ash (*Fraxinus pennsylvanica*) have proven to thrive as street trees (Figure 3-4) (145). Unfortunately, some species with wide ecological amplitude also possess other undesirable characteristics such as weak structure, susceptibility to diseases and pests, and nuisance fruits that limit their use as urban trees.

Other types of adverse sites for trees may also be found in nature. Areas with very shallow clay soils developed over limestone are very similar to some urban soils. Trees found growing in these areas, such as chinkapin oak (*Quercus muehlenbergii*) do well in urban landscapes. A tree selected from a dry or droughty section of its overall geographic range appears to have better coping capacity for urban sites than does a tree of the same species from a more climatically favorable part of its range (244). Pioneer species (i.e., those trees that colonize open fields or newly formed land surfaces) usually have the capacity to endure a great deal of environmental adversity, and they are often successful urban trees.

Roloff et al. (473) developed a matrix system to select species for urban habitats based on drought tolerance and hardiness characteristics in their natural environment. The focus was plants for central Europe, but the list of 250 species is applicable to the north temperate climates. This method could be used to rate species for other climates as well.

Soil pH

Some species of trees have specific soil pH requirements. *Rhododendron* sp. and mountain laurel (*Kalmia latifolia*), for example, require a highly acid soil. Other trees, such as redbud, thrive in slightly alkaline soil. In order to avoid future nutritional problems, trees with specific soil pH requirements should be selected for areas where soil acidity or alkalinity fall within a suitable range (Figure 3-5).

Drought

Where water conservation is important, plant trees that conserve water. Many tree species have morphological and physical characteristics that restrict water loss by special adaptations, including stomatal closure, thick leaf cuticles, leaf presentation to reduce direct radiation, and high root:shoot ratios. Drought tolerance can vary among closely related species in the same genus and even among cultivars of the same species (173). Unfortunately, many temperate landscape trees—such as green

Figure 3-5 Some tree species plants have specific soil pH requirements. A species more tolerant of alkaline soils than pin oak should have been chosen for this site.

ash (*Fraxinus pennsylvanica*)—are considered "water spenders" in that they use water inefficiently and continue to transpire large amounts of water after initial stress (105).

Hardiness

Climatic extremes limit the variety of trees that can be grown in any region of the world. Most southern trees cannot survive cold northern winters. Freezing stress can increase disease (492). Many northern trees will not survive in the south because of the hot summers, or insufficient chilling in the winter. Species that occur naturally over a very broad geographic area may consist of several distinct populations, or provenances, with different genetically controlled attributes. A plant from one area within the species range may not be able to survive over the entire range of the species (481). For example, red maple (*Acer rubrum*) is native from central Florida to Minnesota, and trees from one end of the range will probably not perform well at the other end. Knowledge of the hardiness of specific cultivars is important when choosing cultivars of species with such broad natural ranges.

Many horticultural references and nursery catalogs refer to the United States Department of Agriculture (USDA) map of hardiness zones to describe the cold hardiness of plants (Figure 3-3B) (561). Similar hardiness zone maps have been established for other parts of the world and are available online. Many are based on the USDA map of temperature zones for ease of comparison. A world hardiness zone map is also available (Figure 3-6) (404).

When sufficiently hardened off, plants can often survive extreme cold temperatures for the region. Rapid changes in temperature can be more damaging,

Global Plant Hardiness Zones: 30-year Climate Data (1982-2011)

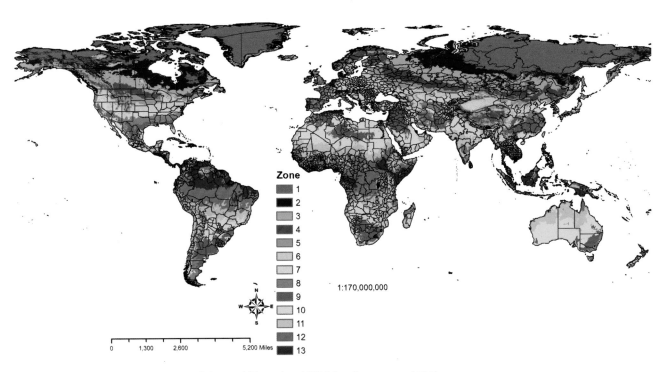

Figure 3-6 Plant hardiness zone map of the world based on USDA hardiness zones (404).

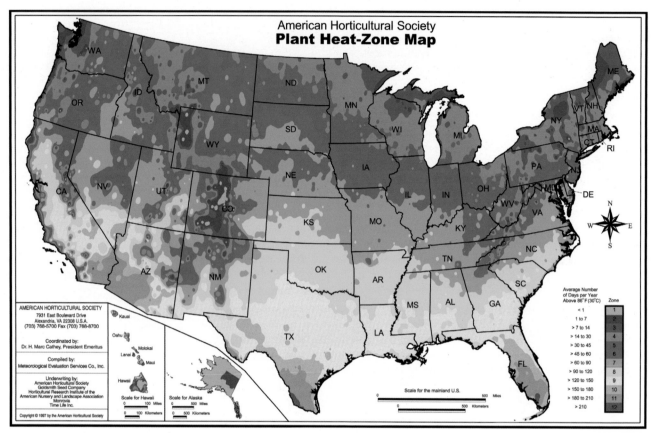

Figure 3-7 In the United States, plants can be coded for heat tolerance (100) to help determine their suitability for a given area. Reproduced with permission of the American Horticultural Society (www.ahs.org).

even if the cold is less extreme. Plants in continental (inland) climates have to be able to survive larger, more rapid decreases in temperature than those in maritime (coastal) climates, where sudden temperature changes are less common. In some northern continental climates, winter temperatures can vary from extremes of 80°F to -20°F (27°C to -29°C) within 2–3 days, or less. During such weather events, dormant trees may become physiologically active for a short period in the warm temperatures and then be injured by a sudden drop in temperature below freezing.

Late spring frosts are particularly damaging to those species that break dormancy early, especially when they are planted in areas where they are marginally hardy. If new shoot growth is killed, secondary growth must develop from axillary buds, leading to additional depletion of stored food reserves.

Extremely low soil temperatures during winter can often cause severe root damage to less hardy plants. The duration of periods of low temperature, the amount of soil moisture, and the depth of snow cover all affect the maximum depth to which the soil freezes and the coldest soil temperatures in the root zone during the winter. Roots of green ash (*Fraxinus pennsylvanica*) trees from even the coldest provenances in Canada were killed at 5°F (-15°C), even though aboveground tissues were hardy to lower temperatures (481). Root killing temperatures of northern temperate woody ornamental trees range from 23°F to -9°F (-5°C to -23°C). Root cold hardiness can vary with tree age and provenance (274, 540). Mature lignified roots can be as much as 20°F (11°C) more cold hardy than young nonlignified roots (540).

Cold is not the only factor determining whether trees will survive and thrive. Heat also has an impact on plants, though the effects are subtler than those of extreme cold. A plant heat-zone map classifies regions of the United States for plant tolerance to heat (Figure 3-7). The zones of the map indicate the average number of days each year that temperatures are over 86°F (30°C), the point at which plants begin experiencing physiological damage from heat. These are called heat days. The zones range from Zone 1 (less than one heat day per year) to Zone 12 (more than 210 heat days per year).

Temperatures are not the only climatic consideration for plants. Plants from dry climates may not perform well in areas with similar temperatures and higher humidity because they lack resistance to fungal diseases commonly found in more humid regions.

Pollution

In some cities, pollution tolerance may be important. Once again, choose species that are tolerant of existing conditions. Pollution can cause conifers to lose their needles prematurely, resulting in the trees being unable to maintain normal photosynthesis levels. When weakened, they may be vulnerable to infectious diseases and attack by secondary pests. Root systems of European beech (*Fagus sylvatica*) exposed to polluted air were smaller than plants grown in unpolluted air, perhaps due to reduced carbohydrate availability (547).

In coastal cities, severe tree damage has been reported within 1,000 feet (300 m) of the ocean from ocean salt spray during storms (503), even on species generally considered salt-tolerant (16). In northern cities, plants near roadways may be subjected to heavy use of de-icing salts (178). Some plants are less tolerant of salts than others (Figure 3-8). Salt-resistant species may have anatomical features that prevent penetration of the salt into tissues, such as resinous or submerged buds, waxy leaves and stems, and smooth twigs (Figure 3-9).

Figure 3-8 Some species are very susceptible to de-icing salt damage. It causes dieback, witch's brooms, and eventually death of the tree.

Appearance

Appearance of a tree is an important consideration, but should only be considered among those selections that are suited for the site. Aesthetic features will mean nothing if the tree cannot survive.

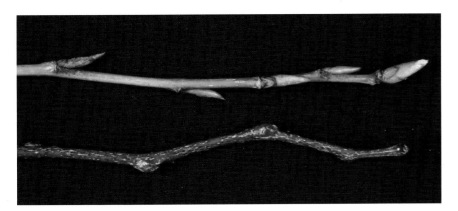

Figure 3-9 Resinous (above, *Populus*) or submerged (below, *Robinia*) buds can prevent penetration of salt into tissues.

Form and Branch Structure

The size, shape, and branch structure of a tree are aesthetically important (Figure 3-10). Low branching, spreading trees are not appropriate along streets but are very useful when screening is desired. Upright selections of trees are quite useful beside buildings and along streets, but look out of place in large, open spaces such as golf courses and parks.

Because deciduous trees are without leaves during the dormant season, the branch structure is a major consideration. A variety of ascending, layered, and weeping branches adds interest in the sometimes uninteresting winter landscape. On a site with many trees, a mixture of trees with attractive summer and winter features is often desirable.

Aesthetic Features

Many trees have especially attractive features or seasonal interest. Foliage, flowers, fruit, and bark can all add beauty and interest. Foliage texture and color may not be as spectacular as spring flowers, but can be enjoyed for much longer. Attractive bark can be enjoyed in all seasons. Don't make the mistake of considering only a single showy feature. Many crabapple cultivars have beautiful flowers for a few days in the spring, but some also have large, messy fruit or severe apple scab disease development later in the season. Hawthorns also have attractive flowers, but most have large thorns that can cause injury when planted in the wrong locations.

Figure 3-10 Tree form and branch structure varies widely and is an important consideration when selecting a species or cultivar.

Cultivars

The aesthetic qualities of a tree are a major factor in the choice of any tree and assurance of the aesthetic qualities of the mature tree is important. Trees of the same species grown from seed are not identical. A cultivar (short for cultivated variety) is a named plant selection, and all individuals possess identical or near-identical traits. Cultivars are usually selected to exhibit specific desirable aesthetic qualities, such as a special flowering characteristic, a unique growth form, or a more attractive fall color. Cultivars have specific and usually appealing names such as 'October Glory' red maple.

Many cultivars can be selected from a single species. Each cultivar will vary in characteristics such as insect and disease resistance, pH adaptability, heat tolerance, drought tolerance, wood strength, central leader dominance, and seedlessness. For example, some crabapple cultivars are more resistant to apple scab disease (Figure 3-11). Growth rate may also vary widely with each cultivar (502).

Vegetative reproduction (or "cloning") is the propagation method most often used to produce cultivars. Propagation by grafting a cultivar onto seedling root stocks does not eliminate genetic variability of root systems, which could cause some variation in performance of trees of the same cultivar. Clonal root stocks are usually not available, except for fruit tree root stocks used with ornamental relatives, such as crabapple. Individual trees have been shown to have desirable root system traits, such as developing deeper rooting (96) and not producing girdling roots (587), but none have yet been developed into clonal root stocks. Rooted stem cuttings and tissue culture propagated cultivars have genetically identical root systems, and they may be more uniform, but no research is available.

Figure 3-11 Know all the attributes of the tree you select. This variety of crabapple has beautiful flowers in spring, but a severe leaf disease defoliates it by midsummer in many years.

Mature Size

The use of large tree species may provide greater benefits than smaller trees and play a role in community image (Figure 3-16). A large street tree ('London Plane,' *Platanus × acerifolia*) can produce net benefits valued at USD $48/year over a 40-year period, even when infrastructure repair was considered. A small tree (crapemyrtle, *Lagerstroemia indica*) produced only USD $1/year in benefits (391).

Large trees are often associated with costly infrastructure damage. Municipal arborists in California identified planting large trees in restricted planting spaces as the most important factor associated with hardscape damage (390). Large species such as willow (*Salix* sp.), poplar (*Populus* sp.), and elm (*Ulmus* sp.) were most often the cause of root intrusion into sewer pipes (455, 472).

Figure 3-12 Fall color can be a very desirable aesthetic feature of a tree.

Figure 3-13 Spikes and thorns can be an undesirable feature of a tree.

Figure 3-14 Interesting bark is a feature that can be enjoyed in all seasons.

Figure 3-15 The mature shape and branch structure of some cultivar selections planted on the same street at the same time can vary widely after many years.

In some residential developments, narrow lots limit the spaces for planting large tree species (493), and very large trees may look out of proportion near small buildings (Figure 3-17). Large tree species should not be planted under utility wires (Figure 3-18).

Growth Rate and Lifespan

The question asked most often in relation to tree selection may be: "How fast does it grow?" Many trees grow faster than is commonly believed. Young oaks can have annual twig growth as great as "faster growing" maples. A person who is older, or who does not plan to live in the same house for many years, may want to have shade as soon as possible. Growth rate is important, but it should not be the primary consideration when selecting a tree. When building a new house and landscaping for investment, a long-lived tree should be a priority.

Rapid growth usually comes at a price. Many fast-growing trees have brittle wood or a short lifespan. Weak or brittle wood can make branches more susceptible to ice and wind damage (273). Longevity is important, but because of site and environmental limitations, urban trees often have a shorter lifespan than woodland trees. An average lifespan for many urban tree species is considered to be 30 to 50 years (418). Trees in small planting spaces cannot be expected to live even this long.

Transplantability

Small trees usually transplant more readily than large trees, although trees over 12 inches (30 cm) diameter breast height (dbh) are successfully moved by qualified contractors with the proper equipment and horticultural knowledge. Moving large trees increases the overall costs of planting and maintenance. Smaller trees will be more economical. In some locations, such as along public sidewalks and streets, small trees are often subject to vandalism, and replacements can increase the cost of surviving trees. Consider all the factors, and make the best choice possible for each situation.

Ease of transplanting has been linked with root morphology and the rate of root regeneration. Species with fibrous roots are typically easier to transplant than species with coarse roots (163, 253, 534, 535). Root regeneration in red oak (*Quercus rubra*) and other coarse-rooted species is predominantly through new root initiation because there are fewer intact root tips at the time of transplanting (529). As an example, the easy-to-transplant pin oak (*Quercus palustris*) had significantly more first-, second-, and third-order laterals than the difficult-to-transplant scarlet oak (*Quercus coccinea*) (535).

Fine root development may play a significant role in transplantability. Root growth was five times as fast for easy-to-transplant Japanese holly (*Ilex crenata*) compared to difficult-to-transplant mountain laurel (*Kalmia latifolia*). Temperature extremes caused greater root mortality in mountain laurel than Japanese holly which contributed to root:shoot ratio that was one-ninth that of holly (631).

Differences in the rate of new root initiation after planting may be an important factor. Species considered easy-to-transplant, such as green ash (*Fraxinus pensylvanica*) and pin oak (*Quercus palustris*), initiate new roots faster than species considered difficult-to-transplant, such as scarlet oak (*Quercus coccinea*) and red oak (*Quercus rubra*) (30, 529, 535, 536, 538).

Difficulty in transplanting may also be related to the main source of stored carbohydrates for growth. In European birch (*Betula pendula*) fine roots were the main reservoir of carbohydrates, whereas larger roots were the principal reservoir in littleleaf linden (*Tilia cordata*). Greater difficulty in transplanting European birch was attributed to the loss of fine roots and the greater carbohydrate reserves associated with them (2).

Because field-grown trees are often transplanted multiple times during production, they usually have a more compact root system and transplant more successfully than uncultivated trees. Nursery standards recognize this and call for larger root balls when transplanting uncultivated trees (12).

Tap-rooted trees, such as white oak (*Quercus alba*), are often considered difficult to transplant. Tap roots are more prominent when trees are young. It is not just having this tap root that makes this species difficult to transplant. Many oak species can be slow to regenerate new roots (30).

The so-called difficult-to-transplant species can be moved successfully if they are moved at the proper time and given the proper preparation and aftercare. Procedures that will make transplanting difficult-to-transplant species more successful include:

- Reducing development of the tap root and encouraging lateral root formation through cultural practices, such as undercutting in the field, or specially designed containers.

- Digging a root ball that exceeds the minimum standard size.

- Taking extra effort in preparing the site to encourage new root growth.

- Providing an extended period of maintenance (especially proper irrigation in dry weather) since these trees will be slower to establish.

Figure 3-16 Large trees enhance the community image and provide greater benefits.

Figure 3-17 Very large trees may be out of proportion for locations near small buildings.

Expected Maintenance

Stress can make trees more susceptible to certain disease problems (491). Newly planted trees may require special measures to protect them from stress-related problems for the first few years until they have overcome transplanting stress. Once established, most trees are susceptible to minor insect pests and diseases, but relatively few are affected to the extent that control measures are required.

Choose species and varieties that will be resistant to serious diseases and insect pests, rather than being forced to control the problem throughout the life of the tree. Seek advice from professionals who are knowledgeable about the problems in your region.

Large trees planted under wires will require regular pruning, as will spreading trees planted in areas where the lowest branches must be continually raised for pedestrian or vehicle clearance. Fruits and flowers may fall and cause a mess or a hazard. Avoid selecting trees having fruits and large flowers for locations near where people walk.

Consider future maintenance of the surrounding infrastructure. If planting close to sewer pipes, bottomland species with aggressive root systems are more likely to cause a problem. Large species and those with shallow root systems are more likely to lift sidewalks and crack pavements (Figure 3-19). Based on inventory data, new street tree planting choices seem to be shifting to species less likely to cause hardscape damage (359).

Figure 3-18 Large tree species are a poor choice for under utility wires.

Certain species have maintenance requirements and other features that render them undesirable for many locations, but don't dismiss them completely. In many urban situations, some of these species are the "survivors." While you may not want to plant silver maples, willows, or poplars along narrow city streets, they can be an excellent choice for large open areas around retention ponds, or along some sections of highway where rapid tree growth is desired. Their shortcomings often pose less of a problem in such locations (309), and they will likely grow better than "higher quality" tree species.

Supply and Demand

In many urban areas, the majority of the landscape tree population is composed of only a few varieties because they are the most readily available, economical to purchase, and easiest to grow. Nurseries often grow large numbers of certain species because they can be produced and sold inexpensively, which makes them popular. It is a cycle that is difficult to break.

Market supply and demand are not always well-matched. Some tree species and cultivars wanted by arborists and landscapers have limited availability, or are not available at all. Others may be in excess supply (546). It takes many years to produce a landscape-sized tree. The supply of certain trees increasing in popularity may be limited until supply can catch up with the demand. The supply of a new selection may never develop if the demand is not perceived, or the cost of production is too great. The consumer must demand a wider variety and be willing to pay more for harder-to-grow varieties, and growers must respond.

If trees are planted on inappropriate sites, useful species may get an unjustified reputation as being "hard to grow." Remember, trees that are not well-suited to the site will be perpetually stressed. Consumers also need to know which trees should not be planted because of chronic problems. The growers and retailers have a responsibility not to sell trees that may only survive a few years in their region, no matter how attractive they may be to the uninformed buyer.

It is not practical to include tree lists for all regions and climates in this publication. Tree selection information is available from a variety of publications such as books, nursery catalogs, and scientific papers. Local information may be available from botanic gardens, universities, professional organizations, extension services and city forestry programs. Many of these sources are easy to access on the Internet. However, the information available may focus on species already widely used and will not encourage use of a greater variety of tree species (507).

Studying the characteristics of trees goes hand-in-hand with analyzing the condition at the planting site. Of course, personal preferences are important as well. Only after all of these factors are considered will it be possible to select the "right tree" for the "right place."

Tree Selection Checklist

The tree chosen must be well matched to the site. First, check the tree characteristics against the site evaluation checklist (Chapter 1). Then, consider the following factors:

- Diversity
- Invasiveness
- Hardiness (cold and heat)
- Mature size and form
- Disease and pest resistance
- Mature size
- Growth rate
- Longevity
- Aesthetic features
- Messiness

Figure 3-19 Large species and those with shallow root systems planted close to pavements are more likely to lift sidewalks.

CHAPTER 4

Choose the Best Season to Transplant

The best time to plant is determined by many factors. Occasionally, unusual conditions—such as freezing temperatures—may make an otherwise impossible job possible.

Planting times are often referred to by season. Many factors contribute to determining the best season for planting. Virtually all recently transplanted trees have greater water demand from the crown than the limited root system can supply. Choice of transplanting season can either minimize or increase water stress.

Favorable environmental conditions and appropriate plant growth stage coincide during fall and spring, making them the preferred seasons, but the terms "spring planting" and "fall planting" must be interpreted carefully. The seasons determined by the calendar are based on the position of the sun relative to the equator and are not closely related to tree planting conditions for any given region. Meteorologists often define the change of seasons a few weeks earlier, but seasons vary with latitude and other climatic influences. To an avid gardener, spring may begin with the long-awaited chance to work in the garden on the first warm day in late winter, though they know growth of most plants will not begin until the soil warms. Autumn is often closely associated with the first frost or when leaf colors begin to change. Growers may begin "fall" planting shortly after the worst heat and drought stress of summer are past so that roots have plenty of time to grow before the soil cools.

The optimum planting time can vary immensely by region and elevation. The time each state in the United States celebrates Arbor Day is an indication of optimum planting conditions for the area. In southern states, Arbor Day is celebrated in the months when there may still be snow on the ground farther north. Arbor Day takes place in April in the majority of states, while in the more northern states, Arbor Day and spring planting season are delayed until May (Table 4-1).

Other important horticultural factors in selecting the best time to plant are the inherent traits of the species, growth stage of the plant, methods of production and transplanting, and level of care after planting. Unfortunately, factors such as labor and equipment availability, weather and construction delays, and customer demands may dictate planting at less favorable times of the year, from a horticultural perspective.

Table 4-1 Arbor Day celebrations usually coincide with the spring tree planting season and vary throughout the United States.

NOVEMBER	APRIL		MAY
Hawaii	Colorado	New Jersey	Alaska
DECEMBER	Connecticut	Nevada	Maine
South Carolina	Washington, DC	New York	North Dakota
JANUARY	Delaware	Ohio	Vermont
Florida	Iowa	Oregon	
Louisiana	Idaho	Pennsylvania	
FEBRUARY	Illinois	Rhode Island	
Alabama	Indiana	South Dakota	
Georgia	Kansas	Tennessee	
Mississippi	Kentucky	Utah	
MARCH	Massachusetts	Virginia	
Arkansas	Maryland	Washington	
Arizona	Michigan	Wisconsin	
California	Minnesota	West Virginia	
North Carolina	Missouri	Wyoming	
New Mexico	Montana		
Oklahoma	Nebraska		
Texas	New Hampshire		

Planting vs. Transplanting

Transplanting is the term used to describe the digging and replanting of field-grown stock. Digging limits season of transplanting. Only a small portion of the root system is harvested with the root ball (see Chapter 9). Though bare-root trees may be harvested with more of their root system (9), root-soil contact is disrupted. This loss of root system functionality when the plant is dug, and the stress resulting from it, is the factor most responsible for limitations on the season when *transplanting* can be most successful. In contrast, container-grown trees are planted without significant root loss and can be *planted* in any season.

Table 4-2 Roots grow best when soil temperatures are above 50°F (10°C) (521). The number of days that soil temperatures are above this level varies greatly from north to south. The longer temperatures are at this level and above, the more roots can grow in a single season.

| LOCATION | ZONE | Date when Soil Temperature at 4 Inches (10 cm) Reaches 50°F (10°C) | | |
		SPRING	FALL	DAYS ABOVE
Tallahassee, FL	8b			360
Atlanta, GA	7b	Feb 26	Dec 15	289
Bowling Green, KY	6b	Mar 25	Nov 17	232
Columbus, OH	5b	Apr 9	Nov 4	205
Ames, IA	4b	May 3	Oct 22	169
Minneapolis, MN	3b	May 14	Oct 16	152

Seasonal Differences

Season of transplanting is important for two reasons. Seasons correspond to specific weather patterns (temperature, moisture) and light characteristics (day length and light intensity) that influence plant growth. Seasons also relate to growth and maturity stages of the plant (dormancy, bud break, leaf drop, bud set, flowering). Fall and spring, when plants are dormant, are typically when trees can be transplanted most successfully without extraordinary follow-up maintenance, making them the preferred seasons. A higher level of posttransplant maintenance will be required if trees are transplanted at less favorable times.

Successful transplanting is dependent on root growth after planting, which is affected by soil temperature and competition for carbohydrates within the tree. When trees are transplanted in the fall at leaf drop, there may still be several weeks of warm soil temperatures (above 50°F, 10°C) that can support active root growth (256, 275, 369). Trees transplanted in the late fall after soil temperatures drop below 50°F (10°C) may not develop any more root growth prior to bud break than trees transplanted early the next spring. There will be little or no root growth until the soil temperature warms again. However, if the soil warms prior to bud break, there may be a short period of active root growth before it is slowed by competition for stored resources by developing shoots (461). Root growth can be most rapid after soil temperatures have warmed and shoot growth has decreased. As soil temperatures increase from 50°F to 79°F (10°C to 26°C), root initiation and growth increase (463, 536). Since a large part of the root system is lost during the digging process, trees planted in full leaf at bud set would be the most prone to desiccation stress. However, this is also a period of significant root growth potential because soils are warm and carbohydrates are available with little competition from expanding shoot and cambial growth (259).

There have been numerous research studies reporting advantages of spring or fall planting for various species. Neither spring nor fall seems to have a consistent advantage. The lack of agreement whether spring or fall transplanting is better may be a result of differences in climate, age, size, type of planting stock, and species (463). Our current knowledge of the advantages and limitations of transplanting trees in different seasons is derived from both research and experience.

Spring

Spring is the traditional tree planting season, and it is the time of year when growers sell the most field-grown stock. All trees can be dug from the field successfully in the early spring because they are still dormant and require little from the root system. Thus, survival is likely to be greatest, and aftercare the least demanding, when trees are planted while still dormant.

Research reports show that spring may be the best season to transplant field-grown sugar maples (*Acer saccharum*). Trees transplanted at bud break had the best root and shoot growth when compared to those transplanted at other times in spring and fall. However, diameter increases were greater in sugar maples transplanted at leaf drop (464). Roots of sugar maples transplanted at bud break grew 8 weeks longer than trees planted at any other time, and had the greatest accumulation of root length by the end of the growing season (463). Tulip poplar (*Liriodendron tulipifera*) (329), Austrian pine (*Pinus nigra*), and arborvitae (*Thuja occidentalis*) (355) trees regenerated more new roots when planted in spring. Twig growth was better in the first 5 years when red maple (*Acer rubrum*) and redbud (*Cercis canadensis*) were transplanted in late spring as annual shoot expansion was nearing completion, compared to trees transplanted prior to bud break. Root growth of Norway maple (*Acer platanoides*) was greater in the first year on late spring transplants (592). Spring-planted hophornbeam (*Ostrya virginiana*) and hackberry (*Celtis occidentalis*) grew better than fall-planted trees (90). Other reports show some tree species performing better when transplanted in the fall.

In subtropical and Mediterranean climates, the best time to transplant palms is in late spring as soil temperature is increasing (84, 288). If irrigation is unavailable, there may be an advantage to transplanting at the beginning of the rainy season, though temperatures may not be optimal (290).

Figure 4-1 Some species that cannot be dug successfully in the fall can be dug in the spring and held for fall planting. Drip ring irrigation is often used to maintain adequate soil moisture in the root ball (Inset: K. Doty)

After being dug in the spring, trees can be held for planting throughout the season with proper care (527). Root balls can be heeled in with mulch or have the sides wrapped with plastic to prevent them from drying out. Irrigation must be more frequent if the root balls are left exposed. Some species, such as hornbeam (*Carpinus* sp.), oak (*Quercus* sp.), and baldcypress (*Taxodium distichum*) that cannot be dug successfully in the fall can be fall-planted if dug in the spring and held for planting in the fall (Figure 4-1).

Summer

Digging trees in full leaf in hot summer weather can induce high levels of stress, and it is not a common practice. Stage digging portions of the root ball over a period of a few days or more, and hardening off in a shaded area with irrigation (see Chapter 6) can improve success of summer digging (200). Trees dug in the spring and container-grown trees can be planted successfully in summer, but they will require more frequent irrigation and monitoring because of the elevated air temperatures and resulting higher water demand from the limited root system.

When transplanted at bud set in late summer or early fall, root growth of sugar maples (*Acer saccharum*) has been found to begin three weeks after transplanting and peak five weeks after transplanting. The peak of root growth was observed earlier in the season when trees were transplanted at other times of the year, or not transplanted at all. Total root length was the same by the end of the growing season, regardless of when they were transplanted (463). Twig growth of Norway maples (*Acer platanoides*) planted in midsummer was equal to, or better than, trees transplanted in early or late spring (594).

Some palm species have their most vigorous growth in the fall, such as ribbon fan palm (*Livistona decipiens*) and needle palm (*Rhapidophyllum hystrix*). These species may do better if transplanted in late summer (287).

Fall

Water stress during the first summer after planting can be the most stressful time for new trees. Trees transplanted in the fall may have additional time for new root growth before the onset of summer heat and stress. However, the fall soil temperatures must be warm long enough after planting to permit new root growth. There should be at least 4 weeks between planting time and when the soil temperature drops to 40°F (4°C) (228). When winter conditions are mild and soils do not freeze, there can be four to five times more root growth before bud break, compared to trees planted in spring (197).

Research shows that fall transplanting did increase root and top growth by the end of the first growing season after planting on littleleaf linden (*Tilia cordata*) (626), northern red oak, (*Quercus rubra*), sugar maple (*Acer saccharum*) (261, 462), and Turkish hazelnut (*Corylus colurna*) (267).

Several studies have shown an advantage for transplanting in early fall compared to late fall. Fringe tree (*Chionanthus virginicus*) had larger leaf area and more root dry mass the following season when transplanted in November (soil temperature 49°F, 10°C) than December (soil temperature 41°F, 5°C) (264). Sugar maple transplanted in early fall (*Acer saccharum*), began root regeneration earlier in the first season following transplanting than trees transplanted in midfall (261, 462). However, early-fall transplanting resulted in reduced growth and delayed establishment in Norway maple (*Acer platanoides*), horsechestnut (*Aesculus hippocastanum*), sweet cherry (*Prunus avium*), European mountainash (*Sorbus aucuparia*), and

European linden (*Tilia × europaea*) compared to late-fall planting (523). Though the late August was considered early fall in this study in Norway, there may still have been considerable stress from warmer weather and a full canopy.

Late-fall (late November through December) transplanting is not advised in climates with severe winters because of an increased risk of desiccation and cold injury (255, 259). Bare-root stock may not be available in fall because of insufficient time to harvest and ship trees after they enter dormancy, though many species can be transplanted successfully by this method in the fall if the stock is available.

Figure 4-2 Frozen soil balls are easier to handle and transport with less chance that the ball will crack and damage the roots. Careful handling of the soil ball is essential.

Evergreens may benefit from a longer duration of warm soil to promote root regeneration after fall planting because they can lose considerable water through their leaves during fall and winter months. Several weeks of 60°F to 70°F (15°C to 21°C) soil temperature at the 6- to 12-inch (15–30 cm) soil depth is especially important for root development of evergreens planted in the fall. When evergreens are planted in the fall, it is imperative that the soil contains an ample supply of water before it freezes. Protection from desiccation with wind screens and antidesiccants through the winter may also be beneficial. Transplanting broadleaf evergreens in fall may be unsuccessful even if all of these procedures are followed.

Winter

Most hardy tree species can be successfully transplanted whenever they are dormant if winters are not severe. Bare-root planting was equally as successful in January as in April in Oklahoma (9). Maximum desiccation tolerance of bare-root trees coincides with January and February harvests in areas where the ground does not freeze (159).

In cold climates, some tree species can be transplanted with a soil ball in winter. On larger trees, the outer 4–6 inches (10–15 cm) of the soil ball can be allowed to freeze before moving it (Figure 4-2). Large soil balls can be easier to handle and transport when frozen with less chance that the ball will crack and damage the roots. Soil balls with high sand or gravel content can be moved with less support while frozen. Frozen ground provides better access for heavy equipment at both the digging and the planting site. Care must be taken to keep the planting hole and backfill soil from freezing before the tree is planted by insulating it with straw or other suitable material (451).

In subtropical and Mediterranean climates with cool winters, palms transplanted in late fall or winter will often have little root growth, and establishment will be slow, subjecting them to unnecessary stress (84). In the tropics, where air and soil temperatures are nearly always sufficient to ensure adequate root and shoot growth, palm species are transplanted year-round (74, 288).

Inherent Traits

We continue to learn from experience and experimentation as various plants are planted under different environmental conditions. Almost all tree species can be transplanted successfully in the spring, but some do not re-establish readily when transplanted in the fall.

Root growth characteristics of different species may contribute to successful transplanting outside the ideal time of year. Root growth potential is the capacity of roots or root systems to extend existing roots and initiate new ones (541). Some species exhibit greater root growth potential when transplanted in the spring (355), others in the fall (357). Species with extensive root lengths within harvested root balls, such as green ash (*Fraxinus pennsylvanica*) and tree lilacs (*Syringa reticulata*) (255), may be transplanted more successfully over a wider range of conditions. Transplanted sugar maples (*Acer saccharum*) may transplant more easily than red oaks (*Quercus rubra*) because they can begin root extension 4–5 weeks earlier (261).

Plant species vary greatly in their ability to tolerate temperature extremes. Cold-hardy plants are best, of course, but occasionally some of the less cold-hardy exotic species are desired in northern climates to create specific landscape

Figure 4-3 Trees moved when the shoots and leaves are actively growing will show the highest water stress and loss rate.

effects. Water stress associated with planting has not been shown to reduce cold-hardiness (10, 430), but it may still be best to install plants known to be of borderline hardiness in the spring so that they will be more established before the first winter.

Figure 4-4 The Missouri gravel bed system uses raised bed of pea gravel to promote fine root development, so that trees can be planted at any time during the growing season. (Photo: University of Minnesota, Department of Forestry)

Growth Stage

Many plants are transplanted most successfully when dormant. The most pronounced state of dormancy corresponds closely with the coldest winter months. Dormancy is initiated in many tree species at the time of the formation and maturation of terminal buds. Many trees are moved more readily after terminal buds have matured, if water stress can be minimized. In general, since evergreens are always subject to water loss through their leaves, they benefit from being moved earlier in the fall and later in the spring than deciduous trees so that new root growth can be initiated sooner in warmer soils. The traditional bare-root planting seasons in temperate climates, late fall and early spring, correspond to periods of high root growth potential in deciduous species (188, 357, 387, 388, 528). A strong relationship between root growth potential and field performance has been demonstrated (164, 188, 388, 467).

Type of Stock

It is possible to plant many species at virtually any time of the year if the appropriate type of nursery stock is chosen. Trees grown in containers can be planted successfully in any season because root loss is minimal. Growth of container-grown trees planted at all phenological stages (leaf drop, root quiescence, root activation, bud break, bud set) was similar to trees that remained in the containers (463, 464).

Using traditional bare-root methods, nursery stock must be transplanted while dormant for a good chance of success. The Missouri gravel bed system (Figure 4-4) uses pea gravel as a medium to increase fine root development, allowing trees to be removed from the gravel and planted, bare-root, during the growing season (63, 150, 527).

Field-grown trees and those grown in in-ground fabric bags are most successfully transplanted while trees are dormant. When moved while in the dormant state, the plant can adjust to the limited water supply from the reduced root system by producing smaller leaves in spring (338). Root loss while leaves are present causes the most water stress because the fully developed crown continues to transpire water. Drought stress can kill plants if transpiration exceeds the limited absorptive capacity of the reduced root system, even if soil moisture is adequate. Though field-grown stock is best dug when dormant, some species can be dug in any season with proper care during and after transplanting (592). Summer transplanting is generally more difficult in arid climates.

Transplanting with tree spades may be successful during the summer partially because the root ball can often be oversized without additional cost. Also, fine root contact with the soil may be less disturbed since the root ball is supported by the rigid blades during the entire process (Figure 4-5).

Figure 4-5 Trees can be successfully moved in leaf with a tree spade, especially if the root ball can be oversized.

Large, mature trees are root pruned and stage dug (see Chapter 6) well in advance of the actual move, if possible. This allows the tree to be moved at any time because there is minimal root loss at the time of the move, and the tree has already had time to adjust physiologically.

Bare-root transplanting of established trees was used to move very large trees before large equipment was available to lift heavy soil balls (Figure 4-6). This practice is being revived primarily because pneumatic excavation tools have become available (Figure 4-7). Contractors doing this kind of work contend

Figure 4-6 Before large equipment became available to move heavy soil balls, large trees were moved bare root. (Photo: Special Collections Department, Iowa State University Library)

they have successfully moved large trees any time of the year, except during shoot expansion or when the soil is frozen. There are practical advantages to this method, such as when access to the planting site is too limited for a heavy soil ball. Horticultural advantages and disadvantages of this method have not yet been investigated through research.

Care After Planting

The expected level of care after planting can also be important in choosing a time to plant. Experienced gardeners may be able to successfully transplant almost any plant at any time of year by providing intensive care tailored to the specific requirements of each plant. Large-scale commercial plantings often consist of a variety of species with different requirements, and the ability to tailor maintenance for each variety or individual plant may be limited. Planting on these large-scale sites may have to be restricted to times when plants will require the least amount of care after planting.

Improper watering is the factor most likely to threaten the survival or limit the growth and establishment of recently planted trees. Carefully monitored supplemental irrigation will be required during the warm summer months for the first year or two in nearly all climates. The absence of natural soil moisture need not delay planting, provided supplemental watering is available for an extended period after planting.

Inadequate rainfall occurs in winter in some tropical and subtropical areas when the soils are warm. Fall and winter planting take advantage of warm soils for root growth and cooler air temperatures for reduced stress, providing adequate supplemental irrigation is provided.

Nutrient deficiencies are not likely to occur during the establishment period, and research has shown that supplemental fertilization is not beneficial until after the tree has become established (see Chapter 8). Controlling serious pests such as borers while the new tree is stressed is important.

Figure 4-7 Pneumatic excavation tools make it possible to transplant large trees bare-root. (Photo: M. Hoenigman)

Research has not provided conclusive guidelines as to which season is best for transplanting. Each study can only focus on a few species under narrow circumstances. Much of our knowledge of the best time to plant individual tree species will continue to come from practical experience. Plants that are well-suited for the planting site and carefully maintained after planting will have the widest latitude in transplanting dates. Substituting a different species or choosing a different type of nursery stock can also extend the planting season. Good results can be obtained on a few plants in a small home landscape that are planted out of season if they receive a high level of care before and after planting. Larger landscapes, where plants often receive less individual attention, are most successfully planted at an optimum time of the year.

CHAPTER 5

Select the Best Quality Trees

Know what to look for in each type of nursery stock.
Root system quality is as important as crown condition.

Proper species selection and good site preparation must be followed by obtaining quality trees. The method used to produce a tree in the nursery can affect its survival in the landscape. Many choices of nursery stock are available. Choosing the best nursery production method for each situation is essential. Individual growers may employ unique and innovative variations on basic production methods. Amount of root loss, soil type, seasonal availability, and handling procedures vary with each type of stock.

Each production method has certain advantages and disadvantages. No single nursery production method fulfills the needs of every planting job. Methods that are practical and economical, and that allow for planting throughout the year are the most widely used. Less versatile production methods may be very well-suited for special situations. Understanding how each production method affects trees after they are installed in the landscape can help in selecting the best type of nursery stock for each situation.

Origin Is Important

It is important to know the source of the trees you purchase. If trees were grown in local nurseries for several years, then there is a good chance that they are adapted to the local climate. Trees produced in nurseries from other regions with the same climate extremes can also be a safe choice. Trees shipped from nurseries in another region with a different climate may not be hardy unless the source of the trees used for propagation was from a region similar to yours, and they possess the natural ability to withstand the climate extremes in your region.

Very little information may be available to the buyer on the source of root stock used for grafted trees. Sources of seed for root stock may vary from grower to grower. Quality growers may be very careful to use root stock from northern parts of the species range to assure cold-hardiness. Others may use convenient nearby seed sources, or from areas where seed of the species is plentiful and easy to collect. Disease resistance of root stock is also a consideration.

Often, growers prefer seedlings with rapid, aboveground growth rates. These seed sources may have low root:shoot ratios and be adapted to climates with minimal stress (65, 111, 189). They may not be the best choice for producing a vigorous root system for stressful urban environments. Growers that are conscious of the need for a vigorous root system will often seek sources of seed with more vigorous root growth, but in the end they may not be well-suited for nursery production if shoot growth is too slow.

Bare-Root Trees

The traditional bare-root method of transplanting trees continues to be used in certain situations. Small bare-root trees are available at garden centers, by mail order, and at local plant sales. Small seedlings are often distributed through Arbor Day and community tree

Figure 5-1 Many field-grown trees are started from seed at nurseries specializing in propagation.

planting programs. Some municipal tree planting programs plant up to 2-inch (5 cm) caliper bare-root stock. Larger caliper trees (3–6 inches; 5.5–15 cm) can be successfully transplanted bare-root, though initial growth after planting may be slower compared to trees transplanted with a soil ball (370). Bare-root stock is not often used by landscape contractors in the United States and Canada, but it is more common in Europe (308, 427).

Trees are often started from seed in prepared beds (Figure 5-1). Introduction of mycorrhizal fungi can improve the growth of seedlings in completely sterilized nursery bed soils sometimes used in forest seedling nurseries (151, 345). Landscape tree growers usually prepare beds with less extreme treatments and do not require inoculation. Seedlings with tap roots may be undercut (root pruned) in the beds to promote a more branched root system (Figure 5-2). Trees are usually grown in sandy or loamy field soils to facilitate bare root harvesting.

The typical size of bare-root trees planted in landscapes is 1- to 2-inch (2- to 5-cm) caliper. These have typically been transplanted once in the nursery as a seedling and grown for 2–4 more years (Figure 5-3). They are mechanically harvested (Figure 6-2) in the dormant season, and held for spring shipping either heeled in with sawdust if winter temperatures are mild (Figure 6-3), or in temperature- and humidity-controlled buildings (Figure 6-4). Bare-root stock may not be available for fall planting if dormant trees cannot be dug from the nursery in time to arrive for the fall planting season at the buyer's location. Often, the seasons are not well-matched between the nursery and the planting site.

Antitranspirant products and hydrogel dips (Figure 5-4) have been shown to reduce desiccation of the roots of bare-root plants when roots are exposed to dry air for extended periods before planting (90, 159, 484, 510), but few growers find it practical to apply at harvest. There may still be benefit to applying them when the shipment of trees is received.

Figure 5-2 Tap-rooted species are undercut (root pruned) in the seedling beds to promote a more branched root system, but often all of the new roots grow straight down with little branching just like the original tap root.

Figure 5-3 Nursery stock ready to be harvested bare-root.

Limitations

Planting bare-root trees is usually limited to smaller planting stock, but even large, mature deciduous trees have been transplanted bare-root using special planting procedures (Figure 4-7). The difficulty of digging out the root system, and keeping it from drying out, increases with size of the tree. Survival rates and growth (565) of small bare-root trees will usually exceed that of large bare-root trees. Evergreens are seldom moved bare-root.

For the best chance of success, dormant bare-root trees should be planted in late winter or early spring to allow time for fine root development before the leaves emerge. Delayed planting of dormant stock often results in rapid bud break from exposure to warm air temperatures above ground before sufficient fine root proliferation has occurred.

In climates that experience severe heat and drought, and the dormant period is shorter or does not occur at all, bare-root planting has traditionally been considered to be more difficult (90). Recent research has shown that it can

Figure 5-4 Hydrogel dips can be used to protect roots from desiccation during handling.

Figure 5-5 Bare-root trees are sometimes put into containers in order to be able to plant them throughout the season.

Figure 5-6 The Missouri gravel bed system can increase fine root development in 8-12 weeks and allow bare-root planting throughout the growing season. (Photo: University of Minnesota, Department of Forestry)

be successful. In Oklahoma, bare-root London plane (*Platanus × acerifolia*), Freeman maple (*Acer × freemanii*), and baldcypress (*Taxodium distichum*) were transplanted without losses in both January and March. Bare-root trees had a 37% greater root:shoot ratio than ball-and-burlap trees when harvested based on total biomass, but this did not result in greater shoot growth after planting. The trees were irrigated for the two years of the study, and this was considered a critical factor in survival and establishment in the Oklahoma climate with hot, dry summers (9).

Under the right conditions, bare-root transplanting can be as successful as ball-and-burlap (9, 90, 276, 278) and using a tree spade (565), though bare-root trees may grow less the first year than trees with root balls. Success of bare-root plantings may be very dependent on the situation. In research studies where transplanting success was high, planting time, handling of plants, and care after planting were optimized. When planting large numbers of trees on commercial projects or municipal tree planting programs, circumstances are not always as ideal, and the results may not be as good. In an analysis of one municipal tree planting program, bare-root survival was so low that for the cost of one surviving bare-root tree, two trees could be planted successfully with a tree spade (115). Though planting bare-root has substantial limitations, success rates can be high if growing conditions and care after planting are favorable.

Variations

Process-balled trees are dug bare-root, and then soil is added around roots to form a soil ball. Burlap and twine can be used to form the soil ball, but more commonly, the bare-root trees are placed in containers (Figure 5-5). Since new roots can begin to proliferate in the soil ball, trees can be held for planting throughout the season. This method can take advantage of low shipping costs from the bare-root nursery, while creating a soil ball locally that can extend the planting season if the trees are properly stored and maintained.

The Missouri gravel bed system allows bare-root stock to be planted throughout the growing season. Bare-root trees are held in a bed of 0.25 inch (6.4 mm) screened pea gravel mixed with 10% (by weight) masonry sand (527) or 40% calcined clay for greatly increased water holding capacity. With proper irrigation, fine root growth can be substantially increased before planting (Figure 5-6) (63, 150).

Figure 5-7 Examples of unacceptable root systems that were shipped by a bare-root producer. Stock like this will never develop a normal root flare.

Soil is sometimes removed from traditional ball-and-burlap and container stock before planting effectively creating a bare-root plant. The primary reason for it is to be able to evaluate the root structure and correct root defects. This bare-rooting process may restrict the planting season, but both experience and research are limited at this point (176).

Selection

When purchasing trees from a local supplier, inspect the grower's stock for root quality. If you must order trees without being able to examine the root systems, use a supplier known for quality trees, and inspect the root systems after receiving them.

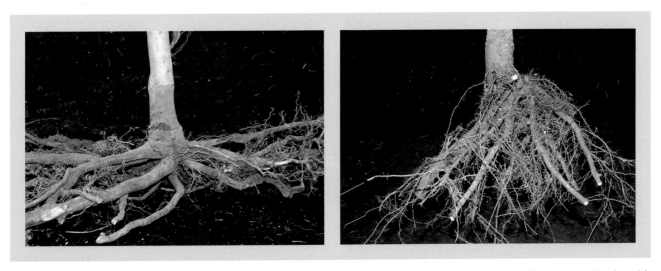

Figure 5-8 The structure of the large, woody roots will be important in the long-term. Root angle is an inherent trait. Species with horizontal roots (left) include maple, elm, birch, honeylocust, and poplar. Ash, hawthorn, *Malus*, linden, *Pyrus*, oaks, ginkgo, Kentucky coffeetree, and baldcypress have oblique roots (right).

Figure 5-9 A simple iodine stain test can confirm the presence of adequate stored carbohydrates in the roots (purple stained cells).

Be sure your expectations are clear, and that the supplier understands you will reserve the right to reject unacceptable trees (Figure 5-7).

When selecting bare-root trees, consider the vigor and structure of the root system. The amount of fine roots is important for absorption of water and nutrients in the weeks after planting, but the structure of the root system will be more important to the long-term health and vigor of the tree (Figure 5-8). Lateral root development is an important factor in root structure development. Seedlings with at least four permanent, first-order lateral roots (woody roots originating from near the base of the trunk, or the tap root) grow much better after transplanting than those with fewer lateral roots (230, 345, 403). Trees with strong tap roots and little lateral root development will probably not survive transplanting well.

A simple iodine stain test (575) can be performed on a few random woody roots to confirm the presence of adequate stored carbohydrates that will be needed for new root growth (Figure 5-9).

Root spread should be adequate. Table 5-1 describes the relationship between caliper, height, and root spread. Another guideline sometimes used is that the root spread should equal four times the trunk circumference.

Discarding trees with inferior root stems after receiving the shipment result in additional expense, but the investment will be worth it in the long run. Also, reject trees if the roots appear to be dry and dead.

Table 5-1 Examples of recommended minimum root spread for nursery-grown bare-root trees (12).

CALIPER*		HEIGHT		MINIMUM ROOT SPREAD	
inches	cm	feet	meters	inches	cm
0.5	1.25	5–6	1.5–1.8	12	30
1	2.5	8–10	2.4–3.0	18	45
1.5	3.8	10–12	3.0–3.6	22	55
2	5.0	12–14	3.6–4.2	28	70
* Measured 4 inches (10 cm) above ground level					

Trees with a Soil Ball

Moving trees with a soil ball (commonly referred to as a root ball) is the most common method of moving landscape-sized trees in colder climates (e.g., Hardiness Zones 2 through 6) where growing trees in containers is impractical. The planting season is longer than for bare-root stock, but digging can still be a limiting factor. Trees dug in the dormant season can be held for planting throughout the season with adequate care. Though the amount of root system moved with the tree is small (598), undisturbed fine root contact with the soil is a major factor in the success and versatility of this method.

The most common way of moving trees with a soil ball is often referred to as the ball-and-burlap method. Soil balls are supported for shipping by wrapping them with burlap (hessian), twine, and sometimes wire. Contractors and municipalities use ball-and-burlap stock frequently. The heavy soil balls may limit homeowners to planting only small ball-and-burlap trees. Trees are also moved with a soil ball using a tree spade (see Chapter 6).

Ball-and-burlap nursery stock is usually grown from smaller bare-root "liners" obtained from another nursery specializing in propagation, and then grown to sizes 2.5 inches (6.25 cm) caliper and larger. The larger sizes of liners may be the same stock that is planted bare-root directly into the landscape. Cultivar selections may be bud-grafted onto seedling root stock, or grown on their "own roots" (rooted cuttings or tissue culture). The graft union should be visible just above the soil surface on bud-grafted stock (Figure 5-10). If it is not visible, then the root system may be too deep (see Selection section). Today, almost all root balls are dug mechanically except those that are too large for available equipment. Root balls are wrapped with burlap (hessian) and supported with twine or wire (see Chapter 6).

Figure 5-10 The graft union (arrow) should be visible just above the soil surface on bud-grafted stock.

Limitations

Ball-and-burlap trees are usually dug while they are dormant in spring or fall to minimize postplanting stress. However, trees can sometimes be transplanted successfully in summer using special procedures such as stage digging, and hardening off in a shaded area (see Chapter 6) and given adequate care after replanting (200, 592). Root pruning also may increase survival rates of summer transplants (223). Summer transplanted trees will require an increased level of care after planting, especially watering. The heavy root balls can be expensive to transport and can limit the distance of distribution from the nursery.

Variations

If performed correctly, root pruning can result in a more branched and dense root system in the root ball (Figure 5-11) and reduce stress after transplanting (223, 598). The European nursery standards

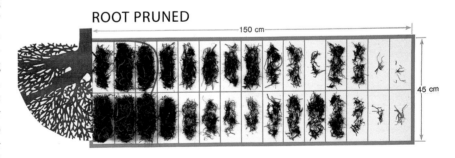

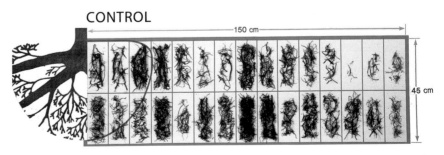

Figure 5-11 Correct root pruning procedures can increase the density of roots at the perimeter of the root ball substantially, but root density in the interior is unchanged (upper left segment). If there is too much time between root pruning and transplanting, root loss will still be very high (598).

Table 5-2 Examples of recommended minimum root ball sizes for nursery-grown plants (12, 14). The European Standard is based on trunk girth (cm). The American Standard is based on trunk diameter. Some values have been slightly rounded to merge standards. Smaller root balls of European stock may be explained by the transplanting requirement. Trees collected from other landscapes or wild lands usually have root systems that are less dense and more spreading than nursery-grown plants. Consequently, the root ball size must be increased to the next largest size class of plant.

MAXIMUM TRUNK SIZE				TIMES [3]	MINIMUM ROOT BALL DIAMETER				RATIO[5]	
Diameter[1]		Girth[2]		Transplanted	European Standard		American Standard[4]		European	American
cm	inches	cm	inches	—	cm	inches	cm	inches	—	—
2.5	1.0	8	3.1	2	25	10	40	16	9.8	16.0
3.8	1.5	12	4.7	3	35	14	50	20	9.2	13.3
5.1	2.0	16	6.3	3	45	18	60	24	8.8	12.0
6.4	2.5	20	7.9	3	55	22	70	28	8.6	11.2
8.0	3.0	25	9.8	4	60	24	80	32	7.9	10.7
9.6	4.0	30	11.8	4	70	28	105	42	6.9	10.5
11.1	4.5	35	13.8	4	80	31	120	48	7.0	10.7
12.7	5.0	40	15.7	5	90	35	135	54	7.1	10.8
15.9	6.5	50	19.7	5	120	47	165	65	7.3	10.0
19.1	7.5	60	23.6	6	130	51	190	75	6.8	10.0

[1] Measured 6 inches (15 cm) above the ground up to and including 4-inch (10 cm) size, and 12 inches (30 cm) above the ground for larger sizes.
[2] Measured 1 m above the soil.
[3] Specified only by the European Standard. Using the same criteria, most field-grown trees in the U.S. would be twice transplanted.
[4] Root balls less than 20 inches (50 cm)—depth not less than 65% of diameter, root balls 20 inches (50 cm) and greater—depth not less than 60% of diameter.
[5] Trunk diameter:root ball diameter.

specify trees by both size and the number of times they have been transplanted (Table 5-2). American standards do not, but most field-grown trees are transplanted twice during production. Root pruning may be essential on wild-collected trees, due to the less dense and more spreading nature of their root systems.

Because root pruning results in a substantial loss of roots, top growth can be slowed and trees may take longer to reach marketable size (342). Repeated root pruning can reduce the number of large roots and increase the number of small roots at the edge of the root ball (206, 223), which should improve root regeneration after planting (202). Timing may be an important factor. Root pruning only in the last year in the nursery did not slow growth, but did reduce the number of large roots at the edge of the root ball. Root pruning only in the last year did not increase the number of small roots (3–5 mm), but there may not have been enough time for the regenerated roots to grow to the 3 mm minimum size recorded. Roots less than 3 mm at the edge of the root ball should also be an advantage in root regeneration after planting (206).

Roots must be pruned so that a portion of the regenerated roots is contained in the final root ball. The pruning cuts must be at least 2–3 inches (5–7.5 cm) inside of the perimeter of the final root ball size (308, 598). Root pruning should be timed to take place early enough so that vigor is not reduced at digging, but not so late that the regenerated roots have once again spread widely when the tree is harvested (Figure 5-11). In some situations, trickle irrigation alone may promote a dense root system with limited spread if surrounding soils remain dry and less conducive to root growth (220, 444), but may not alter the size or number of roots cut at the perimeter of the root ball or improve survival (223).

In-ground fabric bags are used to restrict root spread for greater ease in harvesting and to reduce the size of the root ball for economy in shipping (Figure 5-12). The nonwoven fabric sides of the bag are designed to constrict roots as they penetrate the fabric, creating a dense proliferation of roots within the bag. The numerous small roots near the edge of the root ball facilitate regeneration of new roots more quickly after planting (202, 460, 563, 613).

Tree size should be within specified limits for the size of the fabric bag (Table 5-3). Trees grown for too long in the bags may become root bound and stunted. Trickle irrigation may be necessary in both the nursery and the landscape after planting to avoid drought stress from the restricted root system and small root ball (262, 460). Bags can be difficult to remove if many roots are protruding through the fabric after it is dug (18).

Figure 5-12 In-ground fabric bags are a system in which plants are grown in the ground within specially designed fabric bags. The bags are intended to limit root growth outside of the bag and to develop a more branched root system in a smaller root ball, but research data have not always been supportive of this method.

Table 5-3 Examples of recommended minimum fabric bag sizes for nursery-grown plants (12).

CALIPER*		HEIGHT**		FABRIC BAG DIAMETER	
inches	cm	feet	meters	inches	cm
1½	3.8	4	1.2	12	30
2	5.0	6	1.8	16	40
2½	6.3	7	2.1	18	45
3	7.6	8	2.4	20	50
3½	8.9	10	3.0	22	55
4	10.2	12	3.7	24	60

* Deciduous trees measured 4 inches (10 cm) above ground level
** Shrubs and evergreens

Results of research studies have been mixed on how well the bags actually perform in use (103, 114, 207, 278, 315, 336). Species variation seems to be a major factor.

Testing a similar concept, a piece of similar fabric was placed underneath the tree at the time of planting in the nursery. The fabric prevented roots at the bottom of the root ball from becoming large and increased the number of roots in the top third of the root ball on a tap-rooted species, live oak (*Quercus virginiana*) (223).

Balled-and-potted, also known as field-potted, stock is dug with a ball of earth and placed into a container instead of being wrapped with burlap. This method provides the flexibility of root balls without the precise digging and wrapping involved with ball-and-burlap. In temperate climates, the trees are usually dug in early spring or early fall, potted, and sold after the tree has had a chance to adjust to the stress of transplanting and the roots have filled the soil inside the container (135). In climates without extremely cold winter temperatures, nurseries can keep trees in these aboveground containers for more than one season, enlarging the container and pruning the roots periodically (Figure 5-13).

Figure 5-13 A type of balled-and-potted system. If the plants are held in the container for more than one season, the diameter of these containers can be enlarged. Sometimes, the container wall is replaced with burlap and twine for shipping.

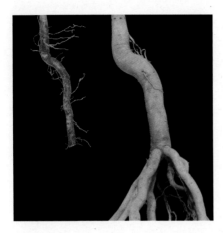

Figure 5-14 Root pruning young seedlings (left) produces adventitious roots at the cut end of the primary root that grow rapidly in the first year after transplanting (right). Many of the small natural lateral roots above the regenerated roots may be lost as well. A deeper adventitious root flare results.

Field potting is also feasible during the hot summer months after plants have made their initial flush of growth. Ideally, these plants should be dug early in the morning, potted, and moved immediately to a shady holding area with overhead sprinkler irrigation. The plants should be held in this area until sufficient root regeneration occurs and leaves remain turgid throughout the day.

Field soils will have different drainage characteristics in containers with bottoms and may become poorly drained. This method should only be used with well-drained soils or bottomless containers. However, if the soil is too sandy and the roots have not filled the entire container, the root ball can fall apart when the container is removed.

Selection

Trees should be selected and tagged at the nursery whenever possible. Trees selected should be specially marked so that species and cultivars can later be identified. It is best to mark the trunk on the north side for later reference when replanting (see Chapter 7).

Table 5-2 describes the relationship between trunk size and root ball diameter based on American and European standards. Other published standards vary somewhat and may be more specific to local conditions. Norwegian standards call for a larger root ball diameter that is four times the stem girth (circumference) or a 12:1 root ball diameter:stem diameter ratio for all sizes of trees (417).

Figure 5-15 The depth of the adventitious root flare is determined by the length of the primary root remaining after the seedling is root pruned, sometimes referred to as the root shank. In some cases, the adventitious root flare can be 12 inches (30 cm) or more below the soil surface.

Figure 5-16 A visible graft union is evidence that the tree was planted at the correct depth and should not be considered an imperfection.

Figure 5-17 Liners are sometimes planted so that the graft is below the soil in order to prevent sprouting from the understock. The root system will then be too deep.

Figure 5-18 Nursery cultivation practices that cause soil to accumulate near the base of the trunk can add to the depth of the roots in the root ball if not removed before harvesting.

It is not uncommon for the large, woody structural roots to be located too deep in the nursery. Nursery practices were first blamed for deep root systems without supporting data (53, 383). More recently, research has shown that the uppermost roots can average 3–4 inches (7.5–10 cm) deep in the growing fields and in harvested root balls (458, 589). The average depth may not be alarming in itself, but a substantial number of individual trees may have roots that are much deeper to achieve this average.

Several causes of deep roots in the nursery have been identified. Root pruning seedlings produces adventitious roots at the cut end of the primary root that grow rapidly (260, 281, 322). Many of the small, natural lateral roots above the regenerated roots may be lost as well (Figure 5-14). Honeylocust, sugar maple, and pear can lose up to 60% of these lateral roots in the first year after seedlings are transplanted (281). These vigorously growing adventitious roots and lack of natural lateral roots above them often develop into an "adventitious root flare" deeper in the soil than the natural root flare. The depth of the adventitious root flare is determined by the length of the primary root (root shank) after pruning (Figure 5-15). Even if the tree is planted at the original depth and the graft union is visible above ground, the adventitious root flare can be 12 inches (30 cm) or more below the soil surface.

Sometimes, the graft union is buried below the soil surface in the nursery because it is considered an imperfection, rather than as a positive sign that the tree is planted at the correct depth (Figure 5-16). Burying the graft union may also help to reduce sprouting from the root stock (Figure 5-17), and protect the graft area from herbicides. When trees are planted with the graft below the soil, it increases root flare depth by 2–4 inches (5–10 cm). Cultivation practices can cause

Figure 5-19 If the root system is too deep in the nursery, the root system may be confined to the bottom portion of the root ball.

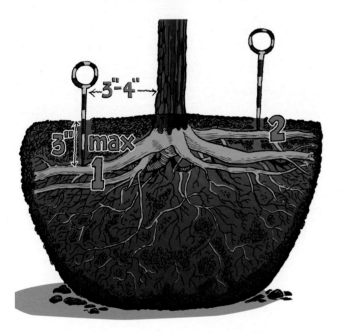

Figure 5-20 At least two structural roots should be within 1–3 inches of the soil surface, measured 3–4 inches from the trunk. They should be closer to the surface on root balls 20 inches (50 cm) or less in diameter. A surveyor's chaining pin can be used to probe the root ball before planting.

soil to accumulate near the base of the trunk (Figure 5-18). Sometimes, mounding soil around the base of the trunk is deliberate in order to create an area of drier soil around the base of the tree, where weeds will not readily germinate. This excess soil can increase the depth of the roots in the root ball if not removed before harvesting. Though trees with deep roots may grow well enough in the high quality soil of the nursery, they may struggle to survive when planted with the uppermost roots at the same depth on difficult urban sites with heavy soils and poor drainage (144, 383, 544).

Select trees with several major lateral roots close to the soil surface (593) (Figure 5-20). In the grower's field, these are often the most vigorous trees in the row. On trees over 2 inches (5 cm) caliper, a pronounced root flare may have started to develop, indicating strong formation of lateral roots. On smaller trees, use a simple test. Grasp the trunk about 4 feet above the ground and gently move it in a circular or rocking motion. If the first roots are too deep, the trunk will pivot deep in the soil, and a small gap will form between the trunk and the surrounding soil. A space around the trunk may have already opened from natural trunk movement in the wind. If the tree is planted at the proper depth, the trunk will pivot at or just below the surface, and no space will develop around it (Figure 5-21).

Whether preselected in the field, or not, when the trees arrive at the planting site, be sure the root ball diameter and depth (Table 5-2) are appropriate for the size of the tree, that the soil is firm, indicating adequate roots in the ball, and that the structural roots are at the correct depth. The ANSI Z60.1 American Standard for Nursery Stock states, "Soil above the root flare shall not be included in the root ball depth measurement" (12). If the depth measurement of the root ball without including excess soil over the root flare does not meet the minimum, the tree can be rejected.

Container-Grown Trees

Container production is used extensively to produce trees in climates without severe winters. Many of the reasons for its popularity are related to business and logistic considerations. In container production, nursery site selection is less soil type dependent than field production because specially prepared media are used in the containers. Containers can be rearranged as needed for efficient use of space. Lightweight, soilless substrate can be less expensive to ship and easier to handle at the planting site. The planting season can be extended to whenever the soil is not frozen.

In warmer regions (e.g., Hardiness Zones 7 through 11) container production is a common method of nursery production. Even large trees are container-grown in climates where overwintering is not a concern. Containers can be as large as 500 gallons (2,000 L). The largest containers are often boxes constructed of wood (Figure 5-22). The soilless substrate used in containers is well-drained to minimize the perched water table at the bottom of the container. Since there is no digging process to cause root loss, trees can be available from the nursery throughout the year.

Figure 5-21 A space will open at the base of the trunk from wind movement when the root system of a small tree is too deep (left), compared to a tree planted at the proper depth (right).

Limitations

The aboveground containers provide little protection from cold winter temperatures. In the north, cold, root-killing temperatures in the container

Figure 5-22 Container production is used extensively to grow trees in climates without severe winters. The largest containers are often boxes constructed of wood.

Figure 5-23 Light container soil media is needed for good drainage in container production, but can become excessively well-drained once installed in the landscape.

Figure 5-24 Pot-in-pot container production systems make the plants more stable and less susceptible to cold winter soil temperatures.

media can limit the use of containers in nurseries to smaller plants, which can be covered over the winter. Larger container trees sold in these regions are generally shipped from warmer climates and may not be hardy. The situation could change in the future as recent research has shown that the warm daytime temperatures from solar radiation on the dark containers may be more damaging than nighttime low temperatures (407), and this is more controllable during production.

Container substrates must be well-drained in order to provide sufficient aeration while in the pot. Once the container root ball is planted in the landscape, water moves easily from the coarse container soil to the finer textured landscape soil, and the root ball holds less water than it did in the container (Figure 5-23) (119, 411, 525). Containers are often irrigated more than once per day in the nursery. Irrigation is likely to be less frequent in the landscape, resulting in high levels of water stress, even though root loss was minimal (262). More frequent watering will be required than for ball-and-burlap stock for at least the first season, especially if planted in summer.

Variations

Trees in aboveground containers are subject to being blown over, often resulting in substantial increases in maintenance expense. In-ground container production systems reduce blow over and provide a more stable soil temperature. Pot-in-pot systems (20, 266, 469, 477) involve sinking an outer pot (socket or holder) into the ground and inserting a second pot (the pot that is harvested with the plant) in the pot that is buried in the ground (Figure 5-24). Roots growing between the pots are lost when harvested. This can make moving them in summer more stressful than traditional container systems. Soils in pot-in-pot containers can be 29°F (16°C) cooler in summer (489, 494) and less

Figure 5-25 Extreme low-profile containers are more suited to the spreading nature of root systems, but impractical to use commercially. (Photo: B. Appleton)

likely to have root damage. Since the trees are grown on wider spacings than typical containers, crowns are larger and trunk taper is improved.

A wide and shallow root system can speed establishment of trees after planting (539). Low-profile containers are wider than conventional containers and allow for more natural lateral root development. An early low-profile container developed for research was 30 inches (76 cm) in diameter. Circling roots were less likely to develop, and they resisted blow-over during production and after planting (Figure 5-25) (394). They were not practical for commercial use. Less extreme designs have been incorporated into commercial nursery production. Many of these designs consist of panels that can be combined to make the desired container size and many incorporate air root pruning features (Figure 5-26) (see the following section on Selection). Trees grown in low-profile root-pruning containers had larger trunks 5 years after planting than other types of containers (214). The shallow wide root ball of low profile containers may

Figure 5-26 Low-profile container designs have been incorporated into commercial nursery production. Some are constructed out of available materials, and many incorporate air root pruning features.

be an advantage when planted on poorly drained sites. Traditional taller container designs may be well-suited for landscape sites where the most consistent soil moisture is found in deeper soils.

Table 5-4 Examples of recommended minimum container sizes for nursery-grown trees (12).

CALIPER*		CONTAINER SIZE	
inches	cm	class	liters
0.75	1.8	10	34–43
1	2.5	15	45–60
1.25	3.0	25	94–112
1.75	4.5	45	153–187
2	5.0	65	221–246
2.5	6.3	95/100	340–416
* Deciduous trees measured 4 inches (10 cm) above ground level.			

Selection

Root systems of container-grown trees should be well-developed and hold the soil ball together when it is removed from the container, but should not be pot bound. Trees should be the appropriate size for their containers (Table 5-4) (12).

Many root defects are related to the container production. Because the natural spread of the root system is restricted by the container, lateral roots reaching the

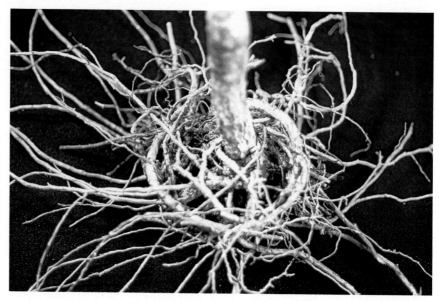

Figure 5-27 Circling roots can develop inside containers and cause problems after planting.

Figure 5-28 Containers designed to minimize circling roots may have ridges that deflect circling roots or openings that air prune roots. Roots may still grow extensively against the inside of the container wall, even though they don't circle extensively.

sides are deflected. Circling roots were the first to be recognized as a problem. Circling roots can strangle the tree a few years after planting, as both the roots and the stem grow larger (Figure 5-27). Various pot designs with ridges and openings were developed to minimize circling roots as early as the 1980s (Figure 5-28) (18, 20, 449, 612).

When roots encounter the wall of these improved container designs, they can still be deflected in other directions, and many container designs have since been developed to reduce these defects as well. Designs include openings in the sides and bottom to air prune roots (kill the root tips that become exposed to the air), shapes to deflect roots, and chemical treatments to stop root tips as they reach the container wall. Tests of numerous container designs have shown that they can reduce the number of circling and deflected roots, but ascending, descending, or kinked roots can still develop (Figure 5-29) (7, 216, 219, 374). Though the number of root defects differed with container design, there was no difference in tree growth during nursery production, or for the first 5 years after planting in the landscape (214, 216). The consequences of root defects may not become evident until it is too late to correct them.

Root defects caused by container walls persist after repotting or transplanting unless pruned (638). Multiple layers of circling roots that develop within the root ball from successive stages of production can be difficult to detect. Most defects are hidden from view because they are found below the substrate surface (Figure 5-30) (217). Slicing root ball edges reduces circling roots, but not descending roots (219).

Another approach has been to apply a coating to the inside wall of the pot containing copper hydroxide or to use a fabric liner impregnated with the same compound, in order to stunt the roots as they contact the inside of the container (Figure 5-31) (24, 30, 31, 33, 93, 376, 385). The copper compound must be applied to the entire interior wall of the container. Applying the chemical only in stripes to save money is not effective (21). Root response to the copper treatment may or may not result in better root growth after planting (67, 530). In the correct concentration, the copper compound does not appear to be toxic to the plant (3, 376, 478). Not all species respond well to the copper treatments (51, 530, 638).

Figure 5-29 Ascending, descending, or kinked root defects can develop in container production, even if circling roots are prevented by pot designs.

High soil temperatures (112°F to 122°F; 45°C to 50°C) on the sun-exposed side of the pot can kill roots (67, 185, 312, 328, 378, 429, 637). Heat stress on roots during production can cause an inhibition of root growth for up to 4 months after the plants are installed in the landscape (377, 489). High soil temperatures from sun exposure, or saturated soils in the bottom of the container from overirrigation, may help to eliminate circling roots, but they are not good management practices.

If the structural roots are too deep in the container, vigor can be reduced (87, 193, 194, 257). Root defects can be increased as roots are deflected up and back across the root ball, and a dense mat of roots can fill the soil above the woody roots that form the root flare (162, 215, 217) (Figure 5-32). This result can make it impossible to plant the woody roots at the correct depth without destroying a substantial portion of the root ball.

Tree Quality

Since most trees are expected to have a long life expectancy, it is important to plant good quality trees. The quality of a tree at planting can have a large impact on longevity in the landscape. Tree quality is based on trunk, branch, crown, leaf, and root characteristics.

How a grower produces and handles trees can affect performance after planting. In an evaluation of similar trees shipped from 12 different nurseries, great variation was found in root development, tissue moisture content, and growth after

Figure 5-30 Multiple layers of circling roots can develop from successive stages of production.

Figure 5-32 If the structural roots are too deep in the container, a dense mat of roots can fill the soil above the woody roots that form the root flare. This result can make it impossible to plant at the correct depth without substantial root damage. (Photo: D. Fare)

Figure 5-31 The plant on the left was grown in a pot with a copper compound applied to the inside wall of the container to minimize circling roots and root growth against the container wall. The plant on the right was grown in an untreated container. (Photo: B. Appleton)

Figure 5-33 The practice of heading back trees in the nursery to stimulate branching can result in an undesirable group of branches originating at the same point. If excess branches have not been removed at the nursery, prune them out at planting time.

Figure 5-34 Trees with codominant stems and included bark in crotches (above) should be avoided. The bark should push up to form a small ridge in the crotch (below).

planting (334). This variation could be due to differences in plant genetics, cultural practices, or shipping conditions. Higher rates of fertilization in the nursery increased shoot and root growth after planting (62).

Trees produced by all nursery methods should meet certain basic quality standards. Published standards are often a minimum standard for the industry (e.g., American Standard for Nursery Stock). The best growers offer plants that exceed the minimum standards. The Florida Grades and Standards (11) go one step further and not only describe minimum criteria for acceptable quality plants, but also higher quality grades. It allows the nursery industry to precisely communicate the attributes of its product.

Only healthy trees with well-formed tops that are characteristic of the species should be planted. The proper relationship between caliper and height for trees is well described in the American Standard for Nursery Stock (12). Heights greater than those listed for a given caliper indicate a spindly trunk that may not be capable of standing upright without support when in full leaf. A tapered trunk decreases in diameter with height. On small caliper trees, rigidly staking a tree prevents trunk flexing and can contribute to a poorly tapered trunk. A staking system that allows some side-to-side movement of the trunk encourages taper development (270). The base of the trunk should be examined for evidence of girdling roots, mechanical injury, and gnawing injury by rodents.

The better the branch structure when the tree is purchased, the less pruning will be required after planting. Trees that have been properly trained and pruned in the nursery should develop a structure which will be resistant to damage from winds and other outside forces. Proper distribution of branches also promotes development of good trunk taper. Both staking and removing the lower branches prematurely can reduce trunk taper. Removing lower branches can also reduce root development, which could affect transplanting success (635). Trees grown for street plantings and other landscape uses where pedestrian and vehicle traffic are expected nearby must often be pruned up higher, but no more than the lower half of the trunk should be pruned free of branches (12).

Branches on broad-leaved trees should be well spaced, both vertically and around the circumference, for strong attachments and unrestricted flow of water and nutrients in the trunk. The practice of heading back the leader to encourage lateral branches in the nursery can lead to several branches originating at the same point (Figure 5-33). This can result in a very weak structure that is susceptible to storm damage as the tree grows. The central leader should be re-established in the nursery. If still present when purchased, it is very important to prune out some of these branches, leaving those with the best position and branch attachment (see Chapter 8). Conifers normally form numerous branches (whorls) at the same level with each year's growth.

Branches should diverge from the trunk at a wide angle except in cultivars that normally grow in narrow, upright (fastigiate) forms. Two or more nearly equal-diameter stems are known as codominant stems. Trees with codominant stems or included bark (bark imbedded between two stems) in the branch crotches should be avoided (Figure 5-34). These should not be present in the lower two-thirds of the tree. Pruning wounds on the trunk should not exceed 1-inch (2.5 cm) diameter or 25% of the circumference of the trunk, whichever is smaller, and should be completely closed. Good nursery practices include pruning to develop good branch structure early in production. Large pruning cuts or little callus formation indicate that pruning was delayed too long.

Figure 5-35 Abnormal growth differences at the graft union can be a sign of a weak graft union that may break in heavy winds.

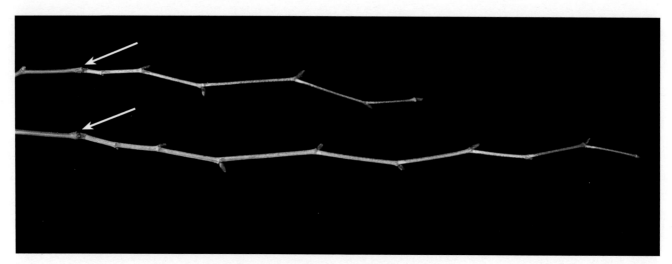

Figure 5-36 Comparison of twig growth and bud development from a vigorous tree (below) and a stressed tree (above). Stress reduces twig extension. The arrows indicate the beginning of the current season's growth.

On grafted trees, abnormal growth differences at the union can be a sign of a problem (Figure 5-35). Weak graft unions can break in heavy winds, even years after planting. Substantial differences in bark characteristics above and below the graft usually indicate that the root stock is not the same species as the scion. This is often acceptable, but know the origin of the root stock to be certain that the roots will be adapted to the planting site. Certain species are very prone to producing basal sprouts from the root stock. If the scion dies during an early stage of production, it is possible for a sprout from the root stock to replace it without being noticed. Be sure that the tree is true to cultivar name.

Trees should exhibit adequate twig growth during the most recent 2–4 years and have well-formed buds (Figure 5-36). Normal twig growth may vary from 4–48 inches (10–120 cm) annually and should be characteristic of the species. Trees should be vigorous specimens free from insects and diseases. Trunk bark should be firm, with no indication of fungus cankers or galls, insect borers, dieback, frost cracks, sunscald, or mechanical injury.

Palms that have been subjected to long-term stresses caused by severe nutritional or water deficiencies often display a constriction of the trunk that corresponds to the period of time during which the stress occurred (Figure 5-37). The constrictions inhibit the translocation of water and nutrients in the vascular system. Such trees are also less able to withstand wind damage. Only specimens that have not developed severe constrictions of the trunk area should be selected. In addition, nutrient deficiencies are common in palms (75). Trees that exhibit symptoms of nutritional deficiency should not be selected.

To obtain the best trees possible, you must be sure that the source is compatible with your region, and this includes the root stock. The nursery production method must be right for the time and place you are planting. And of course, the vigor and health of the trees must be excellent. Choosing high quality trees, along with choosing the right tree and proper site preparation all contribute to planting success.

Figure 5-37 Constriction of a palm trunk is caused by long-term stress. Avoid plants with evidence of this type of constriction.

CHAPTER 6

Maintain Quality to the Planting Site

Equipment used to transplant trees has changed with time, but the need to maintain quality from the nursery to the planting site has not.

Trees are most vulnerable to damage and stress during the time between digging and replanting. Like a goldfish being transported home from the pet store in a plastic bag, anything that goes wrong can have serious consequences. When a tree is dug from the field, the physical size and functional capacity of the tree root system is reduced, and water stress can develop quickly. Mechanical injury can easily occur when the tree is being moved. The many years of hard work put into producing a quality tree can be compromised very quickly if not carefully handled.

Most trees are obtained from the grower already dug and wrapped, but thorough knowledge of the procedures used in transplanting nursery stock can be valuable in judging the quality of the trees when they arrive at the job site. Digging field-grown stock, storing until they are shipped, and loading and unloading the trees requires specialized knowledge and equipment. The grower may be responsible for assuring that the trees arrive at the job site or retail outlet in the same excellent condition as when they left the nursery, but sometimes their responsibility ends when the trees are loaded on the truck. The cost of harvesting and shipping can be a substantial portion of the cost of the tree and should not be considered of secondary importance. If care is not taken during these steps, quality trees ready for harvest may not be quality trees when received by the customer.

Tying Branches

Tops of spreading or low-branching trees should be tied before digging to facilitate handling and to avoid damage during harvest and shipping (Figure 6-1). On taller trees, the branches can be tied more easily after the tree has been dug and tipped. Limbs should not be tied so tightly that the bark is compressed by a sharp bend at the base of the branch. Care should be taken to avoid injuring the bark and splitting or breaking branches.

Figure 6-1 Tops of spreading or low-branching trees should be tied to facilitate handling and to avoid damage during harvest and shipping.

Bare-Root Trees

Root Spread

Smaller deciduous trees are often dug bare-root. The American Standard for Nursery Stock (12) lists minimum root spread standards in relation to tree size for the United States. Table 5-1 provides a summary of these specifications that could also serve as general guidelines where local standards do not exist. Trees collected from native stands should be dug with a root spread one-third greater than the spread of roots listed in the table.

Digging Procedures

Nurseries digging dormant bare-root trees usually have well-drained friable soils so that trees can be dug with less damage to the roots. Nurseries dig deciduous trees in the fall after they go dormant. Mechanized harvesting equipment is used for lifting the trees from nursery rows (Figure 6-2). Pruning the tops and roots may be required before planting.

Overwinter Storage

Fall harvesting has advantages. Fields are not usually as wet as in the spring, avoiding the possibility that wet conditions could delay harvest. Fall-dug trees can be available at the appropriate time for spring planting, even if the trees are being shipped to an area with an earlier spring season.

In climates without harsh winters, trees can be heeled in with sawdust or mulch for the winter (Figure 6-3). Buildings with controlled temperature and humidity are also used (Figure 6-4). Cold storage is necessary to meet the normal winter chilling requirements of the fall-harvested trees. Below freezing storage temperatures reduce the rate of respiration and disease incidence, but induce high moisture stress. The optimum storage temperature for most trees is just above freezing (106). Root regeneration of seedlings is increased by cold storage until the maximum requirement of each species is met (599). The rate of root regeneration decreases if stored too long, possibly due to carbohydrate depletion (158, 384).

Figure 6-2 Bare-root trees being harvested in the nursery.

Figure 6-3 In mild climates, bare-root stock harvested in the fall is often heeled in outdoors, until it is shipped in spring.

Figure 6-4 Bare-root stock can be stored over winter in buildings with controlled temperature and humidity.

Trees lose water from both roots and stems while in cold storage (45). Moderate water stress can reduce root regeneration. High water stress can stop root regeneration (552). Trees harvested during complete dormancy are more resistant to desiccation during storage than trees harvested in early stages of dormancy (101, 159, 401).

Heeling In

When storing a limited number of trees at the job site for a short period, trees should be heeled in by covering the roots and lower portion of the stems with moist soil or mulch (Figure 6-5). The trees should be shaded to keep the tops cool. Do not attempt to overwinter trees in cold climates by heeling in.

Breaking Dormancy

Buds on some tree species become quite dry during winter storage and need rehydration to induce them to break dormancy after planting as bare-root stock. Sweating is the term used to refer to the process that forces bud break and active growth. The main goals are to rehydrate the root systems and to increase the humidity and temperature surrounding the trees. These conditions stimulate growth to start.

Sweating is best done inside a building where the temperature can be maintained between 50°F and 70°F (10°C to 21°C). Soaking the roots in water for several hours ensures proper hydration. The dormant trees can be laid flat between

Figure 6-5 Bare-root trees should be heeled in by covering the roots and lower portion of the stems with moist soil or mulch until ready to plant.

layers of moistened burlap, straw, or similar material and covered with a tarp or a sheet of plastic to create a humid environment. Once the buds begin to swell (usually within 3–7 days), the trees are ready to be planted.

Not everyone agrees on which trees would benefit from sweating, but collectively they include: maple (*Acer*), serviceberry (*Amelanchier*), birch (*Betula*), especially river birch (*Betula nigra*), hornbeam (*Carpinus*), hickory (*Carya*), hackberry (*Celtis*), redbud (*Cercis*), hawthorn (*Crataegus*), ash (*Fraxinus*), honeylocust (*Gleditsia*), Kentucky coffeetree (*Gymnocladus*), sweetgum (*Liquidambar*), apple and crabapple (*Malus*), mulberry (*Morus*), blackgum (*Nyssa*), pear (*Pyrus*), oak (*Quercus*), willow specified (*Salix*), European mountainash (*Sorbus*), lilac (*Syringa*), cypress (*Taxodium*), and linden (*Tilia*) (247).

Shipping

Conditions during shipping are as important as during storage. Covered, temperature-controlled trucks should be used for long-distance transport. Roots must be packed in moist peat moss, straw, sawdust, or wood chips.

Trees with a Soil Ball

Root Ball Size

Larger sizes of deciduous trees, and all but the smallest evergreens, are often transplanted with a soil ball. Nursery grown stock can be dug by hand or with mechanical devices specially designed for nursery conditions (Figure 6-6).

Published standards for root ball sizes are intended to assure that they are of sufficient diameter and depth to encompass enough of the root system for the full recovery of the plant. Table 5-2 lists recommended minimum root ball sizes for trees based on standards from the United States and Europe for trees up to 8 inches (20 cm) caliper.

The final root ball size may vary from these guidelines depending on factors such as the species of tree and the type of soil in which it is growing. Species that are normally difficult to transplant may benefit from larger root balls more than those of species that are easily moved. Increasing the root ball diameter by 20% did not increase growth of sugar maple (*Acer saccharum*), a species not considered difficult to transplant, after planting (265). When root-ball diameter was increased by 40%, leaf area of seven species was

Figure 6-6 Growers use mechanical root ball digging machinery. Many have tracks that allow access to wet fields in the spring (lower). The machine in the upper photo has a rotating blade that produces a round root ball. (Upper photo: I. Solfjeld)

increased inconsistently in the first year, but not twig growth (523). Trees collected from native stands should be dug with a root ball at least one size larger than standard (Table 5-2).

Table 6-1 Estimated weight of soil balls.

Ball Diameter		Ball Depth		Approximate Ball and Tree Weight			
inches	cm	inches	cm	lbs	kg	U.S. tons	Metric tons
10	25	8	20	34	15		
12	30	9	23	55	25	–	–
14	35	11	28	91	42	–	–
16	40	12	30	124	56	–	–
18	45	14	35	193	88	–	–
20	50	15	38	254	115	–	–
24	60	16	41	392	178	–	–
28	70	19	48	624	283	–	–
32	80	20	50	867	394	–	–
36	90	22	55	1216	552	–	–
42	105	25	63	1877	853	–	–
48	120	29	74	–	–	1.5	1.3
60	150	32	81	–	–	2.4	2.2
72	180	34	86	–	–	307	3.4
84	210	36	91	–	–	5.4	4.9
96	240	38	96	–	–	7.4	6.8
108	280	40	100	–	–	9.9	9.0
120	300	40	100	–	–	12.2	11.1

Soils balls are heavy. Table 6-1 lists approximate weights. Water adds to the weight, but root balls should never be allowed to dry out to make them lighter. A mass of soil without roots should be avoided. Heavy clay on the bottom of a ball adds considerable weight and contains few roots. If the root ball is dug shallower than normal for this reason, add extra width to make up for the missing roots. The physical properties of many soils, however, require a greater depth to ensure that the soil ball will not fracture during transport to the new site.

Forming the Root Ball

In the temperate climates, trees with soil balls are generally dug when they are dormant. Trees that will be transplanted during winter should be selected in the fall and mulched with straw or wood chips before the ground freezes.

Growers digging large numbers of trees during the busy and short harvest seasons use mechanical diggers for greater efficiency (Figure 6-6). Trenching machines and backhoes are sometimes used to rough-dig larger trees before shaping the soil ball by hand (Figure 6-7).

Figure 6-7 On larger trees, backhoes can be used to rough-dig very large trees before shaping the soil ball by hand.

Hand-digging procedures vary somewhat by size of the root ball. Digging, wrapping, and handling root balls correctly takes skill, experience, and specialized equipment. If not done correctly, the root ball will break apart, roots will be damaged, and the tree may not survive.

The soil will be easier to dig and will hold together better when moist. The tree will be less stressed if well-watered. If the soil is excessively wet, the root ball will not be stable enough to hold its shape (Figure 6-8), and damage to fine roots will result.

The major roots should be within 3 inches (7.5 cm) of the root ball surface on root balls greater than 20 inches (50 cm) in diameter, less on smaller root balls (see Chapter 5). If the roots are too deep, excess surface soil should be removed before or after digging, and the root ball depth should meet standards after it is removed.

Root balls should have a rounded top edge and uniformly tapered sides. Smaller balls may be nearly oval in profile. Larger root balls should be 6–12 inches (15–30 cm) smaller at the base than at the widest point just below the rounded top edge (Figure 6-9).

Figure 6-8 When root balls are too wet, or if they lack adequate roots, they can be easily distorted during handling and transport, causing damage to many fine roots.

Figure 6-9 Smaller root balls are nearly oval in profile (left). Larger root balls should be narrower at the base (right).

Supporting the Root Ball

Root balls are wrapped with burlap and twine to support the root ball during transport. It is important that the burlap and twine are very tight and secure. Use only natural fiber materials that will substantially deteriorate in 90 days, and will be decompose completely after a year. Multiple layers can deteriorate a little slower, but not long enough to interfere with root growth. Synthetic materials will cause the death of trees in the landscape when not removed. Some natural fiber materials are chemically treated to render them resistant to decay. They can still be intact and very strong after 2 years, and starting to girdle roots (351).

Machine-dug trees are sometimes placed directly into wire baskets lined with burlap. The baskets can be ordered in many sizes, and final tightening around the root ball can be easily accomplished with the twist of a hook (Figure 6-10). The top of the soil ball is tied closed with twine. This system provides excellent support for the root ball during shipping, but the basket does not rust away for many years and should be at least partially removed after planting to avoid root constriction or

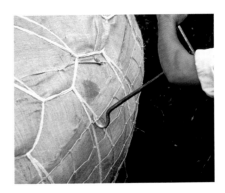

Figure 6-10 Final tightening of wire used to support the root ball during handling can be easily accomplished with the twist of a hook.

Figure 6-11 Wire baskets are sometimes used to support the soil ball during shipping, but the basket does not rust away for many years. Standard baskets have wire high on the root ball where it can later girdle roots if not removed at planting.

a hazardous situation if the wire protrudes above ground (see Chapter 7).

Most baskets are designed so that the wire comes up high on the sides of the root ball and the top wire loops are folded over the top of the root ball and tied together (Figure 6-11). On newer designs the wire comes only part way up the side of the root ball (Figure 6-12). For most soils, this new design provides adequate support for the root ball during shipping and may reduce root girdling because the flare roots usually develop above the wire. Outside of the United States, other types of wire support for root balls use smaller gauge wire and may rust away faster (Figure 6-13). Plastic baskets intended to break as the roots grow against them were introduced in the 1980s (187), but never became widely used.

On large root balls, drum lacing and top lacing are often supplemented with a layer of wire fencing or stiff wire cloth to provide additional support instead of a manufactured basket (Figure 6-14).

Figure 6-12 Low-profile baskets (top) provide adequate support for the root ball while reducing the risk of root girdling because the flare roots usually develop above the wire.

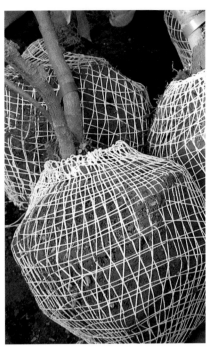

Figure 6-13 Some wire support systems for root balls use smaller gauge wire and may rust away faster (above). String nets can be used to support smaller root balls. Use only natural fiber materials that will decompose completely if not removed at planting (above right).

Figure 6-14 Large root balls are often drum laced, top laced, and wrapped with wire cloth for extra support. The wire must be removed during the planting process.

Summer Digging

Growers have techniques at their disposal to reduce water stress in trees dug with foliage in summer. Stage digging is a process by which portions of the root ball are dug over a period of a several days or longer, while being generously watered (Figure 6-15). This process allows the tree to adapt to the stress gradually.

Trees dug from the field in-leaf continue to transpire at a high rate for at least a few days before adjusting (475). When trees dug in-leaf are stored for at least a few days in a protected holding area, they are said to be "hardened off." Hardening off is used to acclimate trees to root loss and to minimize transpiration and water stress. In addition to heeling in the root ball with wood chips and irrigating to keep it moist, ideally the foliage should be shaded, shielded from wind, and misted frequently with water during daylight hours. It may be necessary to harden off trees for up to 2 weeks to be sure trees will survive summer digging. In the holding area, the process of root regeneration may be initiated, and the tree may also drop a few leaves, reducing transpiration. Therefore, the tree may be able to establish more quickly once moved to the more stressful landscape site (200).

Winter Digging

A few extra precautions are required when trees are moved with frozen soil balls. Although the term "frozen soil ball" is commonly used, in reality, only the outer 4–6 inches (10–15 cm) of the ball soil should be allowed to freeze. If the ball is allowed to freeze too deeply, or get too cold, root damage is possible. Root systems are less tolerant of cold temperatures and may be severely injured or killed if exposed to extreme freezing temperatures in the root ball. Root-killing temperatures vary with species.

After the root ball is dug and the outer 4–6 inches (10–15 cm) is allowed to freeze, the root ball should be mulched to prevent further freezing during storage or transport. The root ball must be protected from thawing during the moving process, or it could fall apart.

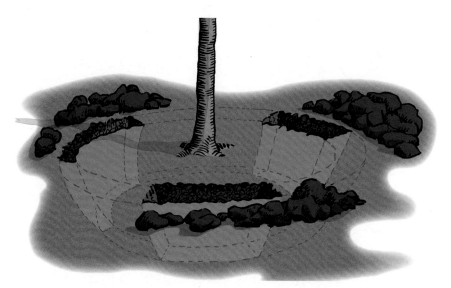

Figure 6-15 Stage digging can improve success when trees are dug in summer. Portions of the root ball are dug over a period of a several days or longer to give the tree a chance to adapt to the stress gradually.

The planting location should also be heavily mulched before the ground freezes or digging may be impossible. After the hole is dug, both the hole and the backfill soil should be mulched to prevent them from freezing before the tree is planted. After the tree is planted, it should be mulched.

Moving the Soil Ball

It may take more than one person to lift even a small ball. A tree should never be lifted by the trunk. Trees weighing up to 500 lbs. (225 kg) can be moved short distances on a hand pushcart (Figure 6-16). Moving larger balls, or small root balls longer distances, will require powered equipment. Bucket loaders are often used, but can cause damage to the soil ball and tree trunk (Figure 6-17). Several kinds of specialized equipment and accessories for conventional power equipment are available for lifting root balls (Figure 6-18).

In-Ground Fabric Bags

Trees growing in fabric bags in the field may be dug with a hand spade. For greater efficiency, large numbers of trees can be lifted out of the ground with specialized tractor-mounted equipment (460). The root balls are transported in the bags with no additional wrapping. The top of the bag is sometimes laced together with twine. The bags must be removed before planting. Growers may remove the bag and replace it with burlap or a container before shipping to make the tree more appealing to the buyer, especially for retail customers.

Storage

Field-grown ball-and-burlap plants are best dug in late winter or early spring while they are still dormant, but are sometimes held for planting until later in the season. If cared for properly, trees with root balls can be stored (heeled in) for several months without damage (527) (Figure 6-19). This allows nurseries to dig trees in the spring and have them available throughout the season. The trees are placed in an area with good

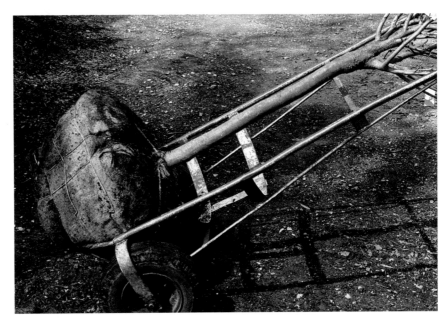

Figure 6-16 Hand carts are useful for moving small trees. Many designs are available commercially.

Figure 6-17 Bucket loaders are often used to move root balls, but can cause damage to tree trunk.

Figure 6-18 Several kinds of specialized equipment and accessories for conventional equipment are available for lifting root balls.

surface drainage and covered with a loose, damp medium to help keep the root ball moist. Composted wood chips or sawdust are often used for this purpose. Sometimes, they are temporarily replanted in holes lined with geotextile fabric until sold (Figure 6-20). Because decomposition of fresh wood chips, and especially sawdust, can produce a large amount of heat, provision must be made for regular watering, if and when temperatures in the mulch approach 90°F (24°C). Wrapping root balls in plastic shrink-wrap is another way to prevent evaporation from the root ball (Figure 6-21).

For long-term storage, partial shade and an irrigation system are beneficial. A dilute solution of a soluble fertilizer should be applied to the root balls two or three times during the growing season. The root ball may need to be watered several times a day for several weeks (up to 2 months on larger trees) until the trees have fully acclimated, and then once a day until the trees are sold. A bed of wood chips or sawdust settles rapidly. Additional mulch may have to be added from time to time to keep the root balls covered.

If mulched in for several months, roots may begin to grow out of the root ball and into the mulch (Figure 6-22). The natural tendency is to try to preserve all new root growth when the tree is moved, but doing so may be

Figure 6-19 Ball-and-burlap trees being stored until needed for planting. Close spacing helps to protect from sun and wind exposure. Trickle irrigation is being used to keep root balls moist.

Figure 6-20 Some growers place the root ball back into the hole lined with a geotextile fabric for long-term storage.

problematic. When the tree is moved, the mulch will fall away and the roots will be exposed. The original burlap is often deteriorated to the point that the root ball must be wrapped with a new layer of burlap, or a second layer may have to be added just to protect the new roots. During wrapping, the roots will be bent at a sharp angle and pressed against the surface of the root ball. The roots should not be left in this position. It will be difficult to position them in their original orientation and fill around them with soil at the planting site even if the outer layer of burlap is

Figure 6-21 Plastic shrink-wrap is another way to prevent evaporation from the root ball during storage and shipping.

Figure 6-22 When root balls are held in mulch for several months, roots may begin to grow out of the root ball and be difficult to orient correctly when planting. It is best to remove them before planting.

removed. If the roots are not straightened they will grow kinked or develop circling roots. It may be best to prune off the new roots. Wrapping the sides of the root ball in fabric coated with the same copper compound used to coat the inside of containers will inhibit this root growth, but it may only be practical to use on larger root balls that are planned to be stored for many months (Figure 6-23).

Shipping

For their size and weight, harvested root balls are very fragile. Even with the support of lacing and wire baskets, visible damage can incur while handling the trees. This is generally seen as cracking and loosening of the soil near the top and sides of the root ball and compaction at the bottom of the root ball. When the soil shifts within the root ball, fine roots are torn or broken. If the root ball is dropped, or roughly handled, major root damage can result. Mechanical damage to the root ball is often greater from handling the tree than from the transportation process. While in transit, 88% fewer shocks were measured than during the handling operation (342).

Trees are usually tipped horizontally when shipped. When trees are being loaded on a truck or trailer bed for shipping, care must be taken to avoid injuring the tree or breaking the soil ball. Blocks and strapping are used to secure the root ball. The trunk of larger trees may be supported with a specially made stand (Figure 6-24). One side of a large root ball may be flattened to help stabilize it during shipping (Figure 6-25). The trunk and branches should be padded with several thicknesses of burlap or carpet to prevent bruising wherever contact is made.

Trees should be covered when transported on an open bed (Figure 6-26). Even dormant trees and their root balls can be desiccated when transported

Figure 6-23 Wrapping the sides of the root ball in fabric coated with copper compound will inhibit growth of roots into surrounding mulch during long-term storage. The fabric should be removed along with any roots that penetrate it (bottom) before wrapping the root ball with burlap to move it.

Figure 6-24 The trunk of larger trees can be supported with a specially made stand to stabilize it on a long trip.

uncovered at highway speeds. Covering is absolutely imperative when trees are transported with leaves. A Saran™ cloth or burlap tarp will protect foliage from wind while driving. A layer of wet burlap under the tarp will help to keep leaves moist (Figure 6-27). Be careful to avoid heat build-up under the tarp while parked in the sun. In warm weather, trees in-leaf should be covered immediately before being transported, and the cover should be removed immediately after arriving at the destination.

The importance of keeping the soil ball moist during and after shipping cannot be stressed too strongly. Excessive drying of the soil ball can be a serious problem, especially if the trees are in-leaf.

Figure 6-25 Some growers flatten one side of large root balls to stabilize them during shipping. The root ball volume does not have to be altered to create this shape. (Photo: J. Urban)

Figure 6-26 Cover trees when transporting them on an open bed, even when they are dormant.

Figure 6-27 A layer of wet burlap under the tarp will help to keep leaves moist when trees are moved with foliage.

Once the soil ball dries, it can be very difficult to rewet the ball thoroughly until after it is planted. The outer few inches of a small root ball can contain 50% of the total soil volume. When this outer layer of soil is allowed to dry out excessively, half of the fine roots can be damaged.

Wrapping the root balls in plastic shrink-wrap keeps the root ball soil moist during shipping (Figure 6-21). It is easy to forget that soil balls may arrive at the planting site dry if it has been a few days since they were dug at the nursery. Inspect trees thoroughly when received, and continue to monitor them until planted. A short delay of just two or three days before planting can also result in serious drought stress.

Figure 6-28 Tree spades are available in many sizes. This one digs a root ball 125 inches (3.2 m) in diameter. (Photo: The Davey Tree Expert Company)

Mechanical Tree Spades

Many models of tree spades are designed for moving trees with trunks 4–10 inches (10–30 cm) in diameter. These machines are similar to the mechanical diggers used in the nursery, but truck-mounted tree spades are designed to dig, transport, and replant the tree directly into a previously tree spade–dug hole (Figure 4-5, Figure 6-28).

If the job calls for only a few trees and the distance between the nursery and planting site is short, it is often economical to use a tree spade. Tree spades are used to remove trees that have outgrown their space in the landscape because it is quick and leaves minimal disturbance. The size and weight of the truck and soil ball may limit access to some areas. Tree spades cannot usually be used on hillsides.

The same ratio of tree caliper to ball size should be followed as for other methods of digging soil balls. As with other transplanting methods, trees in-leaf should be covered while being transported. Because trees are usually transported a short distance, and the root ball is constantly supported by the spades throughout the process, success rates for trees moved with a tree spade in-leaf are usually very good. Because spade dug trees in-leaf cannot be hardened off after digging special care after planting is required.

Palms

Palm trees are monocots and do not have true wood. They do not have a vascular cambium and are not capable of generating new tissue to cover injured areas. Avoid any mechanical damage to the trunks of palms. Terminal buds of palms must always be carefully protected from damage, since it is only from this structure that palms develop new growth.

Digging

Palms have an adventitious root system composed of numerous fibrous primary roots that arise independently and periodically from the root initiation zone at the base of the stem (555). Nearly all palms produce new roots from the base when

Figure 6-29 Palms are often moved with very small root balls. (Photo: E. Gilman)

roots are cut. Root pruning 4–6 weeks prior to digging may be helpful in stimulating new root production (80)

For most species, root balls with a 12-inch (30 cm) radius from the trunk and 12 inches (30 cm) deep are adequate because they capture over half the roots (Figure 6-29). The few species, such as cabbage palms (*Sabal palmetto*), that must grow nearly all their new roots from the trunk after transplanting, need a root ball only large enough to protect the root initiation zone, about 6 inches (15 cm) out from the trunk (71, 123, 288, 292). Species that grow about 30% or more of their roots below 12 inches (30 cm) deep, such as pindo palm (*Butia capitata*), Chinese fan palm (*Livistona chinensis*), and queen palm (*Syagrus romanzoffiana*), would benefit from a root ball about 24 inches (60 cm) deep (288). Mexican fan palm (*Washingtonia robusta*), Senegal date palm (*Phoenix reclinata*), royal palm (*Roystonea regia*), and queen palm (*Syagrus romanzoffiana*) roots have higher survival rates if the roots are cut farther from the trunk and would benefit from larger root balls (78, 80).

Storage

Palms not immediately replanted should be heeled in like any other tree. Transferring palms to containers is another good way to hold trees. Irrigation and protection from excess sun are essential.

Transporting

Some or all of the palm leaves are often removed prior to transport. The proper method varies with species and circumstances. Complete leaf removal to reduce transpirational water loss greatly improves survival of species like sabal palm (*Sabal palmetto*), which must generate an entirely new root system when transplanted. With Canary Island date palms (*Phoenix canariensis*), pygmy date palm (*Phoenix roebelenii*), queen palms (*Syagrus romanzoffiana*), and Mexican fan palms (*Washingtonia robusta*), leaf removal resulted in the least amount of new leaf and root growth and offered no benefit (72, 289, 292). Some lower leaves can be removed to improve aesthetic quality by eliminating leaves that are likely to die and turn brown from transplant stress (289).

Palms are lifted in most instances by means of a strap or sling placed just above the estimated balance point on the trunk. The small size and weight of the root ball offers no logical means of lifting by the ball. Nylon slings should be used because they offer a high degree of protection for the palm trunk. When a sling is being attached to the trunk, the surface must be protected from burn or compression marks that will form permanent scars.

When many single-stemmed palms are to be transported, they can be literally laid flat or shingled on a flatbed trailer. The tops should always be tied securely.

Transplanted palms with long slender trunks should have a supporting timber attached to its trunk during transport. This important protective support is justified because the alternative is the possible loss of the essential terminal bud and the ultimate death of the palm.

Large Trees

Before modern heavy equipment was available to handle the weight of large root balls, trees 15 inches (38 cm) and greater in trunk diameter were moved bare-root (175) (Figure 4-6). The practice of moving large trees bare-root is regaining popularity, but no research data is available to support the successes of practitioners. Trees up to 26 inches dbh have been reported to be successfully moved with this method. Trees have been moved any time except during active twig expansion, as long as the soil is not frozen. Conifers have also been moved with this method.

Pneumatic excavation tools have made excavating the soil much more economical. Many of the spreading roots can be moved with the tree. Typically, roots are excavated to a radius of 1 foot (30 cm) for each inch dbh. These long roots must be carefully bent back toward the trunk, tied securely, and not allowed to dry out during the entire process. Large trees are heavy, even without a soil ball, so a crane or other special equipment is required.

Large trees can be moved with a soil ball as well, but the process requires extensive knowledge of both horticulture and heavy equipment. Several accounts of moving large trees have been published (113, 316, 413, 421, 422, 452, 497, 600).

Figure 6-30 Special chain harnesses are usually needed to support and lift larger root balls.

Mature-sized trees have been moved successfully, but the cost is very high, and it may take decades for them to fully establish on the new site (see Chapter 10).

Proper root pruning prior to transplanting can help to minimize water stress. Some contractors install sprinkler heads throughout the crown after planting to cool the foliage and reduce transpiration. Research on small trees suggests this practice may be beneficial for only a few weeks (44, 49).

Trees up to 12 inches (30 cm) dbh are typically moved with standard ball-and-burlap procedures, using winch trucks and cranes to lift them. Special chain harnesses are usually needed to support and lift larger root balls (Figure 6-30). Winch trucks specially designed for tree moving are owned by experienced contractors who do this work (Figure 6-31). For trees of this size, neither the weight of the root ball nor the size of the crown after tying will be likely to exceed road limits and prohibit transport from site to site. Cranes can be easily rented but may be expensive and require a skilled operator (Figure 6-32).

In special situations, trees have been moved by direct lift from the trunk. The method is sometimes preferred in sandy soils where root balls may break if the tree is lifted by the root ball alone. In this method, one or two heavy steel pins are inserted in holes

Figure 6-31 Winch trucks are used to move large root balls.

drilled through the trunk. These pins are used to lift the tree in the upright position, using a crane. It is best to lift the tree by both the pins in the trunk and by slings on the root ball. The drawback of this method is the injury to the trunk, especially the introduction of decay through the wounds. Plugging the drilled holes with wooden dowels is recommended.

The largest tree spade digs a 14 feet (4.25 m) diameter root ball. It is one-of-a-kind and has been used in locations around the United States (Figure 6-33). Because of the difficulty and cost of transporting this piece of equipment, it is probably only realistic to use this machine on large jobs with several trees to move.

Lifting a very large tree and its root ball requires very specialized equipment and techniques. Trees too large to move with conventional root balls can be moved with a method that uses pipes driven under the root ball to create a platform by which the tree can be lifted (Figure 6-34). This method can be used for even very large mature trees. Root balls can weigh from 100 to 500 tons, and crowns can be up to 80 feet (53 m) tall and just as wide and may have to be lifted with gantries (Figure 6-35). Very few contractors are capable of moving trees of this size. Trees should be root pruned in advance, preferably in stages starting 2–3 years before the tree is moved.

Sometimes, trees are lifted by both root ball and the branches to make them more stable. Tensions must be even on all cables to avoid damaging branches. Using the sound made by the cable when struck with a hammer to judge cable tension (like tuning a piano string) is an example of the very specialized methods used by experienced contractors. Special trailers with over 100 wheels are used to distribute the load (Figure 6-36). Each wheel has a separate hydraulic leveler to keep the tree perfectly vertical at all times and independent steering to maneuver in

Figure 6-32 Cranes are often used to lift large trees.

Figure 6-33 This largest tree spade ever built digs a root ball 14 feet (4.25 m) in diameter. (Photo: Environmental Design)

Figure 6-34 Pipes can be driven under the root ball to create a platform by which large trees can be lifted.

difficult places. These large trees may be too wide for roadways or too heavy for bridges, and are usually not moved very far. Extremely large trees (up to 500 tons) have been moved with a crawler-transporter (Figure 6-37).

The weight and size of the tree, as well as the requirement for relatively level terrain, limit where this equipment can be used. These large trees are transported in the upright position because of their great size and weight. Height and width of the crown, as well as weight of root ball, may require special permits restricting where they can be moved. Utility wires and light poles may have to be moved. This is a job for an experienced contractor.

Once at the new location, it is likely that the entire site will have to be constructed around the new tree. The tree will usually be set at a predetermined elevation, with soil filled around and under the root ball to bring it to final grade. Because of the size and weight, very large trees are often moved in summer or winter when the ground is dry or frozen. The trees have already been root pruned up to several years in advance to help minimize stress. The trees will essentially be deriving moisture from the root ball whether at the new site or old. The rigid boxes and sophisticated lifting systems probably result in less root ball shifting (fine root loss) than standard ball-and-burlap trees. Excellent postplanting care is always part of such a major project. Considering these factors, moving trees in summer is not a major concern.

A guarantee may not be offered on large trees, but individual contractors may have different policies. A one-year guarantee may have some value in case of a complete failure, but since it takes many years, or even decades for the largest trees to become established, the majority of transplant failures may occur several years after transplanting, when diligent maintenance seems less important and watering is reduced for a tree that is only partially established. The tree may then decline slowly over many years without an obvious reason. Do not move trees larger than 12 inches (30 cm) in diameter if you are not prepared to provide regular irrigation for many years.

Figure 6-35 A gantry being used to lift a very large tree with the root ball on a platform. (Photo: The Davey Tree Expert Company)

Figure 6-36 A very large boxed tree on a special trailer with over 100 wheels and special leveling and steering systems. (Photo: T. Thornhill)

Figure 6-37 A huge tree on crawler-transporter (note the man standing by the treads). (Photo: T. Thornhill)

Container-Grown Trees

Hardening off, heeling in, and other long-term storage procedures are not an issue with container-grown trees, since they are not usually moved from the nursery growing area until they are shipped. However, shipping and storage conditions at the receiving end are of concern. When trees arrive at the planting site, they require irrigation once or twice daily. Since soilless container media is well-drained and frequently irrigated in the nursery, the container trees will also have to be watered frequently after leaving the nursery to avoid drought stress.

Figure 6-38 A large tree at its new site before the landscape is constructed around it. (Photo: The Davey Tree Expert Company)

Trees must arrive at the planting site in excellent condition. Reject trees with broken or undersized root balls, container trees with circling roots, trees with injury from rough treatment, and trees that have been drought stressed. Plant only the highest quality plant material for the best chance of success.

CHAPTER 7

Make Sure the New Roots Get a Good Start

Planting practices have improved over time.
Techniques used in the 1980s are considered inadequate today.

P lanning and preparation leading up to planting day can be extensive if done properly. Planting itself must also be done with care and not rushed. It may take only a short time to plant a small tree, but how it is done will have a lasting influence on future tree development. Mistakes made when planting trees are usually impossible to correct later, including planting the roots too deep. Shortcutting the planting process can cause the tree to fail after a short time, or to struggle for many years and never reach its full potential as a healthy, vigorous addition to the landscape. Attention to detail taken at planting time will pay dividends for years.

The Planting Hole

It's Easy to Dig Too Deep

For trees grown in the field, or in containers, the planting hole should be no deeper than the root ball. The root ball must be supported by firm soil underneath to prevent settling. Most new roots will grow horizontally from the sides of the root ball, so compacted soil at the bottom will not substantially affect overall root growth. The depth of each hole must be measured carefully and matched to the root ball that will be placed in it. If the hole is initially dug too deep, add soil to the bottom and tamp thoroughly to provide a firm base. For bare-root trees, the hole should be deep enough so that the woody structural roots are just below the surface. The roots of many urban trees are too deep, and digging the planting hole too deep can contribute to this problem.

Wider Is Better

Research studies (32, 117, 396, 596) and the experience of horticulturists and gardeners have shown that trees benefit from larger planting holes. A larger hole means a greater volume of loose cultivated soil for rapid initial root growth. Widening the planting hole is the only way to increase its size; digging a deeper planting hole is not helpful. A planting hole that is two to three times the width of the root ball is optimum for most situations. Even trees transplanted with a tree spade will benefit from a planting hole at least twice the diameter of the root ball (59, 449).

The planting hole soil provides less resistance to root growth plus more air spaces for oxygen. In many urban soils, root growth from the bottom half of an 18-inch (45 cm) deep root ball will be reduced by inadequate drainage and aeration. Since the most vigorous root growth is likely to occur near the surface, this is where digging efforts should be concentrated to have the greatest impact on future root development. The planting hole can be dug three times as wide so roots can spread, without three times the work. A hole with sloped slides uses the majority of the digging effort to excavate surface soils where the roots will grow most vigorously.

When preparing the wide planting hole, it may not be necessary to remove all the soil, and then put it back in the hole. It may be more efficient to first dig a planting hole about 12 inches (30 cm) wider than the root ball. Then before the hole has been backfilled, break down the sides with a spade to widen the hole near the surface where root growth will be most rapid (Figure 7-1). Another alternative is to rototill a 12- to 24-inch (30–60 cm) ring of soil around it as deeply as possible. A heavy-duty tiller may be required in dense, compacted soils. Steering the rototiller in a circle around small root balls may be difficult. When mechanical tilling is not possible, deeply cultivating the soil around the root ball manually after planting may still be more efficient than actually digging a large hole and refilling it. This can often be done quite easily with an air excavation tool.

Figure 7-1 The planting hole should be only as deep as the root ball. A hole with sloped sides is easier to dig and provides an increased volume of friable soil for vigorous root development from the upper half of the root ball. Breaking down the sides of a traditional hole can reduce the work involved.

The root ball may contain as little as 5% of the original fine roots, which are necessary for absorbing water (see Chapter 9). A planting hole only 25% greater in diameter than the root ball with vertical sides can hinder quick growth of the roots. The regenerated root system will reach less than 10% of its original size in the backfill before encountering the poor quality site soils that can slow root growth. A hole three times the diameter of the root ball with sloped sides will allow the root system to grow rapidly to 25% of its original size before being slowed by the poorer quality site soil—enough to avoid extreme stress under normal conditions. The well-aerated surface soil is increased up to 10-fold by the shallow wide configuration (Figure 7-2).

Concerns are occasionally expressed that this saucer-shaped hole will collect water and funnel it toward the root ball. On poorly drained sites, if the water level was easily raised in the narrow bottom of the saucer-shaped hole, it is possible that the lower roots could be killed. While this concern is valid in extreme situations, when the site is poorly drained, most of the root growth is expected to be in the upper half of the planting hole soil where drainage is better. The upper half of the saucer-shaped planting hole contains over 75% of the backfill soil. The upper quarter contains approximately 50% of the soil, and probably more than half of the roots since growth conditions are always best near the surface. Water could completely saturate the lower three-quarters of the planting hole for extended periods and affect less than half of the root system. However, this should not be used as a reason to avoid correcting drainage problems.

Obviously, the roots must spread beyond the planting hole if the tree is to thrive on the site. If the site soil is compacted and difficult to penetrate, roots may circle inside of the hole,

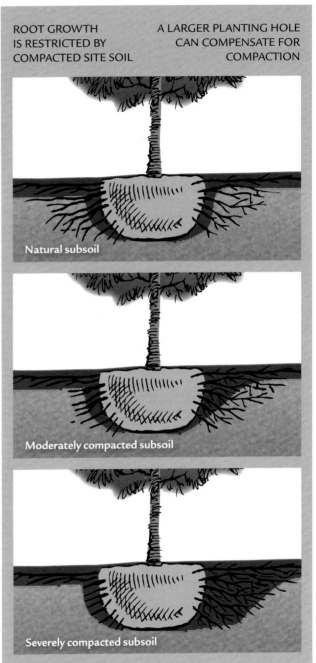

ROOT GROWTH IS RESTRICTED BY COMPACTED SITE SOIL

A LARGER PLANTING HOLE CAN COMPENSATE FOR COMPACTION

Natural subsoil

Moderately compacted subsoil

Severely compacted subsoil

Figure 7-2 The more compacted the site soil is, the larger the planting hole needed to support rapid initial root growth (right side).

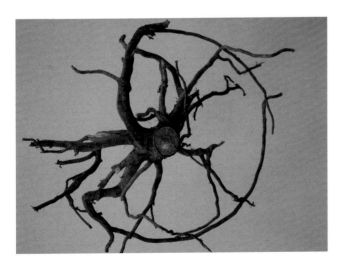

Figure 7-3 If the site soil is difficult to penetrate, the roots may circle inside of the hole, just as they often do inside of a container. Though some roots of this red maple did circle, many roots were able to penetrate the compacted clay site soil.

Figure 7-4 If roots have difficulty penetrating compacted site soils, a hole with sloped sides will allow them to grow toward the better soils near the surface and continue to spread, rather than being trapped in the planting hole. Roots that are able to penetrate the site soil along the slope will grow more slowly.

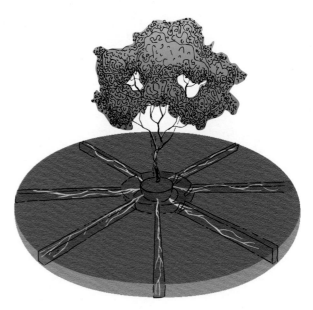

Figure 7-5 Radial trenches filled with amended soil have been used successfully to encourage root growth beyond the planting hole in compacted soils.

just as they often do inside of a container (Figure 7-3). If the roots are unable to grow into the compacted subsoil, a hole with sloped sides will allow them to grow back toward the surface soils and continue to spread (Figure 7-4). Radial trenches with amended soil have been used successfully to encourage root growth beyond the planting hole (Figure 7-5) (141). The sharp corners of square planting holes have been used to lessen the tendency for major roots to circle the hole (Figure 7-6), but the only research study to test this planting hole shape showed no benefit (32).

Figure 7-6 The sharp corners of a square hole are intended to discourage roots from circling around within the perimeter, but research has yet to support this claim. (Photo: T. Kirkham)

Get the Roots Right

Allowing the roots to be too deep in the hole is the most common mistake made during planting, and it is nearly impossible to correct when discovered several months, or years, later. Higher mortality and slower growth vigor often result from trees having deep root systems (27, 28, 87, 89, 476, 590). A tree with deep roots may appear to be growing normally without comparison to a tree with roots at the correct depth (Figure 7-7). Even a slight reduction in growth will reduce the ecosystem services provided by the tree. Root depth should be checked, and rechecked, starting when selecting the trees from the nursery and one final time just before backfilling the planting hole.

Figure 7-7 This hackberry (*Celtis occidentalis*) was planted 7 years earlier with the root system 12 inches too deep. The tree has a healthy appearance, but growth is a fraction of what it should be.

Figure 7-8 When Turkish Hazel *Corylus colurna* trees were flooded, only trees planted 12 inches (30 cm) deep died. (Photo: S. Day)

Consequences of Deep Roots

Research shows that deep-planted ball-and-burlap Yoshino cherries (*Prunus × yedoensis*) can have greater defoliation, chlorosis, and leaf curl (604). Container-grown live oak (*Quercus virginiana*), sycamore (*Platanus occidentalis*), baldcypress (*Taxodium distichum*), crapemyrtle (*Lagerstroemia indica × Lagerstroemia fauriei*), oleander (*Nerium oleander*), and goldenraintree (*Koelreuteria bipinnata*) trees had reduced growth when planted just 3 inches (8 cm) below grade (27, 28, 88). Collar rot and basal canker diseases have been reported on mature sugar maple (*Acer saccharum*) when the roots were planted too deep (154). An increase in the number of girdling roots has been associated with deep roots of several species (192, 604).

Site Quality Is a Factor

The effects of deep root systems are magnified on sites with heavy, poorly drained soils. This includes many of our neighborhoods, commercial properties, and parks developed in the past 40 years—virtually anywhere the land has been reshaped with heavy equipment. Areas with clay soils will have the most severe problems.

A tree growing vigorously in the nursery with deep roots will usually perform poorly on an urban site if planted at the same depth (see Chapter 5). Nursery sites are typically chosen because of high quality soil. Under these conditions, there was no growth reduction of liners planted with the graft union up to six inches below grade (213, 320). On a favorable site, planting Turkish hazelnut (*Corylus colurna*) 6 and 12 inches (15 and 30 cm) below grade had no effect on growth over a 7-year period. When the site was flooded for a season, 40% of the trees planted 12 inches (30 cm) deep died (144). No trees planted at grade were lost (Figure 7-8).

Variable site quality in the landscape also contributes to the difficulty in predicting how an individual tree will perform with deep roots. While up to 60% of

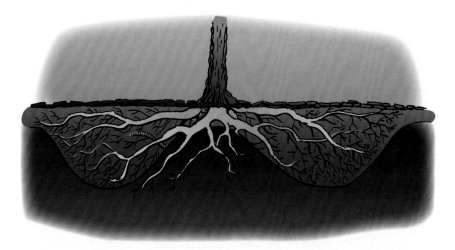

Figure 7-9 Bare-root trees should be placed in a hole that is both wide enough and deep enough to accommodate the entire root system. It can be helpful to mound the soil up in the center of the hole to support the weight of the tree from beneath the trunk.

Figure 7-10 Bare-root stock can be root pruned to remove damaged, girdling, or excessively long roots.

trees may have deep root systems on some sites, it is only one of many factors affecting tree performance (590).

Species Response Varies

Some species are more tolerant of deep roots than others. Survival of Yoshino cherries (*Prunus × yedoensis*) and bougainvillea goldenraintree (*Koelreuteria bipinnata*) planted below grade was reduced, but not red maple (*Acer rubrum*) or green ash (*Fraxinus pennsylvanica*) (27, 604). Red maple and green ash are bottomland species and have evolved to tolerate periodic soil deposits from flooding. Production of adventitious lateral roots on the buried portion of the stem after planting too deep is not typical, and occurs mostly on very young trees of bottomland species. (192, 215, 257).

Bare-Root Trees

Desiccation of roots of bare-root stock during handling is a concern. Several types of synthetic gel and clay- or cornstarch-based root dips and antidesiccant sprays designed to prevent desiccation of bare-root stock are available. These root dips may aid in preventing desiccation of root that are exposed to the air (15, 159), which can result in better seedling survival and growth of seedlings used in reforestation (4, 149, 484, 550, 621). In landscape situations, root dips have not proved to be beneficial alone (34, 47, 313, 433, 434) and typically do not aid in establishment when adequate soil moisture is available. The difference may be because the benefits are most likely to be derived from these compounds in drought or in low-maintenance situations (279, 371). When used in combination with biostimulants and auxins, water-retaining polymer root dips did improve tree vitality and growth (39, 433).

Bare-root trees should be placed in a hole that is both wide enough and deep enough to accommodate the entire root system (Figure 7-9). The original depth of the tree in the nursery can often be determined by observing a color or texture difference on the trunk bark, but this may not be the best depth to replant the tree if it was already too deep in the nursery, or if the natural root flare has been replaced by a lower adventitious root flare (see Chapter 5).

Root pruning is often needed on bare-root stock. Unusually long roots may be pruned back to the standard minimum spread in order to fit into the hole without bending (minimum root spread standards are listed in Table 5-1). Damaged or diseased roots and lateral roots that could later girdle the main roots or trunk should be cut off (Figure 7-10). The roots should be straightened or pruned to prevent kinking, crowding, and crossing of main roots.

Trees with a Soil Ball

Locate the Roots in the Root Ball

It is not uncommon for the root flare to be too deep in the root ball (see Chapter 5). It is always best to select trees having roots at the correct depth in the nursery. If root depth was not checked in the nursery before digging, be sure to do it before planting.

Many tree cultivars are bud grafted onto seedling root stocks. Evidence of the slight crook or dogleg in the stem and bark texture change should be approximately 1–2 inches (3–5 cm) above the soil surface for a young tree (Figure 7-11). Even when the graft union is visible, the roots can still be too deep.

It is not usually practical to remove the burlap over the root ball to locate the roots before placing the root ball in the planting hole. A surveyor's chaining pin can be used to carefully probe for roots through the burlap to estimate root depth (Figure 7-12). With a little practice, you can tell when you encounter roots a few inches below the surface.

Figure 7-11 Evidence of the bud graft above ground indicates that the tree is planted at the same depth as in the propagation nursery, but the adventitious root flare could still be too deep if the root shank was too long.

Figure 7-12 Probing with a surveyor's chaining pin is an effective way to determine the depth of roots in the root ball.

The American Standard for Nursery Stock (12) states only that "soil above the root flare shall not be included in the root ball depth measurement." As long as the root ball is of the correct depth without including the soil over the roots, the root ball can be raised so that the structural roots will be at the correct depth (Figure 7-13). This can help to reverse any negative effects from being planted too deep during production (86).

If the root ball does not meet specifications without the excess soil over the roots, the tree may have to be rejected. In extreme cases (Figure 7-14), only the bottom of the root ball may contain roots, and on poorly drained sites, these roots may not survive long after planting. Most of the root ball soil may contain no roots.

Be sure the depth of each planting hole is appropriate for the root ball to be placed in it before placing the heavy root ball in the hole. After the tree is in the planting hole, the burlap and the twine should be removed from the top of the root

Figure 7-13 As long as the root ball is the correct depth without including the soil over the roots, the root ball can be raised so that the structural roots will be at the correct depth.

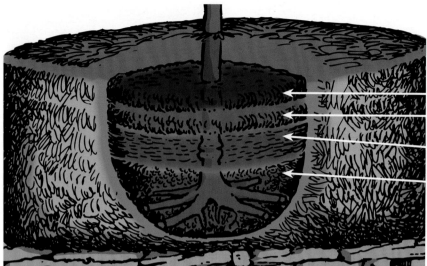

Soil from planting too deep in the landscape

Soil accumulated from cultivation in the nursery

Soil from liner being planted too deep in the landscape nursery

A few inches of soil over structural roots is normal

Figure 7-14 Many steps during production and planting can increase the amount of soil over the root ball. The root system may be very undersized as a result.

ball to confirm root depth visually. Make any necessary final adjustments before backfilling with soil.

Adjust Root Ball Height

If the structural roots have been located within 3 inches of the surface (see Chapter 5), the root ball should be planted with the top surface at the same level as existing grade. Slightly higher, up to one-quarter of the root ball above grade (559), may be preferable to allow for settling (Figure 7-15). Field soil root balls tend to "flatten," and soilless substrate in container root balls decomposes and causes settling (222) over time. Do not plant so high that the cut ends of the uppermost structural roots at the edge of the root ball are above the surrounding grade. If the roots are too shallow, especially on a species with shallow horizontal roots, there will not be enough soil covering them to prevent desiccation after exposure from erosion or frost heaving (Figure 7-16).

Figure 7-15 Planting slightly above grade, as much as one-quarter of the root ball depth, allows for normal settling and "flattening" of the root ball.

Figure 7-16 If the root ball is planted too shallow, there may not be enough soil covering the roots to prevent exposure by erosion or frost heaving.

Though the roots may be covered with a couple of inches of soil when planted, roots increase in size over time. Flare roots thicken faster on the top side, and the amount of soil over them is gradually reduced (Figure 7-17). If planted too shallow, both thickening and frost heaving can eventually result in excessive surface roots.

If a few roots are several inches above the main group of roots with a gap of more than 3–4 inches (8–10 cm) in between, planting deep enough to cover the upper roots with soil would place the main group of roots deeper than 4 inches (10 cm). If only a few small upper roots represent a minor portion of the roots in the root ball, it may be possible to cut them off and raise the main group of roots to the correct depth without stressing the tree excessively (Figure 7-18). If too many roots are removed, it may stress the tree. Removing these upper roots along with the excess soil on pin oaks slowed establishment for 3 years (257).

Even if no roots are originating on the buried portion of the trunk or primary root, above the main group of roots, the soil may contain many roots that have grown up into that soil from below. Removing these roots along with the soil can also reduce growth after planting (257).

Risk of Exposure

When the extra soil is removed from the top of the soil ball, there have been reports of cold damage, sunscald, and borer problems in the newly exposed bark tissue. This could actually be a portion of the original primary (tap) root, in some cases. Late fall plantings may be the most susceptible to cold damage. Earlier plantings may have time to harden off normally. Thin-barked trees are most susceptible to sun injury.

In November, green ash (*Fraxinus pennsylvanica*) root tissue from just below the soil surface was as cold-hardy as stem tissue, while root tissue from

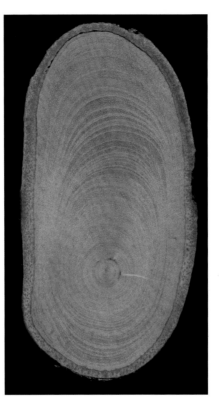

Figure 7-17 Root flare roots thicken faster on the top. Over time the amount of soil over them will be reduced.

Figure 7-18 Sometimes there can be a few small roots above the main group of roots, but these are usually not able to support the plant if the lower roots die because they are too deep.

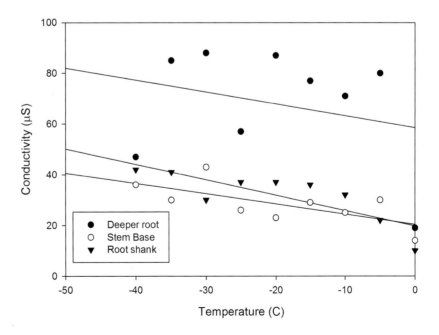

Figure 7-19 Green ash (*Fraxinus pennsylvanica*) root shank tissue from just below the soil surface was as cold-hardy as stem tissue, while root tissue from several inches deeper in the soil was less cold-hardy than stem tissue.

Figure 7-20 When the root ball is planted correctly, the burlap and twine will be exposed if they are not removed. Exposed, burlap and twine decompose very slowly and could cause girdling at the base of the trunk. Remove as much as possible before back filling the hole.

several inches deeper in the soil was less cold hardy than exposed stem tissue (Figure 7-19). There was no apparent difference earlier or later in the season. Based on this data, primary root tissue recently exposed by planting high, but not yet hardened off when a rapid drop in temperature occurs, could be less cold hardy. Until this is better understood, exercise caution when removing soil and exposing tissue that is accustomed to being covered by soil.

Leaving the extra soil in place above grade to be removed slowly or erode away over time, may help to protect sensitive trunk tissues from sudden exposure. In one study, there were no adverse effects of the exposed root balls reported (88). If the soil is removed, replacing it with organic mulch may provide protection from sun and cold damage initially, exposing the trunk tissues gradually as it decomposes. The mulch should not be maintained at this initial depth indefinitely. Trunk protection may help to prevent sunscald but research is not conclusive (see Chapter 8).

Root Ball Wrappings

Burlap (hessian), twine, and wire used to cover and support the root ball during transport and storage can cause injury to trees if left in place after planting. The reasons given by contractors for not removing the wrappings (or the critical portions of them) are not usually horticultural. The extra time it takes to remove the wrappings may increase the cost of planting, and it may be more difficult to straighten the tree without breaking the root ball if it begins to lean after planting. Thoroughly stabilizing the lower part of the root ball at planting will keep firm root balls from shifting, and they will usually not have to be straightened later.

It is often assumed that natural burlap and twine will decompose rapidly after planting. Burlap and twine may decompose very slowly when left exposed and dry (Figure 7-20). Burlap over the root ball can repel water and cause the root ball to dry out. Under some conditions, they sometimes remain strong for several years—long enough to cause serious constriction of the basal trunk area or constrict new roots. Natural burlap may be treated with preservatives to prevent rapid decomposition.

Figure 7-21 The treated burlap on this root ball had not decomposed in 2 years (top), and it girdled the new roots growing through it (at arrows, bottom).

Figure 7-22 Nylon twine does not decompose and will girdle the base of the trunk if not removed.

Figure 7-23 Burlap and twine should be removed after the root ball has been placed in the hole. It no longer serves any useful purpose and can constrict the trunk and roots.

In one study, treated burlap showed little sign of decomposition in 2–3 years (351) and was also observed to persist up to 14 years. As roots grow through the burlap and increase in diameter, they can be girdled by the burlap fibers (Figure 7-21). The tree cannot become established as long as the burlap is present to girdle the new roots growing out of the root ball. Synthetic burlap does not decompose, and roots will not develop normally when this material is left around the root ball. Synthetic twine that is not removed from the base of the tree will girdle the trunk (Figure 7-22) and could cause death of the tree in a few years. Sometimes, the trunk will break at the point of constriction.

After the soil ball has been placed in the planting hole and stabilized by tamping soil firmly around the lower quarter of the root ball, cut off and remove the burlap and twine from the top and sides of the root ball (Figure 7-23). A fresh layer of natural burlap and twine could be covering other less biodegradable materials if the root ball was rewrapped.

When wire baskets were first introduced for supporting the root ball during handling, it was assumed that they would rust away in a few years. We now know that wire baskets can last 30 years or more. Usually, the top of the root flare roots grow against one of the upper horizontal wires as they increase in diameter (Figure 7-24, top). As the roots grow against these wires, the roots will become partially girdled. Transport of water and nutrients to the trunk and carbohydrates to the rest of the root system are restricted (169). The root tissue may eventually grow around the wires and graft together on the other side (299, 229, 367, 368),

Figure 7-24 This wire basket did not rust in 30 years. Roots may eventually grow over the wires of baskets used to support root balls (above), but vascular flow can be interrupted for several years (below), leading to stress and secondary problems.

but it may take several years to reestablish unrestricted vascular transport (Figure 7-24, bottom). Flow of water and nutrients can be constricted in one or more of the major lateral roots for many years, and the resulting chronic stress could lead to serious secondary problems.

It is usually just the upper horizontal wires that interfere with root growth. To prevent future interference with roots, cut off at least the top half of the basket before backfilling (Figure 7-25). Removing the upper part of the basket will also eliminate potential tripping hazards from protruding wires. Wires can also be dangerous later when stump grinding if the tree is removed. Removing the entire basket may be necessary to eliminate this hazard. Wire support systems using thinner gauge wire (Figure 6-13) may rust away faster, but there are no published research reports on any of these alternative types of root ball support systems.

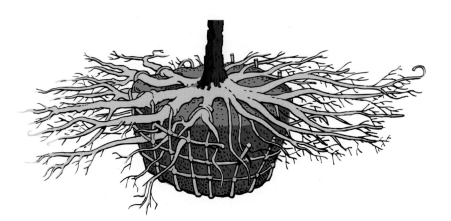

Figure 7-25 If the upper half of the basket is removed before backfilling, most future root problems will be prevented.

Figure 7-26 Roots growing vertically down the container wall at any stage in production can cause the tree to be less stable after planting in the landscape unless cut to allow new roots to grow straight out. (Photo: E. Gilman).

Container-Grown Trees

Roots can be too deep in container root balls as well. Always check to see that the first roots emerge from the stem near the soil surface. This is especially important for containerized trees that have been dug from the field and grown in containers for a few months, since they may have been planted too deeply in the container or may have settled after planting.

Though many containers have been developed to prevent roots from circling around the inside of containers, the problem is still frequently encountered in the landscape. It is common practice to disrupt these circling roots on the surface of the root ball by making several vertical cuts, or "slashes," on the outside of the root ball before planting.

Methods that disrupt circling roots do not eliminate descending, ascending, and kinked roots. Containers designed to prevent circling often direct roots contacting the wall down to the bottom or up to the surface. These roots can persist after planting in the landscape (Figure 7-26). Root ball "shaving" is cutting off the outer surface of the root ball to remove all roots on the root ball surface (Figure 7-27). It results in a more normal root system with roots growing more radially from the trunk (218). Root growth after planting trees from containers without shaving was one-quarter of that of field-grown trees and resulted in reduced tree stability (222).

Figure 7-27 Slashing (left) is less effective than shaving (right) in eliminating root defects in container-grown trees.

Root disruption techniques do cause root injury and may lead to increased stress after planting, but reports are conflicting (25, 60, 157, 227, 229, 372). Butterfly pruning resulted in severe dieback of Shumard oak (*Quercus shumardii*) seedlings (25). Moderate short-term stress from cutting and disrupting the circling roots is preferable to the long-term consequences of allowing root defects to persist.

Though superficial root defects on the surface of container root ball can be corrected by these techniques, additional root defects may also be present deep within the root ball if the tree was first grown in a smaller container during earlier stages of production (Figure 5-30). Butterflying the root ball may also disrupt interior circling roots if they were not formed high in the root ball. This may explain the severe dieback associated with this technique (25).

Palms

Palm root balls are sometimes planted deeper to make heights more even. However, it is recommended that 2 inches (5 cm) of root initiation zone (often visible as a portion of the trunk where roots form above ground) remain above the soil line (Figure 7-28). Pygmy palms (*Phoenix roebelenii*) planted with the visible portion of the root initiation zone buried can grow as well as trees planted at original depth. When planted deeper, new roots may form up to 6 inches (15 cm) above the root initiation zone, but tree survival is decreased (73).

Directional Orientation

Tree root systems and crowns may develop asymmetrically in response to sun (568, 591) and prevailing wind exposure (Figure 7-29). Recommendations vary on how to orient the tree when transplanting, and strong research support for any of them is lacking. Some growers have reported more

Figure 7-28 When transplanting palms, it is recommended that 2 inches (5 cm) of root initiation zone remain visible above the soil line.

sunscald damage when trees are not planted with the same orientation as they grew in the nursery.

On a small tree, where the crook in the stem from bud grafting is still visible, it is sometimes recommended to place the scion of budded trees toward the afternoon sun to reduce the possibility of sunburn in the crook just above the graft union (269). If strong prevailing winds are a concern, it may be best to orient the most or largest roots toward the prevailing wind during the season when the tree will be in full leaf (381). More roots grow on the windward side to more evenly distribute stress among the roots. Placing the side with fewest or smallest branches toward the afternoon sun so that it will be favored with more light and balance the crown over time has been recommended (269).

Since the asymmetry in the tree has developed, at least in part, as a response to different environmental conditions around the tree, it is probably safest to orient it so that it faces the same compass direction as it did when it was growing in the nursery. Turning the tree may expose less-acclimatized bark from the shaded north side to direct sun. This orientation is suspected of increasing the chances of sunscald, especially on thin, smooth-barked species.

Concern for appearance may override any of these other biological considerations for orientation. The best-looking side of a tree may have to face a certain direction. If the tree cannot be oriented as before, it is very important to protect the trunk on thin barked trees from sunscald (see Chapter 8).

Figure 7-29 Tree crowns and root systems may develop asymmetrically in response to sun and prevailing wind exposure. In the northern hemisphere, branches on the north side (right) can be longer and the leaves are more shade adapted. Rotating the tree when transplanting could increase stress.

Backfilling

On planting sites having high-quality soil, it is doubtful that the backfill will require amending. On poor quality sites, soil amendments may be advisable to improve soil structure, water-holding capacity, or drainage. When refilling the planting hole, the backfill soil should be free of large soil clumps and rocks.

Backfill Soil Modifications

Backfill soil amendments are often very controversial. Soil is usually amended by adding compost or sand. But unamended is not the same as unmodified. Removing the soil from the planting hole and then backfilling the hole with the same soil does modify the soil. The topsoil layer is mixed with the subsoil. Structure is often improved as it is cultivated. The soil is not as compacted when it is returned to the hole as it was before the hole was dug. A study comparing three types of backfills consisting of unamended soil, amended soil, and new topsoil produced no difference in root development in any of the backfills (597). Unamended is not the same as unmodified.

The majority of published research reports indicate that amending the backfill soil does not cause an increase in root development or tree growth (107, 117, 166, 168, 203, 271, 293, 304, 314, 428, 468, 511, 596, 597, 609), including palms (289). Specific combinations of certain amendments and site conditions have proven beneficial (58, 112, 141, 295, 428, 630) or detrimental (98, 495) to tree establishment.

Most research is not done on poor-quality urban sites. On these sites, backfill soil amendments may be beneficial, but probably not as important as the preparation of a large planting hole. Amending a large area around the tree will be most effective. Organic matter will improve structure, drainage, and fertility in most soils. Well-decomposed organic matter is best. To amend heavy clay soils, soil from the hole is often mixed with equal volumes of compost and sand. If compost alone is added, add 5% by weight (10% by volume, depending on the material). If sand alone is added, 50% or more by volume may be required depending on soil type. If too little sand is added to a clay soil, the mix could be worse than the original soil (526). Test the pH of both the compost and sand. These materials are often alkaline and may not be appropriate for some tree species. It may be more practical and economical to bring in quality topsoil rather than to amend the backfill on the site.

Hydrophilic polymer gels are sometimes added to the backfill soil to increase available water for newly planted trees. Research has not shown that the use of hydrogels can consistently increase root or shoot growth of trees after planting (203, 442, 443, 572, 622). This may be because the roots quickly grow beyond the polymer-amended backfill in narrow planting holes.

Figure 7-30 The use of power augers can cause a heavy glazing of the planting hole wall in clay soils. Break down the sides of the hole to eliminate the glazed surface and make a wider hole.

Barrier at the Soil Interface

The interface between backfill soil and undisturbed soil is sometimes blamed for poor root growth into the undisturbed site soil. Glazing can pose a barrier to root growth when digging a hole with mechanical equipment. Clay soils will glaze much more readily than loamy and sandy soils, but some roots will grow through the numerous small cracks in the glaze. Though partial glazing may not be a serious problem, it is best to eliminate the potential for trouble by using a spade to break up the glazed surface before planting (416). Sloping the side of the planting hole is a better way to eliminate glazing (Figure 7-1). The use of power augers can cause a heavy glazing (Figure 7-30) of the soil wall under certain circumstances (35). If holes are dug several hours before planting, the soil surface may become dry and very hard. It is best to break up the dry surface to expose some moist soil before planting.

If the backfill soil is amended, a discontinuity of soil properties may be created between the backfill and site soil. The abrupt change in soil properties may include changes in texture, structure, bulk density, aeration, water movement and availability, pH, and chemical composition. Soil water movement can be hindered across the interface between two soil types, but in reality, the rate of lateral water movement from site soil to backfill and root ball soils is negligible compared to the rate at which water is being absorbed by the roots, and the interface may not be of major practical importance. Well-aerated backfill soil may help to aerate the undisturbed soil around the planting hole, but it has not been measured.

After roots grow through the interface between the backfill and the site soil, poor-quality site soil immediately restricts root extension and growth. A study comparing three types of backfills consisting of unamended soil, amended soil, and new topsoil showed that root growth in the undisturbed site soils outside of the planting hole was less than root growth in all of the backfill soils, including unamended backfill. This finding was attributed to poorer root growth in the compacted clay site soil after crossing the interface, rather than to an inability of the roots to cross the interface (596). The lack of vigorous root growth in poor site soil beyond the interface can be mistaken for a restriction at the interface.

Filling the Planting Hole

The first lateral roots of bare-root stock should be planted within approximately 1–2 inches (2.5–5 cm) of the soil surface. While holding the tree in the correct position, add loose soil around the roots and tamp it lightly until no air pockets remain, without causing the tree to settle deeper in the hole. Add water to settle the soil around the roots, and then add more soil if necessary. Check to be sure that the first lateral roots are just below the soil surface.

Figure 7-31 The root ball will dry out faster than the backfill soil until new roots are produced. A raised ring of soil formed around the edge of the root ball will create a basin that can be filled with water.

When backfilling around a root ball, the soil should be tamped firmly around the base to stabilize it, but the rest of the soil should be tamped only lightly, or left to settle on its own. Soaking will assist in settling the soil naturally. Excessive tamping can compact soil and slow water and air penetration and root growth. The soil can be mounded slightly between the root ball and the edge of the planting hole to allow for settling, but do not cover the root ball with soil. The top of the root ball should be level or slightly above surrounding grade to allow for settling, and the structural roots should be within 3 inches of the surrounding grade. If water is expected to percolate slowly in the soil, or if the planting site is not level, a raised ring of soil can be formed around the edge of the root ball to create a basin that can be filled with water (Figure 7-31).

Trees transplanted with tree spades require special procedures. The fit between the root ball and the sides of the hole is never perfect. Wide spaces—and, therefore, air pockets—often occur, especially if the hole is slightly shallower than the root ball or if the blade pattern was rotated slightly (Figure 7-32). The root ball will eventually settle and close the open space around the root ball, but this process could take time. If there are open spaces, roots will not be able to regenerate, and the surface of the soil ball will dry out. Use a hand spade or shovel to loosen the soil around the edge of the root ball, and fill all of the spaces with loose, friable soil. A better procedure would be to cultivate the soil 12 inches (30 cm) deep around the root ball (Figure 7-32). An air excavation tool can also be used to loosen the soil around the root ball. This will permit rapid growth of new roots into the surrounding friable soil (23, 59).

Appropriate planting methods may be the only way to provide for the rapid initial root growth needed to get the new tree through the most critical stress period. The care taken in planting the tree correctly will also have a lasting effect.

Figure 7-32 When trees are transplanted with a tree spade, there is often a gap around the root ball (top). Fill all of the spaces with loose, friable soil. A better alternative would be to cultivate the soil around the root ball to facilitate rapid new root growth (bottom).

CHAPTER 8

Support, Train, and Protect the New Tree

Care for the new tree begins at planting.

Figure 8-1 Quality nursery-grown trees should have a strong central leader and good branching pattern. Minimal pruning should be required at planting.

Figure 8-2 Temporary support may be required to train a new central leader after the original is damaged.

Once the roots are in the ground, it may seem like the planting job is done, but there is still work to do. It is a good time to carefully prune for good branch structure. Some trees may have to be supported or protected. Mulching will conserve soil moisture and reduce root competition. Be sure to complete these important steps.

Pruning at Planting

Trees pruned correctly in the nursery should not require major structural pruning at planting. However, branches damaged in handling will need to be pruned, as well as small upright stems because they often grow into codominant stems. Most nursery-grown trees should already have a strong central leader and good branching pattern (Figure 8-1). Properly trained young trees should require minimal corrective pruning as they mature.

Traditional recommendations to reduce or thin the crown at planting have been proven unnecessary for successful transplanting, through research and experience. Pruning to totally compensate for root loss is not possible. Recommendations sometimes call for removing 20%–30% of the branches and leaves, but a tree can lose as much as 90% of its water-absorbing root system during transplanting. Most studies indicate that moderate crown pruning at planting has little or no effect on the future growth of roots or shoots (160, 161, 269, 305, 490, 501, 554).

When a tree is planted during the dormant season, leaf expansion will be reduced the next season because of the reduced water supply from the roots (338). A tree dug in summer with a crown of full-sized leaves will be less able to adjust to the sudden water stress from root loss. Complete manual defoliation to reduce transpiration was detrimental to survival and growth of trees planted in late summer (254). Too much pruning can ruin the natural shape of the tree and reduce total leaf photosynthesis enough to reduce root growth.

Pruning Deciduous Trees

Structural pruning is an important procedure when planting, if the tree has not been adequately pruned in the nursery. The central leader should never be pruned. If the terminal has been accidentally broken, it should be pruned only as far as the next strong lateral twig or bud, which can form the new terminal leader. Some temporary support may be required to train a new central leader (Figure 8-2).

Even high-quality nursery stock may require some minor structural corrective pruning to promote good branch structure. Broken, weak, or interfering branches should be removed (Figure 8-3), as well as branches with included bark (Figure 5-34). Pay close attention to new growth at the top of the tree. Depending on when the grower last pruned the trees, there could already be some recent growth at the top that could develop into codominant stems. To prevent development of codominant stems, remove the small-diameter, upright-oriented stems in the top half of the crown and preserve the larger one as the main leader.

Larger-diameter branches in the middle and lower crown may also need pruning in lesser quality trees. Rapidly growing lateral branches can compete with the central leader for dominance and develop weak branch attachments that could eventually fail. Cut back these vigorous laterals to slow their growth (Figure 8-4) (205). Cut them off completely about two years later to fully establish a strong central leader.

Limbs below about 8 feet (2.5 m) are not permanent in most situations. However, they do contribute to increasing stem diameter and taper while the tree is

Before Pruning   After Pruning

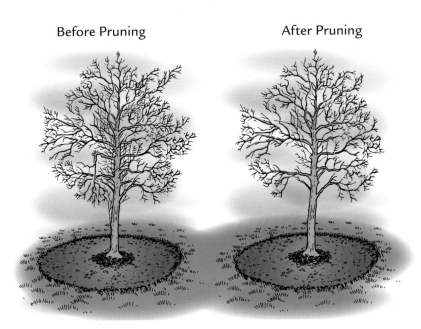

Figure 8-3 Broken, weak, and interfering branches should be removed at the time of planting. Maintain the typical form of the species.

young. Let them grow as long as possible, but keep them small by pruning so that they will be less than one-third the trunk diameter when it is time to remove them. The permanent branches should be evenly distributed around the trunk.

For strong attachment to the trunk, branches should be no more than one-half of the diameter of the trunk measured immediately above the branch attachment, and with no included bark. If a branch is too large in relation to the trunk, selectively thin the branch or reduce the branch length. This technique will reduce the weight of the branch and slow its growth, so that it will develop a stronger branch attachment (205, 221).

Figure 8-4 Rapidly growing lateral branches can compete with the central leader for dominance (left), and develop weak branch attachments. Cut back these vigorous laterals at planting to slow their growth (center). Cut them off completely about two years later to fully establish a strong central leader (right). (Modified from Gilman 2012)

Pruning Evergreens

Most narrow-leaf and broadleaf evergreens require little pruning at planting time if they were properly pruned in the nursery. If possible, pruning should be restricted to 1-year-old wood. The growth habits of evergreens influence pruning practices. Species of fir (*Abies*), Douglas-fir (*Pseudotsuga*), pine (*Pinus*), and spruce (*Picea*) develop characteristic whorls of branches. Most of the growth occurs from closely placed buds near the end of the previous year's growth. Pruning can eliminate these buds, and they may have few or no latent buds, resulting in permanent disfiguration of the tree.

Figure 8-5 Branch pruning cuts should be just outside the branch collar.

Species of arborvitae (*Thuja*), false cypress (*Chamaecyparis*), hemlock (*Tsuga*), juniper (*Juniperus*), and yew (*Taxus*) readily break lateral buds and, if necessary, can be moderately pruned before new growth appears. The terminals should be pruned back to a lateral branch, but the natural form of the tree should be maintained. Corrective pruning should be completed early in the spring to allow the new growth to cover any exposed inner branches.

Broadleaf evergreens should be pruned at planting to remove injured branches and to develop good branch structure. Heavy pruning is not recommended until after the first growing season, or later if the trees have not recovered well.

Making Proper Pruning Cuts

When removing a live branch, pruning cuts should be made just outside the branch collar (Figure 8-5). If no branch collar is visible, the angle of the cut should approximate the angle formed by the branch bark ridge and the trunk. Flush cuts make larger wounds, may increase decay, and should be avoided.

A reduction cut should be midway between the branch bark ridge and a line perpendicular across the cut stem. The retained lateral branch should be at least one-third the diameter of the pruning cut, and with as narrow of an angle as possible (Figure 8-6).

Stubs and rough wood callus over slowly and are more susceptible to fungal and bacterial infections. Tearing the bark on large limbs can be avoided by using a standard three-cut procedure (221).

Wound Dressings

Figure 8-6 Reduction cuts are used to slow the growth of lateral branches. The best angle is midway between the branch bark ridge (arrow) and a line perpendicular across the cut stem.

Wound dressings and tree paints have not been proven to be effective in preventing or reducing decay. They are not usually recommended for routine use on pruning cuts unless specified for control of disease, borers, mistletoe, or sprouts. During certain seasons in some areas of the United States, wound dressings are beneficial in preventing invasion of certain vascular disease fungi, such as *Verticillium* and *Ceratocystis*, as well as weakly pathogenic canker fungi. Wound dressings are sometimes used to reduce drying back of the inner bark and cambium, and to prevent deep weather checking due to drying of the inner wood. Certain wound dressings (335) and wrapping wounds with polyethylene plastic wrap (386) may reduce dieback of uninjured cambium and promote wound closure.

Pruning Palms

In the past, it has been common practice to remove two-thirds or more of the leaves of palms (Figure 8-7). This removal often occurs at the time of digging to facilitate transport. For species like sabal palm (*Sabal palmetto*), which must generate an entire new root system when transplanted, complete removal of leaves greatly improved survival rates because the practice reduces transpirational water loss. For this species, these leaves will quickly yellow and die if left in place. For most palm species, leaf removal offers little or no benefit (see Chapter 6). Leaves tied for transport should be untied when planting (286). Allowing leaves to remain tied could result in fungal infections in the crown under high-moisture conditions (72).

Current recommendations for species where no specific research data is available is to remove no more than one-third of the lower leaves if the palm tree is moved with a small root ball. These leaves often die in the first few months and require pruning later (291). It is not necessary to remove any

Figure 8-7 Two-thirds of the leaves are typically removed from sabal palm *(Sabal palmetto)* at transplanting, and the remaining leaves are often tied over the terminal bud. Recent research shows that this may not be necessary for most other palms.

leaves of palms grown in containers or moved with a tree spade (292). If some palm leaves have been pruned off before moving the tree, additional leaf removal may not be necessary at the planting site.

Support Systems

Staking, guying, and bracing refer to the methods of mechanically supporting the trunk of a planted tree to keep it in an upright position. Staking may present a hazard for people who may trip or fall over the supports. Staking too rigidly for more than a year can reduce trunk taper on small trees and leave them too weak to stay upright on their own after the stakes are removed (270). Stakes can become less rigid over time as a result of wind movement (542).

Support systems should be used only when necessary. Ball-and-burlap trees that were not staked remained upright in ambient wind conditions and were tolerant of moderate to heavy simulated wind loads in pulling tests seven months after planting (5). Container-grown (156) and bare-root trees may require support until lateral or anchor roots develop, but seldom for more than one year. Large evergreens may need to be guyed for up to two years because of the high wind resistance of the foliage and extra weight of snow and ice accumulation during the winter when the soil is wet and offers less resistance to uprooting. Extremely windy climates, or other unusual circumstances, may also call for extensive use of support.

Risk of Tree Damage

Wires can girdle the trunk in as little as two years (Figure 11-13) (22). In one survey, wire ties caused damage to over half of all trees within the first 3–5 years after planting (66). Trunk constriction occurs less often on publicly owned trees if the contract requires inspection and wire removal two years after planting (325).

Figure 8-8 Planting pit grates and trunk guards often cause injury to the tree as it grows. Many grates are designed to be cut away in segments as the tree grows, but this is expensive.

Figure 8-9 One or two stakes are commonly used on smaller trees. It is important that the tying material be able to resist breaking and unfastening while allowing the tree trunk to flex.

Figure 8-10 Staking systems with more than three stakes do not increase support.

Specially designed trunk guards and grates are often installed to prevent vandalism and to cover sidewalk cutouts. Both may eventually interfere with the growth of the tree (Figure 8-8). While they might be necessary in high traffic areas, they may need to be enlarged or removed as the tree grows in size.

Types of Systems

One or two stakes with separate flexible ties are commonly used (Figure 8-9), but provided inadequate support when tested (156). The stake material, thickness, and depth to which the stakes are driven into the ground are factors in the

Figure 8-11 Low staking can keep the tree in place while permitting the top to move freely so that the tree can develop greater taper. This is most important on small trees.

Figure 8-12 Three-point guying systems have been shown to be among the most effective support system.

strength of the two-stake system. Three stakes will provide better support (5, 156). Additional stakes are sometimes used, but may not provide additional support (Figure 8-10). It is sometimes easier to install stakes before the hole is backfilled.

When staking is needed to keep a tree with a strong trunk in the upright position until sufficient roots develop to anchor the tree, low staking can keep the tree in place while permitting the top to move freely (Figure 8-11). If the trunk is weak, support the tree with a stake about 6 inches (15 cm) above the lowest level at which the trunk can be held upright (270).

Figure 8-14 Palms are often braced by strapping small boards to the trunk, which serve as a place to anchor the angled wooden braces. Nails and screws must never be driven into the trunk of palms.

Figure 8-13 Systems that stabilize the root ball can be very effective. In this simple, economical system, vertical stakes attached to the ends of the horizontal board over the root ball must be 4 feet long; otherwise, they pull out. The supports can be easily covered with mulch after installation.

Figure 8-15 Tree stakes can also serve as guards to protect the tree from vandalism and accidents.

Test have shown that the best support is provided by three-point guying systems (Figure 8-12) and root ball stabilization systems that have structure or straps over the root ball that are anchored into the soil at the bottom of the planting hole (5, 156) (Figure 8-13). Guys are most often used on larger trees. Root ball stabilization systems eliminate trip hazards in heavily used areas.

Large palms are commonly supported after planting. Palms should be braced or guyed. However, nails, screws, and other mechanical devices must not be placed into the trunk. A common method of bracing or guying is to strap short, vertical pieces of boards around the trunk with steel bands. The banded boards serve as supports in which to anchor screw eyes for guy wires, or to attach angled support braces (Figure 8-14).

Stakes sometimes double as guards. Presumably, this is why some are so oversized (Figure 8-15).

Materials

The traditional material for tying the trees to the stakes is a wire slipped through a piece of garden hose, but this material is no longer recommended. Guying material should be wide, smooth, nonabrasive, flexible, and, if possible, photodegradable to avoid injury to the tree if it is not removed (Figure 8-16). It is important that the tying material be able to resist breaking and unfastening while allowing the tree trunk to flex. To prevent injury to the bark, the ties should be examined at least once during the growing season and adjusted if necessary.

Guy wires can be secured by stakes, but specially designed land anchors will be stronger. Experience has often shown that driving stakes parallel to the guy wire will provide the best anchorage. The only research data available indicates that stakes driven into the ground vertically will provide greater strength. An angled stake could support a typical 2.5-inch (7.6 cm) caliper tree to about 50 mph (22 m/s) wind, while a vertically driven stake could support the tree to in excess of 100 mph (45 m/s) wind (516). Galvanized steel cable is best. Turnbuckles can be installed to adjust the length. Compression springs can provide flexibility for trunk movement.

Figure 8-16 Guying material should be flexible, wide, and nonabrasive.

Trunk Wraps

In cool temperate climates, trunks of thin- and smooth-barked trees are wrapped to prevent injury from winter sun. When trunk tissues are exposed to direct sun in winter, trunk temperatures may rise well above freezing on cold, but sunny days. At sunset, or even when clouds move in, tissue temperature can drop rapidly in minutes, resulting in possible injury to the cambium. Damage appears several months later, as dead bark that sloughs off in a long narrow strip (Figure 8-17), usually on the south or southwest sides (363).

The wrapping may, or may not, be protection against this type of injury. Paper wrap has not been shown to be an improvement over an unwrapped trunk (272, 363), but continues to be the accepted standard, and users consider it to be effective in preventing sunscald (17).

If used, the best trunk wrap materials are ones that will buffer temperature extremes, not hold excess moisture against the bark, not encourage insect infestation or disease development, and are bio- or photodegradable in case they are not removed. A white, geotextile (polypropylene fabric) meets these criteria (20). Trunks should be wrapped from the bottom to the top so that the layers overlap and shed water. At the top, self-attach the trunk wrap material by pulling the end through the last wrap around the tree, or secure the wrap with a small piece of weatherproof tape that does not encircle the trunk. Never use wire, nylon cord, or fiber-reinforced tape.

Plastic guards are sometimes used as protection against damage from sun, equipment, and animals (Figure 8-18). Simple, homemade plastic guards were recommended to protect the base of trees against injury from lawn equipment, which can be a major problem for trees in the landscape (284). Small wounds can enlarge to become a serious problem in trees stressed from

Figure 8-17 When sun warms the bark to above freezing in winter or to very high temperatures in summer, damage can occur on newly planted, thin, smooth-barked trees. Planting a tree in a different directional orientation than it was in the nursery may increase susceptibility of some tree species to bark injury from sun exposure.

Figure 8-18 Trunks of small trees can be protected from mowers and string trimmers by a simple 6-inch (15 cm) high piece of flexible plastic drain pipe, slit down the side to place it around the trunk. Deer protection may require a taller guard. The entire trunk is often covered on golf courses to protect young trees from golf balls.

transplanting. The guards can also help prevent small mammals from chewing on the bark at the tree base, which can girdle the stem. Thin-barked trees and palms are most susceptible to damage. The best guards are those that prevent constriction by fitting loosely around the trunk, provide space for air circulation to buffer temperature and prevent excess moisture from accumulating, and protect against physical damage (20).

Mulching

Mulch can improve growth and establishment of newly planted trees (26, 112, 153, 165, 171, 436). Mulching with wood chips at the time of planting resulted in a 400% increase in fine root development in the top 6 inches (15 cm) of soil outside the root ball, partially because grass competition was eliminated (246). Growth increases are likely due to increased moisture availability as foliar nutrient levels were not increased in newly planted trees by mulching (177). Mulch did not improve establishment of North American desert plants (282, 505).

The majority of tree species used in the landscape evolved in a woodland environment and their root systems do not compete well against grasses. Eliminating the grass can increase tree growth (136, 153, 408, 602, 611), though not as much as adding mulch (Figure 8-19) (182, 246).

When rainfall or irrigation is light, mulch can reduce the amount of moisture reaching the root ball (27, 212). Since as little as 4% of the water lost from the root ball is attributed to evaporation from the surface (210), in situations where newly planted trees are receiving a small amount of water at each irrigation, it may be best not to apply mulch over the root ball. This may be the reason that height growth of container-grown Southern magnolia (*Magnolia grandiflora*) was reduced by mulch in the first season when root spread beyond the root ball would have been limited, but not the second (280).

The size of the mulched area needed will depend on the size of the tree. For typical-size landscape trees (up to 2-inch (5 cm) caliper), a

Figure 8-19 Mulching (right) newly planted trees improves growth above and below ground. (Photo: T. Green)

Figure 8-20 Mulch an area three times the diameter of the root ball with 2–3 inches (5–10 cm) of wood chips. The soil ring at the edge of the root ball for holding water will usually be visible through the mulch.

minimum 8- to 14-foot (2.5 to 4.3 m) diameter circle of mulch is best (Figure 8-20). This will cover the area where roots will grow during the first two years after planting (see Chapter 11). Trees will benefit longer from larger areas of mulch, but even a small circle of mulch around the trunk will reduce lawn mower injury.

In northern climates, the soil may warm slower if mulch is applied before the soil warms in spring (402). This is not a problem with established mulch areas because the mulch helps to moderate both winter and summer soil temperatures.

Unless water interception is a concern (see above), the mulch layer should be 2 to 3 inches (5.0 to 7.5 cm) deep after settling. A thinner layer will need replenishment in a short time. A layer any thicker would be out of proportion

Figure 8-21 The common practice of mounding mulch around the base of the tree is of no benefit, potentially damaging to the trunk, and could prevent water from reaching the root ball.

to the size of most new trees, and provide no additional benefits. The mulch should not be allowed to cover the base of the trunk. This could lead to bark injury from fungi or rodents. Mulch is often incorrectly applied up to 1 foot (30 cm) deep in a small circle only about 3 feet (1 m) wide around the tree (Figure 8-21). This is of no benefit to the roots, potentially damaging to the trunk, and aesthetically unpleasing.

Sheets of plastic or geotextile fabric under mulch can be effective in controlling weeds (7). This can be problematic for trees. The geotextile fabric under mulch can sometimes become so clogged with soil and debris that water and air cannot pass through. Plastic can cause roots to grow at, or near, the soil surface, presumably because of reduced aeration in deeper soils (610). Decomposing mulch on top of the fabric or plastic creates an excellent environment for weeds to establish, though the fabric can reduce the time required for weeding when they do grow in the mulch over the fabric (147). Weed shoots and roots can penetrate many of the fabrics. It also prevents the humus from the decomposing mulch from being incorporated into the soil. Avoid the use of these materials under the mulch.

Fertilization at Planting

It is difficult to make general recommendations about fertilizing after planting that would apply to all situations. Length of the establishment period, production method, fertilizer formulation, and maintenance after planting must all be considered. In most cases, applying fertilizer will not improve survival or growth in the first few years after planting.

Lack of sufficient water uptake by the roots limits the growth of newly planted trees more than any other factor immediately after planting, even if the soil is kept moist. Until the root system can grow and absorb more water, adding nutrients to the soil has shown to be ineffective in most cases (143, 166, 168, 172, 199, 226, 258, 276, 279, 280, 410, 438, 445, 501, 562, 564, 634). Only 5%–25% of the nitrogen applied to trees at up to 3 lbs/1,000 ft^2 (1.44 kg/100 m^2) at planting was absorbed by newly planted trees (606). Moderate release of nutrients by decomposition of both surface mulch and organic matter added to backfill soil will be available to meet the tree's modest need for nutrients during this initial establishment period.

Some palms may be an exception. When palm fertilizer (77) was incorporated into the backfill soil at planting, Mexican fan palm growth increased even though all palms in the study received a maintenance application of the same fertilizer every 3 months during the 2-year study (82).

Many factors determine how soon after planting that fertilizing will be effective. Small trees require less time to regenerate their root system and can overcome the water shortage problem more quickly than large trees. Very small trees that overcome postplanting stress very rapidly may benefit from slow-release fertilizer formulations applied at planting. Trees with a constant and ample supply of soil moisture will be less water stressed, regenerate roots and establish more quickly, and benefit from fertilization earlier than infrequently irrigated trees. If the soilless substrate in a container root ball has low nutrient-holding capacity, these trees may require earlier and more frequent fertilization to avoid nutrient deficiency until the roots grow out into the backfill and site soils.

Biostimulants

Many compounds have been marketed as biostimulants to be applied at planting. Contents of these may include growth hormones, nutrients, vitamins, sugars, amino acids, humic acids, extracts of plants, and inoculum of beneficial rhizosphere fungi and bacteria.

Application of organic products, such as humates and plant extracts, at planting has shown limited or no benefit to root or shoot growth of trees. Dose and species responses vary widely (39, 82, 167, 184, 203, 332, 333, 442, 443, 480).

Sugars have been tested as a postplanting treatment to increase growth and establishment of trees. Some sugars can increase root and shoot dry weight or increase root:shoot ratio. Early results are inconsistent among tree species, kinds of sugars, and application rates included in the trials (39, 380, 432, 434, 435). In most studies, the sugar was applied to the soil at least twice.

Paclobutrazol, a growth regulator used primarily to reduce shoot growth of trees, can also increase root growth under certain circumstances. Paclobutrazol applied at planting doubled root growth on black maple (*Acer nigrum*) in the first season when crown growth was not reduced by the paclobutrazol treatment. In the second season, when crown growth was reduced, root growth was not increased (577). The reduction in top growth may have been responsible for the lack of root stimulation in the second year. Species response may vary as well. Growth of green ash (*Fraxinus pennsylvanica*) roots was unaffected by paclobutrazol treatment under the same conditions (577). Gilman (203) reported that paclobutrazol slowed top growth, but had no effect on root growth of transplanted live oaks (*Quercus virginiana*). Root pruning can enhance the growth regulation effects of paclobutrazol treatment (380), making it more difficult to determine an appropriate application rate.

The benefits of mycorrhizal associations of tree roots are well established. Inoculations with mycorrhizal fungi have proven beneficial to trees when planted in soils lacking the appropriate fungi, such as strip mining reclamation sites and sterilized nursery beds. Urban planting sites can be of very poor quality, but this does not necessarily mean that they lack appropriate mycorrhizal fungi for trees. Mycorrhizal inoculum present in urban soils was greater than in forest soil (624), and mycorrhizal colonization of littleleaf linden (*Tilia cordata*) street trees and forest trees was similar (551). Colonization can increase after planting without inoculation (625). Growth rate has generally been unaffected when treated at planting with commercial inoculants (1, 82, 116, 167, 202, 625).

The quality of the inoculum may be a factor. Mycorrhizal colonization of roots rarely exceeded 5% after treatment with commercial inoculants, but was up to 74% when treated with fresh lab-cultured inoculant (174, 623).

Antitranspirants

Antitranspirants are foliage sprays that reduce water loss through the leaf surface (99, 457). These are essentially waxes, resins, and plastics. The spray dries and forms a thin protective film on the leaf surface that usually lasts for several weeks before it weathers off. If the leaves are growing when the spray is applied, the film cracks and eventually loses its effectiveness.

Certain film antitranspirants may be detrimental to normal leaf respiration when used improperly (348), and they can reduce root and shoot growth (457). Due to the reduction in cooling effect of water evaporation from the leaf surfaces, high air temperatures and bright sun may cause heat injury to leaves that have been sprayed. Film-forming antitranspirants are variably effective, depending upon the compound, the tree species, and environmental conditions. On some evergreens, such as pines, the compounds combine with the waxes in the stomatal pores and form impermeable plugs. These plugs reduce water loss, but also reduce photosynthesis due to limited diffusion of CO_2. Some antitranspirants are toxic to certain species and nontoxic to others. In general, antitranspirants appear to be more toxic to evergreens than to deciduous species.

Antitranspirants have been used in summer transplanting with success (254, 269, 303). In colder climates, evergreens may be protected from winter desiccation when a spray is applied in late fall. An additional application may be necessary during a mild period in mid-winter. Another benefit unrelated to reducing water stress is that film-forming antitranspirants can reduce certain leaf diseases such as powdery mildew (437). Despite possible injury, antitranspirants provide a useful method of manipulating the water balance of trees after transplanting if used cautiously (133). A light application is most likely to produce benefits with minimal adverse effects. Antitranspirants should not be used as a substitute for good transplanting practices.

Tree Shelters

Tree shelters are translucent tubes that are placed around small seedlings. The bottom of the tube must be in complete contact with the soil to protect the seedling from animal damage, and the unit is held in place by a stake (Figure 8-22). Originally used to aid in establishment of seedlings in reforestation, tree shelters are sometimes used to aid in establishment and early growth of small trees in nursery and landscape situations (97). They were first used in cool summer climates, where both the greenhouse effect and rodent protection help to increase survival. More recently, they have also proven effective is the southern United States with hot summers (70, 323, 608). They can be ineffective in Mediterranean climates without irrigation (122).

Air temperature, relative humidity, and carbon dioxide concentrations are higher inside the tree shelters, providing a greenhouse-like effect that often results in increased height growth (70, 94, 95, 97, 122, 190, 323, 336, 442, 443, 608, 627) and survival (122, 323, 336, 442, 443, 447, 608). Ancillary benefits include

Figure 8-22 Tree shelters can increase survival and shoot growth of seedlings by protecting them from animal damage and providing a greenhouse-like environment. Roots and trunks may grow slower when tree shelters are used. The effectiveness of tree shelters varies with application.

protection from damage and vandalism (323, 446) and reduced competition with grass (339).

Most studies have shown that tree shelters can decrease caliper growth in the first few seasons, and the trunks of these trees may be incapable of supporting the weight of the top when the tree shelter is removed (94, 95, 190, 336, 543, 608, 627). This reduction in caliper growth may be due to suppression of low branches along the trunk that increase caliper growth of young trees, combined with the lack of movement. Originally used in reforestation plantings, tree shelters were intended to be left in place for at least 5 years until weathering caused them to gradually deteriorate and fall away. A tree that loses support of the shelter gradually is able to develop trunk taper and stand upright on its own (447). Removing the tree shelter prematurely in landscape and nursery situations does not allow time for the trunk to strengthen.

Tree shelters can reduce root development (95, 97, 543), but the reasons are unclear. If removal of the shelter resulted in increased transpiration, severe water stress could result from the smaller root system.

Tree shelters seem to be most beneficial when used for their original purpose—to aid in the establishment of seedlings in reforestation where the tree shelters would remain in place until they deteriorate. In landscape situations, the disadvantages may outweigh the potential benefits.

Final Inspection

The final step in the planting process is inspection. Many items need to be checked:

- Is the planting depth correct?
- Have at least the upper portions of the root ball wrapping materials been cut away?
- Have roots growing against the inside of the container been eliminated?
- Is the trunk straight?
- Is a raised ring of soil needed to hold irrigation water over the root ball?
- Has the tree been pruned to correct structural defects?
- Has mulch been applied to the soil surface around the root ball with only a light layer over the root ball?

- Was the root ball and backfill soil watered thoroughly?
- Have the extra soil, root ball wrappings, pruned branches, and other debris been removed from the site?
- If the tree needed staking, do the ties allow for growth and movement of the trunk?
- And finally, does the new owner or maintenance crew understand how important proper care after planting will be for the survival and good health of the new tree?

It will take several years for the new tree to become established, especially larger trees. Throughout this period an ongoing commitment to maintenance will be required.

CHAPTER 9

Encourage Root Development After Planting

Regenerated roots are produced from the roots cut during planting.
Soil temperatures determine the rate of their growth.

Root systems of trees spread beyond the branch tips when they are growing in an area without restrictions, such as a nursery. The spreading root system has access to a large soil volume and the large quantity of water held in it. When field-grown trees are harvested from the nursery, most of the absorbing root system remains in the nursery. The amount of water available to the roots in the root ball is a fraction of what it was before digging. Even though root loss of container plants is minimal when planted, the roots are confined to an abnormally small volume in the container, very similar to root ball dug from the field nursery. Both container- and field-grown plants face the same challenge initially after planting: marginal or insufficient water absorption by the root system. Until they can grow a normal spreading root system, newly planted trees are dependent on frequent irrigation. Water stress is a common cause of planting failure.

Root Distribution Before Transplanting

An understanding of the spread and depth of the field-grown tree root system before transplanting is necessary to understand the challenge faced by a tree after transplanting when the root system has been reduced to a fraction of its original size. The inherent structure of woody root systems can be categorized into three basic types: lateral, sloping, and tap (Figure 9-2) (618). Lateral root systems (or plate root) are characterized by major roots spreading widely near the soil surface. Sloping root systems (or heart root) have roots growing at many angles. Trees with true tap roots also have substantial lateral roots. Over 80% of trees have a lateral root system (128), and all types have substantial lateral root development near the surface.

In the field nursery, a typical landscape-sized tree— 2- to 4-inch (5 to 10 cm) caliper—will have a root system dominated by laterals that spread two to three times as far as the branches (Figure 9-3). Tree lilac (*Syringa reticulata*) roots were up to twice as long as serviceberry (*Amelanchier* sp.). Root depth did not differ by species and was more determined by soil conditions (191).

The spreading lateral roots regularly develop side branches over their entire length. These divide repeatedly and terminate as fine roots. This network of branch roots, and the constant replacement of fine roots on them, results in the presence of fine absorbing roots virtually everywhere in the top few inches of surface soil. It is sometimes referred

Figure 9-1 The large lateral roots of most tree species grow very horizontally, just a few inches below the surface, and can extend great distances. After tapering noticeably within a few feet of the trunk, the root becomes more rope-like, tapering very slowly.

Figure 9-2 The basic root structure types: tap root, often with large laterals also (left), sloping or heart root (center), and lateral or plate root (right).

to as a mat of fine roots just below the soil surface. Of the total root system (dry weight) of 3-year-old birch (*Betula pendula*) trees, 40% consisted of fine roots less than 1 mm diameter (52). Dominant tap roots are limited to a few genera, such as oaks (*Quercus*), walnut (*Juglans*), hickory (*Carya*), and tupelo (*Nyssa*). Growing in certain container types, or undercutting and transplanting field-grown trees, reduces the dominance of the tap root in these species.

Palm trees are not woody plants, and are anatomically similar to grasses. Root systems of palm species usually consist of numerous closely spaced and rather small, tube-like roots that radiate out from the base of the trunk with little or no branching (Figure 9-4). Little data is available on palm root spread.

Root Loss

Root loss is responsible for slow growth of field-grown trees after transplanting. The greater the amount of both coarse and fine roots lost, the greater the reduction in top growth until the root system is replaced by new growth. Shoot growth was reduced by 10% after loss of 25% of the root system. Shoot growth was reduced 40% when 60% of the root system was removed. Removal of fine roots alone, as would be more typical of bare-root transplanting, resulted in a 30% reduction in shoot growth (8).

Figure 9-3 Tree root systems are typically shallow and widespread. Sinker roots can follow natural openings into deeper soils. True tap roots are rare. Fine roots are present near the soil surface throughout the entire root system. Only a small percentage of the root system of a field-grown tree is moved with the tree in the root ball.

Field-Grown Trees

A substantial portion of the root system of field-grown trees is lost when trees are harvested. The proportion of the root system retained in root balls decreases with increasing trunk diameter. Standard root balls (12) of trees up to 2.3 inches (6 cm)

Figure 9-4 Typical tube-like roots of a palm tree.

Figure 9-5 Root spread of palm has not been extensively studied, but the exposed roots of these palm trees can be seen extending several meters.

Figure 9-6 With the tree roots exposed and painted white, it is easy to visualize how 53% (or more) of root biomass is contained in the root ball, while 18% (or less) of the fine roots are contained in the root ball.

dbh contained 53%–100% of root biomass (191, 208). Trees with 2.3- to 8-inch (6–20 cm) diameter retained 29%–83% of their root biomass (191). However, a much smaller portion, 5%–18%, of the fine roots (<2 mm) is within in the root ball (Figure 9-6) (198, 208, 209, 593). The larger roots comprising most of the biomass can store carbohydrates, but it is the fine roots that absorb water. High levels of water stress can result from the large loss of fine roots. Low-volume trickle irrigation systems used in nurseries can increase the amount of fine roots contained in the root ball (209).

Root pruning in the nursery field can increase the amount of fine root surface area in the root ball by 400%–600% (225, 598), but the percentage of the fine roots moved with the tree is still less than 20% (208, 598).

Bare-Root Trees

A larger root spread can often be moved with a bare-root tree (Figure 9-7), but exposed fine roots are more subject to mechanical damage and desiccation. Cell damage from exposure to air and sunlight, even for a short period, is well-documented by electrolyte leakage tests. Despite evidence of cell damage, green ash (*Fraxinus pennsylvanica*) and sugar maple (*Acer saccharum*) fine roots survived, and tips continued to grow after losing up to 82% of their

Figure 9-7 The root system of a bare-root tree as it is shipped from nursery. Fine roots may not survive, but they will soon be replaced by new fine roots from the many woody roots.

water under controlled laboratory conditions (580). Exposure of littleleaf linden (*Tilia cordata*) roots to ambient indoor conditions up to 48 hours had no effect on overall root regeneration (626). Survival of fine roots under conditions that exist at the planting site may be somewhat different, and roots should be protected from desiccation as much as possible.

Root Injury

Roots are good compartmentalizers (walling off decay to limit its spread) (498). Roots are subject to frequent wounding by elements of their natural environment, such as burrowing animals and natural movement of the soil from freeze/thaw and wet/dry cycles. This wounding takes place in the presence of decay-causing organisms that are always present in the soil. Response to natural wounding in the environment has led to excellent compartmentalization in roots. When woody roots of four species of trees were severed and examined 5 years later, minimal discoloration and decay were found (579). If the process of severing roots was likely to lead to serious root decay, most trees that are transplanted would exhibit extensive root loss from decay fungi.

Producing a New Root System

The Need for Access to More Water

Rapid new root growth is important to minimize water stress after planting (317). Does a tree benefit from roots that are denser than would be found in the natural state? Will those extra roots absorb water from the soil more quickly? If so, will the tree benefit, or will water be absorbed so quickly from the small root zone that the tree will be subjected to more severe drought stress between watering cycles? Has the tree wasted the energy producing the extra roots? Research has not provided answers to all these questions, but it is probably better for roots to grow out into a larger soil volume as quickly as possible, rather than to produce denser root development in a limited soil volume within and near the root ball. A large planting hole,

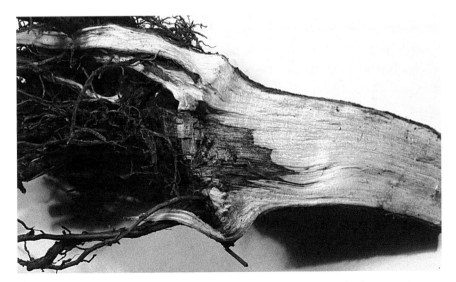

Figure 9-8 Roots are good compartmentalizers, and severing them during transplanting does not lead to extensive decay.

or a large area of cultivated soil around the root ball, will help roots to spread out quickly, as will good care after planting.

The entire container root system may be planted with the tree, but the roots are confined to a small volume of well-drained container substrate. The root ball can become dry between rainfall and irrigation cycles even more quickly than a field soil ball, causing drought stress, even though the surrounding the soil moisture may be ample. A container plant must also develop roots that spread throughout a large volume of soil in order to have access to sufficient moisture to survive without the daily irrigation it received in the nursery.

Root Regeneration

When roots of field-grown or container-grown trees are severed, nearly all of the new roots are produced near the severed end of the root. Numerous new roots are initiated near the cut end as a result of the wounding (Figure 9-9) (218, 592). When a root is severed, new roots formed nearest the cut surface will elongate in the same direction as the original root. New roots forming further behind the cut surface tend to grow at more perpendicular angles to the original root (301).

The rate of new root initiation after planting is affected by many factors. In warm greenhouse conditions (77°F, 25°C), intact root tips of dormant green ash (*Fraxinus pennsylvanica*) began to elongate 7–20 days after planting. New roots were not initiated from severed root ends until 17–29 days after planting (30). In cooler spring or fall field soils, a longer time would be required for new root growth than in the warm soil conditions of these experiments. Tree fine root growth was slowed by approximately half when soil temperatures dropped from 68°F (20°C) to 50°F (10°C) (557). When trees are planted in the late fall, after soils have cooled, substantial new root growth may not occur until the soils have warmed again in the spring. In warmer regions, active root growth may continue all winter if soils are warm.

It is mistakenly believed that if the tube-like roots of all palms are cut during the digging process, they will die back to the trunk, and new roots will originate from the root initiation zone at the base of the trunk. Actually, regrowth response of severed palm roots varies with species and distance from the base of the trunk (79). Less than 1% of all cut cabbage palm (*Sabal palmetto*) roots regenerated new roots,

Figure 9-9 When roots are severed during transplanting, nearly all of the new roots are produced near the cut end.

whereas coconut palms (*Cocos nucifera*) cut roots regenerated new root tips about 50% of the time. For other species of palms, such as queen palm (*Syagrus romanzofiana*), royal palm (*Roystonea regia*), Mexican fan palm (*Washingtonia robusta*), and Senegal date palm (*Phoenix reclinata*), the percentage of roots surviving increases with stub length as well as the number of new roots produced from the root initiation zone (Figure 7-28) on the trunk (79). Many palms may benefit from a root ball with roots cut at least 1 foot (30 cm) from the trunk for better survival of existing roots, and some may benefit from root pruning 4–6 weeks prior to digging to stimulate new root production from the base of the trunk (80).

Time Required to Produce a New Root System

Root extension rate (increase in length) depends on species and a number of environmental factors. Annual soil temperature regime is important. In the upper Midwestern United States (Hardiness Zone 5), with its warm summers and frozen soils in winter, roots grow at an average annual rate of approximately 18 inches (0.5 m) (576, 577). In one season under nursery conditions in USDA Hardiness Zone 6, red oak (*Quercus rubra*) roots grew 21 to 24 inches (53 to 61 cm) (527), and birch (*Betula pendula*) roots grew 35 inches (89 cm) (524). In the subtropical climate of north central Florida (Hardiness Zone 9), where light, sandy soils predominate and the growing season is nearly year-round, annual root growth is more rapid—up to 6 feet (2 m) or more for some oak and citrus species that were studied (99, 207).

Root growth for some species will be higher or lower than average figures. For example, black maple (*Acer nigrum*) roots grew 15 inches (39 cm) in a season, which is near the expected average for the Midwestern United States. Under identical conditions, green ash (*Fraxinus pennsylvanica*) grew nearly twice as much (26 inches, 67 cm) (577). Root growth data for other climates is not available, but it should be possible to estimate using these few published studies and the soil temperature data in Table 4-2.

Root regeneration in the first year after planting is generally better on ball-and-burlap than container-grown deciduous and evergreen trees (60, 207, 263). Arborvitae (*Thuja occidentalis*) is the exception among species studied (132).

As the roots continue to spread out, fine roots continue to develop throughout the root system and increase in density for at least 5 years (307). In general, it will require several seasons to replace the roots that were lost when the tree was dug unless the plant is very small and the growing season is very long.

Environmental Factors Influencing Root Growth

Like most aspects of plant growth, the rate at which roots grow is influenced by numerous factors. Roots can sometimes grow at almost unbelievable rates. Black locust (*Robinia pseudoacacia*) roots grew over 2 inches (56 mm) in a single day, though average daily growth is usually much less (369). Birch (*Betula pendula*) averaged one-quarter inch (7 mm) per day over two consecutive growing seasons (524).

Temperature

Most authors agree that, in temperate climates, root growth starts just before shoot growth in the spring, though considerable variation among species has been reported. Roots are not dependent on actively growing shoots as a source of auxins (369, 496) and are often able to resume growth first in spring. Sugar maple (*Acer saccharum*) roots began to grow at 41°F (5°C), while shoot growth was initiated at 50°F (10°C), but initial root growth may be quite slow at such low temperatures.

Active root growth has been reported to begin when spring soil temperatures reach 52°F to 59°F (11°C to 15°C) (256, 524). Daytime air temperatures usually increase faster in spring than soil temperatures, so the difference in the start of spring growth above and below ground may not be as great as it seems. Substantial root growth can continue throughout the winter in areas with mild winter temperatures.

Maximal root growth in most tree species occurs in early summer. Optimum temperatures for root growth have been reported at 65°F to 89°F (18°C to 32°C), depending on species, with maximum temperatures for active growth reported at 77°F to 100°F (25°C to 38°C) (377, 470, 524, 628). Root growth can be interrupted in midsummer due to unfavorable environmental conditions (drought or high soil temperature) with a second, but smaller period, of active growth in the late summer or early autumn when soil moisture and temperature again become more favorable. Honeylocust (*Gleditsia triacanthos*) is the only temperate tree species reported to sustain growth at root-zone temperatures above 90°F (32°C) (238, 239, 631). Roots of most woody species are killed at 104°F to 122°F (40°C to 50°C) (628).

In temperate climates, root growth slows in the autumn as the soil cools and plants enter dormancy. Roots can continue to grow in all nonfrozen soil, but the rate will be reduced by cold soil temperatures. Reported minimum temperatures range from 35°F to 52°F (2°C to 11°C) (369, 524). Root tissues of woody plants can be killed at soil temperatures of +23°F to -4°F (-5°C to -20°C) (274, 429, 481, 540).

Moisture

As soil begins to dry, development of branch roots is inhibited more than growth of primary roots (633). Root growth stops in most species when soil moisture is reduced to 12% to 14% on an oven-dry basis (369), or -500 mbar soil moisture tension (54). Root suberization (the deposition of a waterproof layer in the walls of cells near the root surface) is accelerated in dry soil. As the effective absorbing surface is diminished, the roots do not regain their full capacity for water uptake until new root tips can be produced. When roots are rewatered immediately after the cessation of elongation, roots may not resume elongation for at least one week. Resumption of root growth takes up to five weeks if water is withheld longer (56). If the soil becomes too dry, some of the smaller roots may be killed.

An increase in soil moisture content above 40% induces almost no additional root growth. Roots are generally not sensitive to soil saturation itself, but secondary effects do have an impact on root growth. In colder climates, wet soils will warm up more slowly in the spring, reducing root growth. Excessive soil moisture reduces soil aeration because the water replaces the air normally held in the macropores of the soil. However, moisture reduces soil strength which can allow greater root growth if aeration is not limiting.

Aeration

Limited oxygen availability in saturated soils does have a substantial effect on the roots of most species. In most soils, 8%–10% oxygen in the soil atmosphere is considered the minimum for good root growth. Below this level, root growth is reduced. When roots are deprived of adequate oxygen, leaf growth rate can be reduced (412). Lack of adequate gas exchange in waterlogged soils can also lead to an increase in carbon dioxide, which is toxic to roots in higher-than-normal concentrations. Roots are killed if conditions become anaerobic.

Roots of some species have lower oxygen requirements (439). In some trees, such as willow (*Salix*), alder (*Alnus*), poplar (*Populus*), tupelo (*Nyssa*), ash

(*Fraxinus*), baldcypress (*Taxodium*), and birch (*Betula*), oxygen can move down to the roots internally through intercellular spaces. Enough oxygen can be transported so that some is released into the soil immediately surrounding the roots (300, 327). This oxygen-transporting tissue within roots is called aerenchyma.

Soil Density

Roots tend to follow the path of least resistance. Old root channels, animal tunnels, pockets of loose soil, cracks, and fissures are often used by roots to penetrate the deeper, denser soils. Species with high root:shoot ratios seem to have a greater ability to penetrate hard soil layers. Compacted soils with high penetration resistance will slow the growth of roots. Bulk densities of 1.4–1.6 g/cc of soil will inhibit root growth (269, 423), although root growth can be reduced at much lower bulk densities, depending upon soil texture (see Table 1-1) and other factors that affect soil strength. Soil strength (penetration resistance) may be more important than bulk density (548). Inadequate soil moisture increases penetration resistance. Species that are tolerant of reduced soil aeration that can accompany high moisture content of compacted soil can develop better root systems in compacted soils. For species that are less tolerant of the poorly aerated conditions and cannot produce new root growth when penetration resistance is reduced by high moisture, overall root development may be reduced (145, 382).

Stored Energy

Carbohydrates are often assumed to be in short supply in transplanted trees on the basis that much of the storage capacity (woody root tissue) is removed. Total carbohydrates stored in the root system may not be substantially reduced since most of the large roots and root biomass are contained in the root ball (191, 209). Levels of stored carbohydrates (amount of carbohydrate per gram of root tissue) can be higher in transplanted trees one year after planting than in trees that are not moved (592). Vigorous regenerated root growth from the smaller transplanted root system probably requires less energy than normal growth of an intact root system. The amount of carbohydrates produced by the crown and stored in the transplanted root system is probably adequate to support a reduced level of overall root growth.

Fertility

Concentrations of fine roots are often encountered in nutrient-rich zones of soil (268, 438, 586). In nutrient-rich soils, the extension growth of the main root is reduced, and development of lateral roots is increased. This results in dense, fine root development in these areas. Conversely, nutrient-poor soils stimulate long roots with poorly developed laterals ("pioneer" roots). Nitrogen fertilization can cause a localized increase in root growth (126, 586), but other parts of the root system may be reduced to compensate (603). Nitrogen fertilization may just alter the distribution of the fine roots, rather than increase it.

Nitrogen and phosphorous can stimulate top growth more than root growth, decreasing the root:shoot ratio (83, 249, 639). Heavy nitrogen fertilization at planting could be counterproductive, reducing root extension and stimulate too much top growth. Contrary to traditional beliefs, increasing phosphorous has not been shown to increase root growth of woody plants unless it is deficient in the soil (586, 636). Fertilization is sometimes promoted on the basis that if fertilizer increases crown development, more carbohydrates will be translocated to the roots and increase root growth, but transplanted trees already have high levels of carbohydrates in the roots (592).

Increasing Root Growth After Planting

Many growers strive for a dense development of fine roots on the basis that it is important for tree survival and new root growth after planting. Many postplanting techniques have been explored to increase root growth after planting.

Cultural Practices

Trees transplanted from the field initially develop a greater number (and cross-sectional area) of roots growing into landscape soil than trees planted from containers (222, 375). Root pruning can further improve root regeneration of field-grown trees after planting (202). Irrigation after planting did increase root development of container-grown trees (214, 375) and bare-root trees (626). Mechanically disrupting root balls of container-grown trees by slicing, butterflying, or teasing (see Chapter 7) did not result in an increase in root growth after planting (601).

Root Stimulants

Auxin treatments can increase the number of new roots initiated near the cut ends. Indole-3-butyric acid (IBA) when applied to roots near the edge of the root ball (366, 370, 448, 536) and as a bare-root dip (433) resulted in more root initiation, but may reduce root elongation (433, 536). This could be counterproductive to the goal of achieving a greater root spread rather than a denser root system close to the root ball. IBA treatment did not increase root initiation of palms (81). Napthaleneacetic acid (NAA) applied as a soil drench after planting also increased root initiation within a few centimeters of the severed root end in linden (*Tilia*) (Figure 9-10) (582). Gibberellin-inhibiting growth regulators, such as paclobutrazol, may also promote root initiation (139) and can increase length and dry weight of regenerated roots in some species if top growth regulation is minimal (577).

Many kinds of root-stimulating products have been marketed over the years (see Chapter 8). Claims usually refer to "better" or "improved" root growth without reference to specific effects on the root system or how they lead into faster establishment after planting. Ingredients range from vitamin compounds to seaweed extracts and growth hormones. The effectiveness of many of these products in stimulating root growth has not been shown convincingly in landscape situations through published independent studies. Use caution when judging unsubstantiated claims. If testing the products on your own, be sure to include untreated plants for a comparison (similar to the untreated control in a scientific experiment) in order to judge whether they are really effective.

Redevelopment of Root Structure

When roots of bare-root trees are not spread out properly at planting, permanently kinked and twisted roots can result (Figure 9-11). Also, proper root development and anchorage will not occur, and vascular flow may be restricted. New root growth will concentrate in the soil depth where conditions are most favorable

Figure 9-10 Application of auxins to the cut root surface at planting can increase root initiation near the severed end. However, these additional roots have not been shown to improve growth or reduce stress after planting.

for root growth, usually near the surface. When trees were planted with the root systems too deep, roots were observed to gradually grow to the upper soil regions. Within 4 feet (1.25 m) from the trunk, root distribution was the same as other trees planted at the proper depth (Figure 9-12) (144). However, the portion of the root system that is too deep may affect tree performance.

Survival of the Fittest

Many new roots are formed at the cut end of a root (Figure 9-10), but the more vigorous roots soon begin to dominate (301, 531, 581). The less vigorous roots persist for only a short time or remain subdominant if they persist (Figure 9-13). Though these numerous small-diameter roots may help absorb moisture during the critical period just after transplanting, their benefit to the tree is short-term. As the root structure is re-established, there would be no advantage or enough space for all of the roots to continue to increase in diameter. Mortality of regenerated roots was high the first winter after transplanting, regardless of the season the trees were transplanted (465), suggesting that some of these roots may begin to deteriorate after just one season.

On Colorado spruce (*Picea pungens*), a species with strong aboveground apical dominance, usually a single regenerated root persisted on each severed root after about 5 years (Figure 9-14, left). Just a slight swelling and a few traces of the small, dead regenerated roots are the only indication on the outside of the root that it was ever severed. On species such as maple, which do not exhibit strong apical dominance aboveground, several regenerated roots may persist (Figure 9-15). Horsley and Wilson (302) describes evidence for apical dominance in roots, but further studies into the mechanism and significance of this pattern are needed.

Large severed roots are often quite visible at the surface of the root ball (Figure 9-16), and there is often great focus on avoiding damage to these root ends. Roots regenerated from the large severed roots may be gone after a few years, leaving only a "stub." What is often not appreciated is that much smaller and less visible roots also regenerate many new roots, and some of these may become the new structural roots. Being smaller, these roots may be more subject to damage from desiccation if the exterior of the root ball dries out.

Figure 9-11 If the roots of bare root plants are not properly spread out at planting, a distorted root system will develop, sometimes referred to as a club foot.

Figure 9-12 Roots usually grow back up near the soil surface, even when planted too deep—if they survive. (Photo: S. Day)

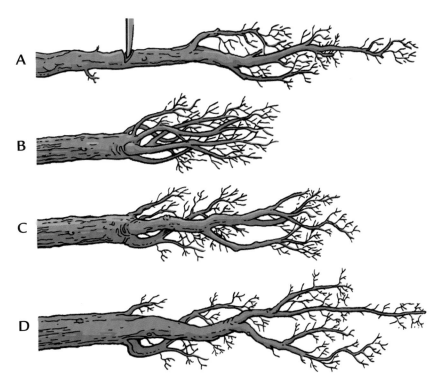

Figure 9-13 Stages in replacement of a severed root. The root is severed at the arrow (A). Initially, many small roots are regenerated from the callus collar at the severed end (B). One root becomes dominant and continues to grow rapidly, while others stop growing or die (C). Eventually, only a single root may remain to replace the original root (D).

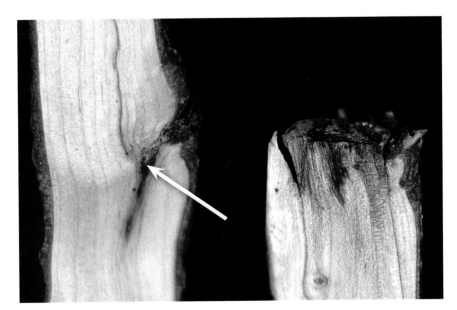

Figure 9-14 A spruce root that is more than a few millimeters in diameter when cut (right) produces a few small, short-lived roots, but they soon disappear leaving only a "stub." When a small 1- or 2-year-old root is cut (left, at arrow), the strongest regenerated root(s) usually dominate and become part of the new root structure, leaving little evidence that the other regenerated roots once were present. There is very little wood discoloration and decay resulting from the cuts.

Figure 9-15 On some species, such as maple, more than one regenerated root may persist, but most of the regenerated roots originally initiated are gone a few years later.

Figure 9-16 Large roots like this may be severed at the edge of the root ball, but often produce few, if any, new roots that contribute to the new structural root system.

Girdling Roots

Girdling roots (Figure 9-17) of field-grown stock (of different origin than circling roots on container stock) can be formed as a result of transplanting (588). When the radially oriented lateral roots (like spokes of a wheel) are severed by transplanting, existing branch roots behind the cuts often begin to grow more rapidly. If normal root development occurred, and roots were not cut, these branch roots would remain small. But after the primary root is cut, they sometimes grow rapidly and become a part of the permanent structural root system. Their perpendicular orientation to the other radial roots and proximity to the base of the trunk results in development of girdling roots as both the roots and the trunk continue to increase in diameter (Figure 9-18). These girdling roots restrict the flow in the vascular system and can cause stress and eventually death of the tree. Evidence that girdling roots result from transplanting is provided by the low incidence of girdling roots found in nature.

Figure 9-17 Girdling roots can restrict the flow of water and nutrients between the root system and the crown.

Container Root Defects

No container shape accommodates the natural spread of a tree root system. When roots encounter the container wall, they can be deflected up, down, or around the inside of the container wall. Some container designs are better at preventing these root defects, but none eliminates them all. If these defective roots are planted with the root ball, they will persist and not function as well as normal roots. Normal radially oriented roots will not develop as well with the defective roots present (218), and establishment and anchorage will be hindered (222).

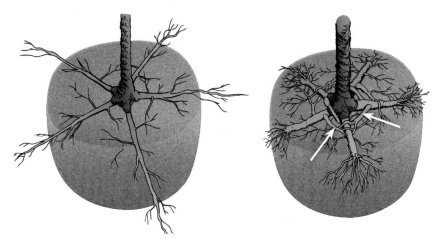

Figure 9-18 Probable mechanism of girdling root formation. The major roots of a tree normally extend out from the trunk like spokes of a wheel (left). These roots and some of their branch roots are severed during transplanting and new roots initiated near the cut ends (right). These grow in the direction of the original root, but growth of existing branch roots is stimulated, and these are positioned to become girdling roots (arrows).

Figure 9-19 Root defects caused by containers can inhibit root development after planting (left). Eliminating the defects by shaving the root ball at planting results in a more normal root system (right). (Photos: E. Gilman)

Development of a normal root system after planting is critical for tree vigor and longevity. Site conditions can influence the speed of regeneration. The tree will need special care during the time it takes for the new roots to grow.

CHAPTER 10

Allow Time for the Tree to Establish

Water stress can reduce twig growth until the root system is fully established on the new site.
The larger the tree, the longer its establishment will take.

A newly planted tree will be under stress and have a greater need for care until its root system can fully develop at the new site. Water stress can occur even with the best of care, especially on hot, sunny days when transpirational water loss from the leaves can exceed the ability of the limited root system to absorb water, even if the soil is moist. The duration and severity of this postplanting stress is affected by many factors.

Defining Postplanting Stress

The term transplanting shock has often been used to describe the stress induced by transplanting. Postplanting stress more completely and directly describes the physiological condition of recently planted trees.

Water Is Limiting

Tree growth is always limited by the factor required for growth that is in shortest supply, even if all other factors are plentiful (see Chapter 1). Common limiting environmental factors are temperature, light, water, and nutrients. After planting, water is usually the most limiting factor. Even if soil moisture is adequate, the limited root system may not be able to absorb enough water to completely satisfy the needs of the tree. Within hours of root severance, water stress can cause the formation of embolisms (air space disrupting water movement) in the xylem and reduce water conductance (110, 340). Temperature, light, nutrients, and other factors are usually less limiting than water for the initial period after planting.

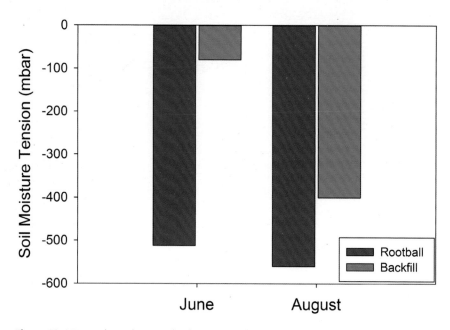

Figure 10-1 Transplanted trees rely almost entirely on root ball moisture for much of the first growing season. Root ball soils dry rapidly, while backfill soils with no roots remain moist. At -500 mbars soil moisture tension (more negative value indicates drier soil), roots will not grow and water absorption is decreased because of increased suberization of existing root tips. Not until near the end of the summer, 14 weeks after planting, did roots absorb significant amounts of water from the backfill soil, but still the root ball soil dried faster (595).

Table 10-1 Soil moisture available to the rapidly expanding roots system of newly planted 1-gallon (4 L) container shrubs increases faster than transpirational water loss by the crown, reducing the frequency of watering (40).

WEEKS AFTER PLANTING	WATER USED PER DAY (Liters)	WATER IN ROOT ZONE (Liters)	WATER SUPPLY (Days)
4	0.5	2	4
11	1.0	6	6
16	1.5	12	8
21	2.0	23	11

Recently planted trees rely heavily on root ball soil moisture for at least the first growing season because that is where most of the roots are located. For ball-and-burlap trees, the moisture contained within the root ball represents only a small fraction of the water that was available to the full root system before transplanting. Well-drained container substrate will hold less water in the landscape (see Figure 5-23), and once planted it will probably be irrigated less frequently than in the nursery. Both field-dug and container root balls hold very little water relative to the transpiration demands of the tree.

Figure 10-1 shows that the root ball soil moisture of a newly planted tree can be very dry for most of the first season even though irrigation was applied three times per week. At the same time, backfill soils just outside the root ball stay very moist because no tree roots are there taking up moisture. It is not possible for water to move from the backfill soil into the root ball as fast as it is being removed from the root ball by roots. Even at moderate soil moisture stress (i.e., -0.4 MPa), root growth can be reduced or stopped (356), and the capacity of roots to absorb water is decreased because of increased suberization of root tips (54). In temperate climates, it can take 4–5 months for enough roots to grow into the soil outside the root ball to absorb significant amounts of soil moisture from the backfill soil (264, 595).

Restoring Balance

Calculating the amount of water held in the root zone in relation to usage by the tree is another way to look at the potential for water stress in new plantings. Table 10-1 shows that the moisture available to the expanding root systems of recently planted shrubs increases more rapidly than does water used by the crown. Four weeks after planting, the shrubs required watering every 4 days. By 21 weeks after planting, the root system had expanded into a much greater volume of soil, more water was available to it, and the watering cycle could be extended to once every 11 days (40). A tree may be considered established when the watering cycle can be extended to at least 2 weeks during warm, summer weather without substantial water stress. This occurred near the end of the second growing season for 2-inch (5 cm) green ash (*Fraxinus pennsylvanica*) trees in Hardiness Zone 5 (595), and in about 6 months after planting laurel oak (*Quercus laurifolia*) in Zone 9 (207).

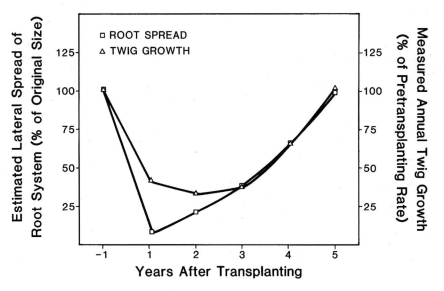

Figure 10-2 Root loss as a result of transplanting causes a corresponding decrease in twig growth. Recovery of twig growth rate is closely related to regeneration of the root system (583).

Signs of Recovery

The water stress resulting from root loss during transplanting reduces overall growth (265, 523, 583). Reduced leaf area allows trees to self-regulate water loss by reducing transpiration (337). Physiological measurements—such as xylem water potential and leaf gas exchange—can be used to track the establishment of trees (46, 173, 487), but are difficult to measure. Growth rate is easier to evaluate. When a tree is fully re-established, the growth rate will recover to pretransplanting levels as the root system regenerates and postplanting stress is reduced (Figure 10-2) (207, 523, 533, 583).

For species with only one flush of growth each year, twig growth may be smaller the second year after transplanting than the first year because future growth is influenced by conditions at the time the bud is forming, and also at the time when the bud is expanding. The bud for the first year's growth after transplanting is large and contains many leaf primordia (preformed leaves) because it was formed under optimum conditions in the nursery. Because the bud expands under conditions of great stress, the expanded leaves are generally small and closely spaced. The bud for the second year's growth is formed under greater stress and may be much smaller with fewer leaf primordial, but it will expand

Figure 10-3 It is easy to see the pattern of growth after transplanting on evergreens because they retain several years of needles. Growth the first year (between arrows) is dwarfed, but with nearly as many needles as before transplanting. The second year, there are fewer needles, but they are closer to normal size.

under less severe stress. The leaves are closer to normal size, and internodal spaces (distance between leaves) will be larger. Because the smaller bud results in fewer leaves, the annual growth extension may be actually smaller than the first year after transplanting, even though the tree may be less stressed (Figure 10-3). Each successive year, the conditions for bud formation and expansion are less stressful as the root system grows, and twig elongation will increase. If conditions on the landscape site are not as favorable as in the nursery, growth may never be as great as it was before transplanting.

Duration of Postplanting Stress

To be considered fully established, the partial root system in the root ball, or the confined root system of the container, must develop into a normal spreading root system with access to soil moisture and nutrients from a large soil volume. This process usually requires several years of root growth.

Tree Size

What is the best tree size to plant? Large trees can be transplanted very successfully, if a large tree is needed (or wanted) immediately. The larger the tree, the longer it will take to establish. A commitment to special maintenance (primarily watering) will be required throughout the longer establishment period, or the tree may not survive. Both the cost of planting the tree and the cost of the maintenance will be higher. A small tree will be less expensive to plant and will establish more quickly.

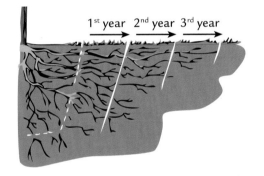

Root system establishment will take longer for large transplanted trees than for small trees. When standard specifications are followed, the size of the root ball or container is proportional to the size of the tree. Root extension rates are similar for large and small trees, but the distance that roots must grow to redevelop the full spreading root system is much greater for a larger tree. A smaller tree requires fewer annual root growth increments to replace the original root system after planting than does a large tree (Figure 10-4) (576). Small container-grown—0.5-inch (12 mm) caliper—oak (*Quercus*) trees were established within the first season (121).

Because vigorous growth returns to a small tree sooner after transplanting, trees of two different sizes planted at the same time may be more similar in size by the time both are established (107, 211, 358, 362, 565, 576), though this may not be true under all circumstances (532). Occasionally, the smaller tree could become larger (Figure 10-5).

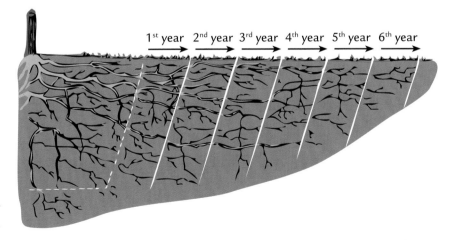

Figure 10-4 Roots grow at a similar rate regardless of tree size, but for a larger tree, roots must grow over a longer distance to redevelop a normal root spread after transplanting. This requires more years of growth and results in a longer establishment period for a large tree.

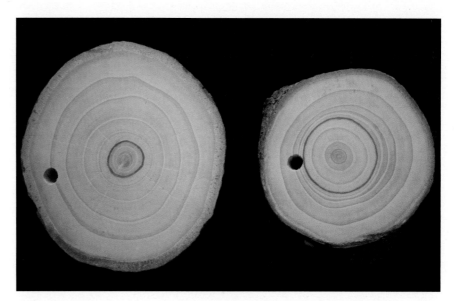

Figure 10-5 Trunk cross sections of transplanted spruces show the growth after transplanting. The diameter of each at the time of transplanting is shown by the circle. Growth rings of the larger transplanted tree was slowed for several years (right). Normal growth of the smaller tree (left) resumes more quickly. By the time vigorous growth returned to the larger tree, the smaller tree was larger in diameter.

Species

"Easy to transplant" usually means excellent survival and fast to establish with minimal care, and it may be related to rate of root regeneration (29). Some species are known for their ease of transplanting, while others are known to be more difficult. Most of this information is experience-based and not always consistent. Some research has indicated that that English oak (*Quercus robur*) recovered from transplanting more rapidly than did honeylocust (*Gleditsia triacanthos*), which is generally considered very easy to transplant (539). Horsechestnut (*Aesculus hippocastanum*), which is considered easy to transplant, was the slowest to establish of five species tested (523). Shoot growth of alder (*Alnus*) recovered in half the time as linden (*Tilia*) trees of the same size (466). Those that are more difficult to transplant, such as many oak (*Quercus*) species, may just be slower to establish and require more care after planting to be successful.

Climate

Root growth after transplanting is highly affected by soil temperature (see Chapter 9). In climates where the soils are warm all year round, roots will grow more rapidly, and trees will become established sooner. In the north temperate climate of the upper Midwestern United States, twig growth of a 4-inch (10 cm) caliper tree can be slowed for four years after transplanting. In other words, the establishment period is approximately one year per caliper inch—4 years for a 4-inch (10 cm) caliper tree (532, 594). In the subtropical climate of northern Florida, roots grow much faster. Trees establish in approximately 3 months per caliper inch—1 year for a 4-inch (10 cm) caliper tree (48, 207). No data is available from other climates, but times can be approximated by comparing the length of the growing season, soil temperature (see Table 4-2), and soil type information.

Of course, stress decreases and growth increases each year as the roots grow. During the second half of the establishment period, the tree may not appear to be stressed. Though stress is less severe, and the associated growth reduction may not be as obvious. Monitoring should be continued, but supplemental watering may be necessary only during dry periods.

Production Method

Establishment of traditional field-grown trees with ball-and-burlap root balls has been compared to container-grown trees and trees grown in in-ground fabric containers. Based on water stress data, field-grown trees usually establish more quickly than trees planted from containers. Container plants can be smaller with minimal root loss at planting, yet take longer to become established. Establishment of in-ground fabric bag trees is variable (48, 262).

Container-grown trees were more dependent on irrigation until established. Under limited irrigation conditions, there was higher mortality in container-grown trees than field-grown trees (202). Ten percent of infrequently irrigated trees died, and new growth was killed when irrigation was cut back to once per week at 10 weeks after planting. Field-grown trees were not affected by a similar reduction in irrigation frequency (211).

Both periodic and chronic stress can reduce growth. If a tree receives a high level of care and a consistent environment is maintained above and below ground, good growth will occur, and the tree will establish faster. Proper care after planting will help to assure survival and to minimize stress.

Cultural Practices

Common sense cultural practices can speed establishment and improve transplanting success. Frequently irrigated trees established more quickly than those receiving infrequent irrigation (211). Pruning (about 20% canopy removal by thinning-out cuts) and irrigation in combination partially can reduce water stress (42), but not without irrigation (350). Weed control can reduce competition for soil resources and speed establishment (350).

It takes time for a tree to establish a new root system after planting. The length of time will depend on tree size, care, and production method. Plan to provide proper care to successfully make it through the through the several years of post-planting stress that can be expected.

CHAPTER 11

Provide the Best Care
After Planting

Proper care until the tree is established is essential for successful tree planting.

Maintenance after planting is an extension of the planting process itself, but those responsible for the care of the tree are not always the ones who planted the tree. The efforts and expense devoted to site preparation, species selection, and planting procedures can all be wasted without proper care after planting. Procedures such as watering, mulching, fertilizing, and pruning that were important on planting day must be continued until the tree and its root system are established. Starting immediately after planting, most trees will require special care for at least the first two years, longer for trees over 3 inches (8 cm) caliper.

Changes Occur Rapidly

Careful and regular monitoring of soil moisture and tree condition is of paramount importance. Particularly important is monitoring the amount of moisture in the root ball. Seasonal rainfall patterns may cause the soil to be too wet at times, and too dry at others. The transition between saturated and excessively dry soil may occur in as little as a week in many urban soils. The transition between adequate soil moisture and initial drought stress may occur in as little as a day in hot, windy weather. Tree condition will change in response to soil moisture changes. The leaves of newly planted trees may be slightly off-color, but should not be showing signs of severe water stress (dull appearance or drooping) (Figure 11-1). Twigs should have no indication of shriveled bark or drooping tips. Check the trunk for discolored sunken bark areas, sunscald, borers, cankers, and mechanical or animal damage.

Figure 11-1 Dull appearance or drooping leaves and expanding shoot tip are the signs of water stress.

Watering

Watering is the most important maintenance practice initially after planting, but specific recommendations vary with different environmental conditions. Watering practices will vary with the amount of local rainfall, sun, temperature, and wind. The amount and frequency of irrigation needed depends not only on the weather but on the moisture-holding capacity of the soil, drainage, and stage of root system establishment. If the soil is poorly drained, it is important to not apply too much water.

Transpiration rates may be very high in the first few days after transplanting (107, 262, 475). Adequate irrigation during this period is extremely important for survival. Overhead misting may help reduce stress for a few weeks after transplanting, but it is ineffective after the tree adjusts (44, 49), and is usually considered only for large, high-value trees.

Mild stress lasting 10 days or less slows growth temporarily, but may not affect total season growth. Stress of 22 days or longer reduced shoot growth for both the current season and the following season (619). Proper irrigation can reduce secondary stress-related problems such as injury from borers, bark cracks, and sunscald (476).

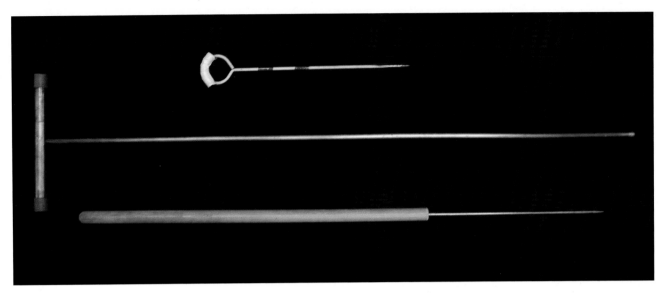

Figure 11-2 Probing with a solid metal rod, such as a tile probe (middle), a surveyor's chaining pin (top), or a simple homemade probe (bottom) can accurately estimate soil moisture with a little practice.

Root growth is slowed up to 90% by dry soils (40, 572). When roots are drought stressed, they mature rapidly toward the tip (suberization), decreasing absorption, and reducing future growth (326). Water stress during periods of active root growth can reduce the root:shoot ratio (389). Applying excessive irrigation may also reduce root growth and increase the time needed for the tree to develop enough root system to survive without irrigation (219).

Monitoring Soil Moisture

The root ball is the primary source of water for the tree until new root growth occurs. In temperate climates, substantial root growth outside the root ball may not develop until midsummer (264) even if the trees were planted the previous fall (see Chapter 4). In hot summer weather, the root ball can become very dry in just 2 or 3 days, while the surrounding soil remains moist throughout most of the first growing season (Figure 10-1) (252, 595). In the first 2 years after planting, the most important place to check the soil moisture is in the root ball.

Low-cost electronic soil moisture meters may be accurate enough to indicate when the root ball should be watered. Probes must be inserted at least 6–8 inches (15–20 cm) with good contact between the probes and soil. High salinity may cause inaccurate readings, especially with electronic meters.

Sampling with a soil profile tube (Figure 1-18) removes a small core of soil that can be easily examined. If the soil retains its shape after compressing it between the fingers, but is not sticky, the moisture content is favorable. The number of times even a small diameter core can be inserted into a small root ball without injuring roots may be limited. Determining soil resistance by probing the root ball and the backfill with a pointed metal rod—such as a tile probe, a surveyor's chaining pin, or common soil injector without the water running—can also be used to estimate soil moisture (Figure 11-2). Very dry soil will resist penetration of the rod and indicate the need for watering. If suction develops when removing the rod and the rod surface is muddy when removed, then the soil is too wet. To get experience with the method, it is very helpful to compare rod resistance to soil samples removed with a core. After a little practice, the rod method of determining soil moisture can be easy and reasonably accurate.

Apply Water Wisely

To water the root ball, apply water near the base of the tree. Water can be applied with a hose when the tree is near a water source and the ground is level. Water applied too rapidly will run off. A raised ring of soil at the edge of the root ball (not the edge of the planting hole) will help to keep water from running off of the root ball (Figure 7-31). When the ground is sloped, even slightly, a soil injector under low pressure (10–20 pounds) can effectively deliver water to the root ball. The injector should be moved to several locations for large root balls. Commercially manufactured systems designed to hold water and release it slowly over the root ball can be helpful if there is a slope or if the soil absorbs water very slowly (Figure 11-3). These devices are usually a plastic bag or rigid container with small perforations to release the water slowly. These systems can be used to apply a measured amount of water on any tree.

The amount of water applied from a garden hose or water tank should be measured as well to avoid overwatering or underwatering. The time required to deliver the appropriate amount of water from a hose can be calibrated by filling a container of known volume and then using the same time and pressure when watering.

When numerous trees are planted in a large bed, an alternative to watering each individual root ball may be necessary. Overhead irrigation with sprinklers may be possible at sites having ample drainage. At an appropriate interval (determined by checking root ball and bed soil moisture), apply water slowly enough that it is all absorbed by the soil. Measure the amount of water applied with a wide-mouth, 4-inch (10 cm) tall container, such as a can, placed in the bed. More than one can may be needed to get an accurate average measurement.

Another alternative is a drip (or micro-) irrigation system designed to apply water directly to the root balls. The components are available at most landscape supply houses and home centers. Depending on the emitter design and root ball size, several emitters may be needed for each root ball. Larger root balls will require multiple emitters or types with higher flow rate and a wider area of application. Soaker hose or leaky pipe irrigation systems can be installed on the soil surface spiraling around the trunk. They also can be covered by mulch so that they are not visually apparent. Time the length of irrigation to apply the desired amount of water. Check these systems often for malfunction or animal damage.

Irrigation systems not properly calibrated and monitored frequently cause the death of many landscape trees. Irrigation systems are often designed with the assumption that excess water will drain away quickly and leave root zone soils at field capacity. This is rarely true in urban soils. Drainage may vary greatly at locations just a few feet apart.

Shrub beds are often irrigated at the same levels as nearby lawn areas, though their needs are often different. Too much irrigation water can easily be applied to the trees. Irrigation water can accumulate in the planting hole and "drown" tree roots even when surrounding soils near the surface are just adequately moist. Plants in shady locations do not need as much irrigation as those in sunny locations, but automatic timers are often set for the same length of time. Irrigation requirements are usually greater during the summer than the spring or fall seasons, even if the amount of rainfall is the same because transpiration from the leaves and evaporation from the soil surface are much higher in the hotter summer months. Irrigation cycles should be adjusted for the amount of current rainfall to conserve water and to avoid overwatering.

Figure 11-3 Manufactured systems designed to hold water and release it slowly aid in supplying measured amounts of water to the root ball.

Amount and Frequency

Guidelines for amount and frequency of watering can only be generalized and are highly dependent on factors such as local weather, site soil conditions, time of planting, and type of nursery stock. To provide for the changing needs of the newly planted tree, and conserve use of water, watering frequency will change throughout the first seasons.

Reference evapotranspiration (ET) data can be used to develop the framework for an irrigation schedule. It simply measures the amount of evaporation during the warmer months. The National Weather Service uses a large water pan with a diameter of 4 feet (1.2 m) to measure the rate of evaporation (Figure 11-4). All the data through the world is collected and compiled into an annual evaporation map (Figure 11-5). Local data is usually available via the Internet. Evapotranspiration in the temperate climate of the Midwestern United States averages 6–8 inches (15–20 cm) per month during the warm summer months.

Figure 11-4 A standard four-foot diameter Class A evaporation pan used in the United States to measure daily evaporation rate. (Photo: Illinois State Water Survey)

Pan evaporation and transpiration rates for woody species are strongly correlated (341). Transpiration of larger trees is approximately 20% of ET (361), but additional moisture evaporates from the soil surface. Irrigating recent plantings at full ET rate proved unnecessary, and 50% ET can produce plants aesthetically pleasing with acceptable growth (396, 499). In a semi-arid climate, irrigation at 33% or 66% ET produced equal or better growth than 100% ET for many species (181).

Root ball moisture can be depleted very quickly during the warm, summer months. In most climates, trees will probably need to be watered about twice each week. Five gallons (20 L) of water every 3 days was adequate to keep a 32-inch (80 cm) diameter root ball well irrigated (506). Shrubs watered every 2 days during the establishment period had greater shoot and root growth than plants watered every 8 days. Watering every other day with just 1–2 gallons (4–8 L) of water per inch of trunk caliper might provide the most even soil moisture for roots, but may not be practical without an automatic irrigation system (499, 617). Trees transplanted in leaf may initially require watering more frequently (211). Applying more water less often will not maintain the root ball at the right soil moisture. Excess water will either saturate the lower portion of the root ball if the planting hole is not well drained, or drain away and be wasted.

Container-grown trees will need irrigation more than ball-and-burlap trees. Very little plant available water is held by pine-bark growing substrate in the container root ball after it is planted (252). When irrigation frequency was reduced 14 weeks after transplanting, laurel oak (*Quercus laurifolia*) trees from plastic containers were water stressed more than ball-and-burlap (207). Ten percent of container-grown trees died immediately following a reduction in irrigation frequency from twice per week to once per week, just 7 weeks after transplanting. The remainder of the trees showed severe water stress and tip dieback. Field-grown and hardened off trees were not affected by the same reduction in irrigation schedule (211). In another study, more container-grown trees died than field-grown trees, and they died sooner (202).

Newly planted trees should be watered for at least two growing seasons in most climates. Even in Florida, where roots grow quickly, 2-inch (5 cm) caliper live oaks (*Quercus virginiana*) watered for 38 weeks grew twice as much as those irrigated only during the first 12 weeks after planting (203). When irrigated for only 6

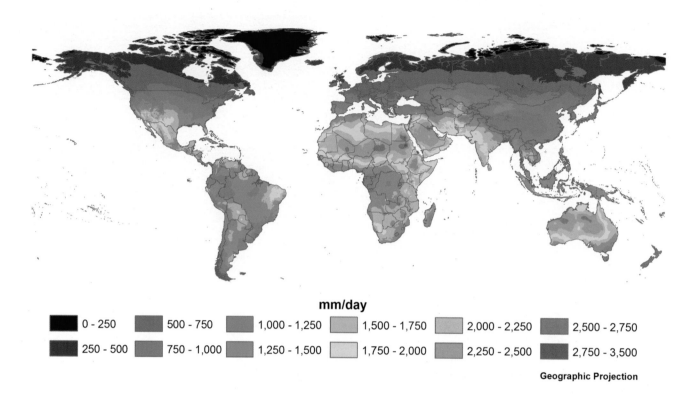

mm/day

■ 0 - 250	500 - 750
250 - 500	750 - 1,000

1,000 - 1,250   1,500 - 1,750   2,000 - 2,250   2,500 - 2,750

1,250 - 1,500   1,750 - 2,000   2,250 - 2,500   2,750 - 3,500

Geographic Projection

Figure 11-5 Using the annual evaporation map one can find the average annual evaporation rate for any location. The evaporation rate varies with temperature, wind speed, sunshine, and relative humidity. The evaporation rate also varies throughout the year. (Source: Food and Agriculture Organization of the United Nations)

weeks, tree mortality was 43% (202). Periodic watering may need to be continued during the dormant season in semi-arid regions, especially for evergreens.

As the root system establishes, the frequency of watering can be reduced and the area watered can be enlarged. The average increase in root spread diameter can be from 3–12 feet (1–4 m) per year, depending on climate (north temperate to subtropical, respectively) and site conditions (Table 11-1). Using these generalized growth rates, irrigation frequency can be reduced when the root spread is three times the root ball diameter, but the irrigation should not be completely stopped. Because of more direct sunlight on the south side of the tree there may be greater water stress on the south side of the tree (568, 591). Increased irrigation may be appropriate on the south side of larger trees to compensate.

Enough water should be applied to this larger root zone area to wet the soil 12 inches (30 cm) deep. For soils with good water-holding capacity, which have not been allowed to completely dry out, this should be about one gallon of water per square foot (40 L/m2) of soil surface area. If using a sprinkler, measure 1.5–2 inches (3.5–5 cm) of water with a wide can or pan. Watering should be continued through the fall season, though the frequency may be reduced. Trees should go into the winter with ample moisture in the soil, especially evergreens. In arid climates, winter watering may be beneficial when temperatures are above freezing.

Treated sewage effluent water is sometimes used to irrigate landscape plants. Salt content may be elevated in effluent water, which can lead to increased ion concentration in leaves and increased visual damage. Visual damage can vary by species and the amount and quality of the effluent water applied (148).

Fertilization

When sufficient levels of all elements essential for plant growth are present in the soil, fertilization may not be necessary for at least the first growing season after planting. A reliable soil test performed as part of the initial site evaluation will be useful to indicate availability of essential nutrients. Water, rather than nutrients, is usually the most significant growth-limiting factor for newly planted trees (see Chapter 10). Later, as the tree develops a greater absorptive root area and becomes more established, fertilization may be desired to maximize growth.

Plant growth is more often limited by a nitrogen deficiency than by any other element. Because nitrogen exists in several forms, and is so short-lived in the soil, standard soil tests do not include it. It may be beneficial to apply nitrogen fertilizer annually to maintain an optimum supply for maximum growth once water stress has been reduced. Starting the beginning of the second season after planting (third season or later for larger trees), fertilizer can be applied to the root zone (Table 11-1). The root zone size will increase faster in warmer climates. Research has shown that up to 6 pounds of nitrogen per 1,000 ft^2 (2.88 kg per 100 m^2) is effective in increasing growth of trees once they are established (410, 562, 564).

A slow-release form of fertilizer should be used to fertilize trees so that the nutrients are available throughout the season. Slow-release fertilizers should have at least half of the nitrogen in an insoluble form, and the salt index should be less than 50 to avoid plant damage (13). A fertilizer N:P:K ratio of 3:1:1 or 3:1:2 should be used for trees, though application of phosphorous-containing fertilizers is becoming increasingly subject to regulation.

Formulations and application methods vary according to the type of fertilizer to be applied. Phosphorous, potassium, and other nonmobile elements are most effective when applied below the soil surface. Slow-release fertilizer formulations can be applied during the fall and winter, and the nutrients will still be available the following spring when they are most effective (409). However, fertilization in the early fall may reduce stem freeze resistance. Broad-leaved and marginally hardy plants may be more at risk (277, 518). Professional arborists often use liquid injection of slow-release formulations. Small amounts of the fertilizer should be injected in many locations in the upper 4–8 inches (10–15 cm) of the soil where most of the fine absorbing roots are located. Homeowners can apply nitrogen effectively

Table 11-1 The estimated root spread diameter of a transplanted tree can be used to determine the appropriate area to water, fertilize, and mulch each year as the root system grows. Root spread estimation is based on a 24-inch (60 cm) diameter root ball and favorable growing conditions. Make adjustments as necessary for root ball size and growing conditions.

CLIMATE	YEARS AFTER TRANSPLANTING			
	1	2	3	4
Subtropical (Hardiness Zones 9–11)	14 (4.3)*	26 (8.0)	38 (11.5)	**
Mild Winters, Long Summers (Hardiness Zones 6–8)	8 (2.5)	14 (4.3)	20 (6.0)	26 (8.0)
Cold Winters, Short Summers (Hardiness Zones 4–5)	5 (1.5)	8 (2.5)	11 (3.4)	14 (4.3)
* Feet (meters)				
** All but the largest trees will be established.				

Figure 11-6 All fertilizer containers have guaranteed analysis stating the amounts and types of fertilizer elements.

by spreading granular fertilizer on the soil surface in the spring, and it will readily move down to the root zone.

Lawn fertilizers containing broadleaf weed killers and other herbicides should not be used in the vicinity of any tree. Some weed killers can be absorbed by the roots and become systemic. They are then translocated to rapidly growing portions of the tree, where they cause injury (Figure 11-7) and sometimes death of the affected plant.

Salt index is a measure of the relative salinity of a fertilizer. Salts in the soil draw water out of the root system, resulting in less water uptake. A salt index of less than 50 is preferred (517). Avoid formulations with high salt indexes, especially where a salt problem may already exist, such as along streets where de-icing salts are used. Slow-release fertilizers have low salt indexes (Table 11-2).

Palms growing in the landscape have different nutritional requirements from dicotyledonous plants. Potassium, manganese, magnesium, boron, and iron deficiencies are often more widespread than nitrogen deficiency. Deficiencies in potassium, manganese, or boron can be fatal. Nutrient deficiencies can be caused by high soil pH, poor soil aeration, cold soil temperatures, and nutrient imbalances. High-nitrogen fertilizers applied directly to palms or to adjacent turfgrass can increase the severity of potassium and magnesium deficiencies (76, 85). For palms, the ratio N:P:K ratio should be 3:1:3.

Mulching

The benefits of organic mulch are well-established and continue to be reinforced in recent studies. A review of published mulch research studies showed surface mulch improved soil physical properties and tree physiology, but there was no improvement in chemical or biological properties (485).

Figure 11-7 Some weed killers can be absorbed by the roots and translocated to rapidly growing portions of the tree, where they cause injury and sometimes death of the affected plant. Curling of the leaves is a common symptom of herbicide damage.

Soil Benefits

Organic mulch reduces evaporation from the soil surface and conserves soil moisture (112, 311, 504). Mulch allowed a 50% reduction in irrigation while still maintaining acceptable growth and appearance (396). Mulch insulates soil from temperature extremes (397, 504). Inorganic mulch, such as stone, provided greater benefits than bare soil (311, 504).

Tree Benefits

Organic surface mulch generally improves shoot and root growth of newly planted trees (26, 165, 485). However, mulch had no effect on the growth of desert plants (505).

Root growth is increased in the soil beneath the mulch (Figure 11-8) as well as in older, partially decomposed organic mulch. The roots in the

Table 11-2 Nutrient content, speed of availability, and salt indexes of common fertilizers (after 517).

FERTILIZER	NUTRIENT CONTENT (%)			AVAILABILITY	SALT INDEX**
	N	P_2O_5	K_2O		
Ammonium nitrate	35	-	-	Quick	105
Ammonium sulfate	21	-	-	Quick	69
Sodium nitrate	16	-	-	Very quick	100
Potassium nitrate	13	-	45	Quick	74
Urea	46	-	-	Quick	75
Urea, sulfur-coated	30*	-	-	Medium	n/a
Urea methylene	40	-	-	Medium	27
Urea formaldehyde	38	-	-	Slow	10
Isobutylidene diurea (IBDU)	31	-	-	Slow	6
Monoammonium phosphate	12	61	-	Quick	25
Diammonium phosphate	20*	49*	-	Quick	34
Superphosphate	-	20	-	Slow	8
Triple superphosphate	-	48	-	Medium slow	10
Monopotassium phosphate	-	52	35	Quick	8
Potassium chloride	-	-	60	Quick	116
Potassium nitrate	-	-	45*	Quick	74
Potassium sulfate	-	-	52*	Medium	46

* Formulations may vary slightly.
** Salt index of a fertilizer is a measure of the salt concentration that fertilizer induces in the soil solution.

mulch will not be at any greater risk of desiccation, since a well-established layer of mulch can hold more water than the soil itself, without decreasing aeration to the soil beneath it (285, 584).

Mulch eliminates competition from lawn grasses for soil moisture and nutrients. In addition to competition for water and nutrients, some lawn grasses may be able to reduce the growth of the trees through chemicals the grass roots produce. This phenomenon is called allelopathy. Fescues have been shown to stunt the growth of southern magnolia (*Magnolia grandiflora*) (269), river redgum (*Eucalyptus camaldulensis*) (392), black walnut (*Juglans nigra*) (553), and sweetgum (*Liquidambar styraciflua*) (573). Combinations of other trees and grasses have not been studied.

Grass   Mulch

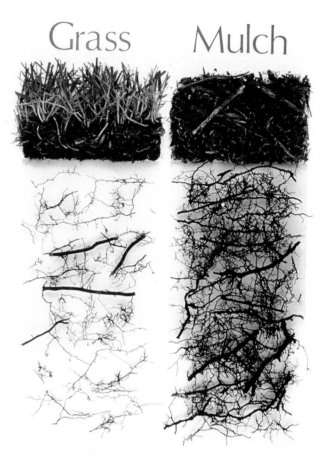

Figure 11-8 Sugar maple *(Acer saccharum)* root density is greater under mulch than when in competition with grass.

Potential Drawbacks

The use of mulch is not without potential drawbacks. A thick layer of mulch can absorb rain and irrigation water before it reaches the roots in the soil and result in increased stress and reduced growth (27, 212). This is most critical immediately after transplanting, when the tree is totally dependent on the very limited amount water held in the root ball.

Application of fine textured organic mulch, such as compost, can cause temporary reduction in soil oxygen to less than 10%, which can affect root function. Under wet conditions, this may occur with as little as a 2-inch (5 cm) thick layer, and the oxygen reduction in the soil can last as long as rainy conditions persist. Under dry conditions, less than 6 inches (15 cm) of mulch did not reduce soil oxygen (251).

Certain mulches can support the growth of undesirable fungi, such as the artillery fungus and stink horns. Mushroom compost has suppressive characteristics against some fungal growth. Incorporation of mushroom compost can reduce nuisance fungi to acceptable levels (137, 138, 170). Pathogenic fungi may be able to survive and be transmitted in mulch. Thyronectria, a canker causing fungus of honeylocust *(Gleditsia triacanthos)* survived in uncomposted wood chip mulch for 143 weeks (346). More Sphaeropsis tip blight developed on Austrian pines *(Pinus nigra)* when mulched with diseased needles (319).

Subterranean termites consumed most, but not all, types of mulches tested in laboratory experiments (155). It is possible that wood mulch could harbor termite colonies around buildings, but no field research studies have been reported.

Some trees such as black walnut *(Juglans cinerea)* produce chemicals that are harmful (allelopathic) to other plants. Wood chips should be composted to break down the chemicals before using them as mulch.

Mulch Materials

Organic materials are best for mulch. Composting before use can help reduce nutrient imbalances, kill many plant pathogens, and increase microorganisms that can suppress disease organisms (297, 298). Research has never indicated that vascular fungal diseases, such as Dutch elm disease, Verticillium wilt, and oak wilt can be transmitted in mulch. However, it would be difficult to prove it is absolutely safe to use potentially contaminated mulch.

Most organic mulch materials provide the basic benefits of mulch, but there can be variation in some of the nutrient properties of specific mulch materials. Common hawthorn *(Crataegus monogyna)* and cherry *(Prunus avium)* mulch improved tree growth more than European beech *(Fagus sylvatica)*. High levels of carbohydrates in hawthorn and cherry wood and allelochemicals from beech wood released as the woods decompose may be responsible for the differences (436). In contrast, differences in soil and leaf nutrient levels in pecan *(Carya illinoensis)* trees were very minor when many types of mulch were applied (177).

The carbon:nitrogen (C:N) ratio of organic mulch materials is important in mulch decomposition. During decomposition of organic matter with a C:N ratio higher than 20, micro-organisms have to supplement their nitrogen demand by absorbing nitrogen from the soil, making it unavailable to plants, and nitrogen deficiencies can develop. In contrast, when the organic matter C:N ratio is lower than 20, excess N is released by the soil microorganisms and available for the plants (134, 353).

Mulch Maintenance

After 5 years, a 3-inch (7.5 cm) layer of surface mulch was half of the original thickness (112). Decomposition can be more rapid in warm, humid climates. As the organic mulch decomposes, new mulch must be added periodically. Every few years, as the new roots spread farther, the mulched area should be expanded in diameter (Table 11-1).

As the mulched area expands, compatible plantings may be added to enhance the landscape appearance. Most trees can tolerate root competition from woody shrubs, groundcovers, and even some perennials. Woodland plant communities are a mix of these kinds of plants, and most should pose no threat in the landscape. When planting in the root zone of existing trees, disturb as little soil as possible to minimize damage to the roots of the tree. Each autumn, shredded leaves can be added to the mulch, recycling the nutrients and organic matter, just as in the forest.

Trunk Protection and Support

Basal trunk damage from lawn mowers and weed whips is a serious problem in landscapes (Figure 11-9). The bark on young trees is thin and very susceptible to mechanical damage, especially in the spring growth period. Because of postplanting stress, the cambium around a small wound can die back farther and become a more serious injury. Homemade and commercially available trunk guards are recommended to prevent mechanical injury to the trunk and to prevent small rodent damage (see Chapter 8). A well-maintained mulched area should eliminate the need to use mechanical tools and mowers near the tree trunk.

Large animals, such as beaver and deer, can cause major trunk and branch damage. Heavy hardware cloth or metal fencing covering the bottom three to four feet of the trunk will provide protection against beaver (Figure 11-10, left). Plastic drainpipe provides adequate protection against antler rubbing by deer in the fall (Figure 11-10, center). Golf courses sometimes use 5- to 6-foot sections of corrugated plastic drainpipe to protect tree trunks from golf balls. White plastic is best when used during the growing season.

Trunk wrap and guards installed at planting (see Chapter 8) can be harmful if not regularly inspected. Moisture held under the wraps has been linked to bark injury. The injured bark can serve as an entrance point for canker fungi, and the wrap may increase incidence of borers (425). Application of an

Figure 11-9 Basal trunk damage from lawn mowers and weed whips result in decay and serious loss of structural support.

Figure 11-10 A variety of materials can be used to protect the trunk against many animals.

insecticide labeled for borer management prior to installing trunk wrap can reduce or eliminate borer infestations for months. Trunk wraps can cause physical injury to the trunk if left on too long (Figure 11-11). In cold climates, it is best to apply trunk wraps only over the winter for sun protection. In hot and dry climates, protection from summer sun may be important, but it may be necessary to loosen the wrap at least once during each growing season to prevent trunk constriction and inspect for borer activity, excess moisture, or canker formation. The same paper

Figure 11-11 In one season, burlap caused constriction of the trunk, and an imprint of the fiber pattern in the bark of this tree.

wrapping may be used to rewrap the trunk if it is still in good condition.

Supporting wires around the trunk from stakes or guys should be checked frequently and adjusted to prevent trunk girdling (Figure 11-13) until they can be permanently removed. Stakes on smaller trees can often be removed after one year. A good test is to move the trunk back and forth to determine if the tree trunk is rigid at the soil line. Re-examine the supports annually until the stakes can be removed. If stakes are required to hold the tree upright for more than a year or two, the roots are not growing properly. Check for problems—such as poor drainage or over-watering—that could be limiting root system development.

Figure 11-12 Spiral plastic tree guards (left) can cause trunk damage (right) when not removed as the tree grows. (Right photo: D. Rideout)

Pruning

Pruning small trees for proper branch architecture should continue in the years after planting. Maintaining a central leader is important for most tree species. Trees properly pruned in the nursery, or at planting, to one dominant trunk with small-diameter spreading branches can revert back to an undesirable form in just a few years following planting. Prune out upright stems in the upper crown that could grow to compete with the main leader, and reduce large lateral branches to slow their growth (see Chapter 8). On large mature-sized trees, branches should eventually be spaced 12–18 inches (30-45 cm) apart and no closer than 40–60 inches (100–150 cm) above one another. Inspect soundness of branch attachments regularly. Prune out branches with weak crotches, dieback, and sprouts along the trunk and from the root stock below the graft union (205).

Pest Control

Insect- and disease-control measures may be required. Trees in a stressed condition following planting are susceptible to many diseases and insect pests, especially borers. Insect and disease problems vary widely with region and species. When necessary, a fungicide or insecticide application may be needed. Only registered chemicals should be used, and application must be done in accordance with the label instructions.

Planting a tree is a simple concept, but it is by no means a simple process. In nature, many seeds fall and only a few of the stronger seeds that land in a favorable location survive to maturity. Survival rates of transplanted trees should be as close to 100% as possible. To achieve this high level of success, the "right tree" must be planted in the "right place" and receive the "right care"—the three basic elements for tree planting success.

Figure 11-13 Wires used in staking and guying can cause injury if not removed soon enough.

References Cited

1. Abbey, T., and T. Rathier. 2005. Effects of mycorrhizal fungi, biostimulants and water absorbing polymers on the growth and survival of four landscape plant species. *Journal of Environmental Horticulture* 23:108–111.

2. Abod, S.A., and A.D. Webster. 1991. Carbohydrates and their effects on growth and establishment of *Tilia* and *Betula*: 1. Seasonal changes in soluble and insoluble carbohydrates. *Journal of Horticultural Science* 66:235–246.

3. Aldrich, J.H., J.G. Norcini, and W.E. Roddenberry, Jr. 1996. Effect of cupric hydroxide-treated containers on *Bougainvillea* propagation and growth after transplanting. *Journal of Environmental Horticulture* 14:181–183.

4. Alm, A., and J. Stanton. 1993. Polymer root dip increases survival of stressed bareroot seedlings. *Northern Journal of Applied Forestry* 10:90–92.

5. Alvey, A.A., P.E. Wiseman, and B. Kane. 2009. Efficacy of conventional tree stabilization systems and their effect on short-term tree development. *Arboriculture & Urban Forestry* 35:157–164.

6. Amoroso, G., P. Frangi, and R. Piatti. 2010. Effect of container design on plant growth and root deformation of littleleaf linden and field elm. *HortScience* 45:1824–1829.

7. Amoroso G., P. Frangi, R. Piatti, A. Fini, F. Ferrini, and M. Faoro. 2011. Evaluation of shrubs for side slope greening and protection in urban landscape. *HortTechnology* 21:359–366.

8. Andersen, L., H.N. Rasmussen, and P.E. Brander. 2000. Regrowth and dry matter allocation in *Quercus robur* (L.) seedlings root pruned prior to transplanting. *New Forests* 19:205–214.

9. Anella, L., T.C. Hennessey, and E.M. Lorenzi. 2008. Growth of balled-and-burlapped versus bare-root trees in Oklahoma, U.S. *Arboriculture & Urban Forestry* 34:200–203.

10. Anisko, T., and O.M. Lindstrom. 1996. Cold hardiness of evergreen azaleas is increased by water stress imposed at three dates. *Journal of American Society of Horticultural Science* 121:296–300.

11. Anonymous. 1998. *Florida Grades and Standards for Nursery Stock*. Florida Department of Agriculture and Consumer Services, Division of Plant Industry, Gainesville, Florida. 110 pp.

12. Anonymous. 2004. *American Standard for Nursery Stock*, ANSI Z60.1. American Association of Nurserymen. Washington, D.C. 113 pp. Accessed April 1, 2012 <http://www.anla.org/docs/About%20ANLA/Industry%20Resources/ANLAStandard2004.pdf>.

13. Anonymous. 2004. *Tree, Shrub, and Other Woody Plant Maintenance—Standard Practices* (fertilization) ANSI A300 part 2. Manchester, New Hampshire: Tree Care Industry Association. 14 pp.

14. Anonymous. 2010. European technical & quality standards for hardy nurserystock. Accessed April 1, 2012 <http://www.enaplants.eu/EXEN/site/quality.aspx>.

15. Apostol, K.G., D.F. Jacobs, and R.K. Dumroese. 2009. Root desiccation and drought stress responses of bareroot *Quercus rubra* seedlings treated with a hydrophilic polymer root dip. Plant and Soil 315:229–240.

16. Appleton, B., R.R. Huff, and S.C. French. 1999. Evaluating trees for saltwater spray tolerance for oceanfront sites. *Journal of Arboriculture* 25:205–210.

17. Appleton, B.A., and S. French. 1992. Current attitudes toward and uses of tree trunk protective wraps, paints and devices. *Journal of Arboriculture* 18:15–19.

18. Appleton, B.L. 1989. Evaluation of nursery container designs for minimization or prevention of root circling. *Journal of Environmental Horticulture* 7:59–61.

19. ———. 1993. Nursery production alternatives for reduction or elimination of circling tree roots. *Journal of Arboriculture* 19:383–388.

20. ———. 1993. The latest word on tree wraps: less may be better. Arbor Age 13(12):8, 11–12.

from the archives of the International Society of Arboriculture

21. ———. 1995. Nursery production methods for improving tree roots—an update. *Journal of Arboriculture* 21:265–270.

22. ———. 2006. Tree stabilization at transplant. SNA Research Conference 51:473–476.

23. Appleton, B.L., and C.E. Whitcomb. 1983. Effects of container size and transplanting date on the growth of tree seedlings. *Journal of Environmental Horticulture* 1:89–93.

24. Arnold, M.A. 1992. Timing, acclimation period, and cupric hydroxide concentration alter growth responses of the Ohio production system. *Journal of Environmental Horticulture* 10:114–117.

25. ———. 1996. Mechanical correction and chemical avoidance of circling roots differentially affect post-transplant root regeneration and field establishment of container-grown Shumard oak. *Journal of American Society of Horticultural Science* 121:258–263.

26. Arnold, M.A., and G.V. McDonald. 2009. Groundcovers, organic and inorganic mulches, and masonry surfaces differentially affect establishment

and root zone characteristics of urban trees. *Arboriculture & Urban Forestry* 35:232–240.

27. Arnold, M.A., G.V. McDonald, and D.L. Bryan. 2005. Planting depth and mulch thickness affect establishment of green ash *(Fraxinus pennsylvanica)* and bougainvillea goldenraintree *(Koelreuteria bipinnata)*. *Journal of Arboriculture* 31:163–170.

28. Arnold, M.A., G.V. McDonald, D.L. Bryan, G.C. Denny, W.T. Watson, and L. Lombardini. 2007. Below-grade planting adversely affects survival and growth of tree species from five different families. *Journal of Arboriculture* 33:64–69.

29. Arnold, M.A., and D.K. Struve. 1989a. Cupric carbonate controls green ash root morphology and root growth. *HortScience* 24:262–264.

30. ———. 1989b. Green ash establishment following transplant. *Journal of American Society of Horticultural Science* 114:591–595.

31. ———. 1993. Root distribution and mineral uptake of coarse-rooted trees grown in cupric hydroxide-treated containers. *HortScience* 28:988–992.

32. Arnold, M.A., and D.F. Welsh. 1995. Effects of planting hole configuration and soil type on transplant establishment of container-grown live oak. *Journal of Arboriculture* 21:213–218.

33. Arnold, M.A., and E. Young. 1991. CuCO3-painted containers and root pruning affect apple and green ash root growth and cytokinin levels. *HortScience* 26:242–244.

34. Askew, J.C., C.H. Gilliam, H.G. Ponder, and G.J. Kever. 1985. Transplanting leafed-out bare root dogwood liners. *HortScience* 20:219–221.

35. Auxt, T., S. Blizzard, and K. Elliot. 1980. Comparison of apple planting methods. *Journal of the American Society for Horticultural Science* 105:468–472.

36. Banko, T.J. 1986. Growth response of azaleas transplanted into beds amended with compost sludge or pine bark. *Proceedings of SNA Research Conference* 31:111–113.

37. Barker, P.A. 1995a. Managed development of tree roots. I. Ultra-deep rootball and root barrier effects on European hackberry. *Journal of Arboriculture* 21:202–208.

38. ———. 1995b. Managed development of tree roots. II. Ultra-deep rootball and root barrier effects on Southwestern black cherry. *Journal of Arboriculture* 21:251–258.

39. Barnes, S., and G.C. Percival. 2006. Influence of biostimulants and water-retaining polymer root dips on survival and growth of newly transplanted bare-rooted silver birch and rowan. *Journal of Environmental Horticulture* 24:173–179.

40. Barnett, D. 1986. Root growth and water use by newly transplanted woody landscape plants. *Public Garden* 1:23–25.

41. Bartens, J., P.E. Wiseman, and E.T. Smiley. 2010. Stability of landscape trees in engineered and conventional urban soil mixes. *Urban Forestry & Urban Greening* 9:333–338.

42. Barton A.J., and C.S. Walsh. 2000. Effect of transplanting on water relations and canopy development in Acer. *Journal of Environmental Horticulture* 18:202–206.

43. Bassuk, N.L. 1990. Street tree diversity: making better choices for the urban landscape. *Proc. 7th Conference Metropolitan Tree Improvement Alliance (METRIA)*, pp. 71–78. The Morton Arboretum, Lisle, Illinois.

44. Bates, R.M., and A.X. Niemiera. 1994. Mist irrigation reduces post-transplant desiccation of bare-root trees. *Journal of Environmental Horticulture* 12:1–3.

45. ———. 1996. Effect of transplanting on shoot water potential of bare-root Washington hawthorn and Norway maple. *Journal of Environmental Horticulture* 14:1–4.

46. Beeson, Jr., R.C. 1994. Water relations of field-grown *Quercus virginiana* Mill. from preharvest through containerization and 1 year into a landscape. *Journal of the American Society for Horticulture Science* 119:169–174.

47. Beeson, R.C. 1994. Root regeneration and water stress of balled-and-burlapped *Quercus laurifolia* (laurel oak) pre-treated with an antitranspirant. Proceedings of the Annual Meeting of the Florida State Horticultural Society 107:186–188.

48. Beeson, R.C., and E.F. Gilman. 1992a. Diurnal water stress during landscape establishment of slash pine differs among three production methods. *Journal of Arboriculture* 18:281–287.

49. ———. 1992b. Water stress and osmotic adjustment during post-digging acclimation of *Quercus virginiana* produced in fabric containers. *Journal of Environmental Horticulture* 10:208–214.

50. Beeson, R.C., and K.G. Keller. 2001. Yard waste compost as a landscape soil amendment for azaleas. *Journal of Environmental Horticulture* 19:222–225.

51. Beeson, R.C., and R. Newton. 1992. Shoot and root responses of 18 southeastern woody landscape species grown in cupric hydroxide-treated containers. *Journal of Environmental Horticulture* 10:214–217.

52. Bellet-Travers, D.M., D.E.B. Higgs, and C.R. Ireland. 2004. The effects of progressive root removal prior to planting on shoot and root growth of *Betula pendula* Roth. *Arboricultural Journal* 27:297–314.

53. Berrang, P., D.F. Karnosky, and B.J. Stanton. 1985. Environmental factors affecting tree health in New York City. *Journal of Arboriculture* 11:185–189.

54. Bevington, K.B., and W.S. Castle. 1985. Annual root growth pattern of young citrus trees in relation to shoot growth, soil temperature and soil water content. *Journal of the American Society for Horticultural Science* 110:840–845.

55. Biddle, P.G. 1998. *Tree Root Damage to Buildings. Volume I: Causes, Diagnosis and Remedy.* Wantage, UK: Willowmead Publishing, Ltd. 376 pp.

56. Bilan, M. 1974. Relationship between needle moisture and root growth in loblolly pine seedlings. In G. Hoffman (Ed.). *Ecology and Physiology of Root Growth*, pp. 219–221. Berlin: Academic-Verlag.

57. Bir, R.E., J.L. Conner, and C. Deyton. 1995. The effect of pine bark soil amendments on bed-grown hybrid ericaceous shrubs. *Proceedings of SNA Research Conference* 40:152–154.

58. Bir, R.E., and T.G. Ranney. 1991. The effect of organic soil amendments on the growth and development of Kalmia latifolia. *Proceedings of the International Plant Propagation Society* 41:395–398.

59. Birdel, R., C. Whitcomb, and B.L. Appleton. 1983. Planting techniques for tree spade dug trees. *Journal of Arboriculture* 9:282–284.

60. Blessing, S.C., and M.N. Dana. 1987. Post-transplant root system expansion in *Juniperus chinensis* L. as influenced by production system, mechanical root disruption and soil type. *Journal of Environmental Horticulture* 5:155–158.

61. Blunt, S.M. 2008. Trees and pavements—are they compatible? *Arboricultural Journal* 31:73–80.

62. Bohne, H., L. Salomon, and D. Gerhard. 2011. Influence of provenance and fertilization in the tree nursery on outplanting performance and N-, P-, and K-content of *Viburnum opulus* L. in shoots and roots. *Journal of Environmental Horticulture* 29:137–142.

Charles F. Irish

63. Bohnert, C.A., C. Starbuck, and S. Anderson. 2008. Amending a gravel based growing medium with calcined clay improves physical properties and seedling growth. *Journal of Environmental Horticulture* 26:149–156.

64. Boland, A.M., P.D. Mitchell, I. Goodwin, and P.H. Jerie. 1994. The effect of soil volume on young peach tree growth and water use. *Journal of American Society for Horticultural Science* 119:1157–1162.

65. Bongarten, B.C., and R.O. Teskey. 1987. Dry weight partitioning and its relationship to productivity in loblolly pine seedlings from seven sources. *Forest Science* 33:255–267.

66. Bradshaw, A.D., B. Hunt, and T. Walmsley. 1995. *Trees in the Urban Landscape: Principles and Practice*. London, UK: E&FM Spon. 272 pp.

67. Brass, T.J., G.J. Keever, D.J. Eakes, and C.H. Gilliam. 1996. Styrene-lined and copper-coated containers affect production and landscape establishment of red maple. *HortScience* 31:353–356.

68. Bresnan, D.F., W.A. Geyer, and G. Rink. 1996. Variation among green ash of differing geographic origins outplanted in Kansas. *Journal of Arboriculture* 22:113–116.

69. Britt, C., and M. Johnston. 2008. *Trees in Towns II: A New Survey of Urban Trees in England and Their Condition and Management.* London, UK: Department for Communities and Local Government. 644 pp.

70. Brooks, K.M., G.J. Keever, J.E. Altland, and J.L. Sibley. 2006. Growth and flowering of crape myrtle in response to tree shelters. *Journal of Environmental Horticulture* 24:155–159.

71. Broschat, T.K. 1991. Effects of leaf removal on survival of transplanted Sabal palms. *Journal of Arboriculture* 17:32–33.

72. ———. 1994. Effects of leaf removal, leaf tying, and overhead irrigation on transplanted pygmy date palms. *Journal of Arboriculture* 20:210–214.

73. ———. 1995. Planting depth affects root growth and nutrient content of transplanted Pygmy date palms. *HortScience* 30:1031–1032.

74. ———. 1998. Root and shoot growth patterns in four palm species and their relationships with air and soil temperatures. *HortScience* 33:995–998.

75. ———. 2005. Nutrient Deficiencies of Landscape and Field-Grown Palms in Florida. Florida Cooperative Extension Service, Institute of Food and Agricultural Sciences, University of Florida Publication #ENH1018. Accessed April 1, 2012 <http://edis.ifas.ufl.edu/ep273>.

76. ———. 2009. Palm nutrition and fertilization. *HortTechnology* 19:690–694.

77. ———. 2011. Fertilization of field-grown and landscape palms in Florida. University of Florida Environmental Horticultural Department. Circ. ENH 1009. 4 pp. Accessed April 1, 2012 <http://edis.ifas.ufl.edu/pdffiles/EP/EP26100.pdf>.

78. Broschat, T.K., and H. Donselman. 1984a. Root regeneration of transplanted palms. *Principes* 28:90–91.

79. ———. 1984b. Regrowth of severed palm roots. *Journal of Arboriculture* 10:238–240.

80. ———. 1990a. Regeneration of severed roots in *Washingtonia robusta* and *Phoenix reclinata. Principes* 34:96–97.

81. ———. 1990b. IBA, plant maturity, and regeneration of palm root systems. *HortScience* 25:232.

82. Broschat, T.K., and M.L. Elliot. 2009. Effects of fertilization and microbial inoculants applied at transplanting on the growth of Mexican fan palm and queen palm. *HortTechnology* 19:324–330.

83. Broschat, T.K., and K.A. Klock-Moore. 2000. Root and shoot growth responses to phosphate fertilization in container-grown plants. *HortTechnology* 10:765–767.

84. Broschat, T.K., and A.W. Meerow. 2000. *Ornamental Palm Horticulture.* Gainesville, Florida: University Press of Florida. 256 pp.

85. Broschat, T.K., and K.A. Moore. 2010. Effects of fertilization on the growth and quality of container-grown areca palm and Chinese hibiscus during establishment in the landscape. *HortTechnology* 20:389–394.

86. Bryan, D.L., M.A. Arnold, A. Volder, W.T. Watson, L. Lombardini, J.J. Sloan, L.A. Valdez-Aguilar, and A.D. Cartmill. 2009. Overview of selected studies on the influence of planting depth on landscape establishment of container-grown trees. In G. Watson et al. (Eds.). *The Landscape Below Ground III,* pp. 126–130. Champaign, Illinois: International Society of Arboriculture.

87. ———. 2010. Planting depth during container production and landscape establishment affects growth of *Ulmus parvifolia*. *HortScience* 45:54–60.

88. Bryan, D.L., M.A. Arnold, G.V. McDonald, W.T. Watson, L. Lombardini, A.D. Cartmill, and Geoffrey C. Denny. 2005. Planting depth and cultural practices. In *Proceedings of Trees and Planting: Getting the Roots Right*, pp. 17–24. Lisle, Illinois. Accessed April 1, 2012 <http://www.mortonarb.org/deeptreeroots/pdf/GRR_Proceedings.pdf#TOC>.

89. Bryan, D. L., M.A. Arnold, A. Volder, W.T. Watson, L. Lombardini, J.J. Sloan, A. Alarcón, L.A. Valdez-Aguilar, and A.D. Cartmill. 2011. Planting depth and soil amendments affect growth of *Quercus virginiana* Mill. *Urban Forestry & Urban Greening* 10:127–132.

90. Buckstrup, M.J., and N.L. Bassuk. 2000. Transplanting success of balled-and-burlapped versus bare-root trees in the urban landscape. *Journal of Arboriculture* 26:298–308.

91. Bühler, O., P. Kristoffersen, and S.U. Larsen. 2007. Growth of street trees in Copenhagen with emphasis on the effect of different establishment concepts. *Arboriculture & Urban Forestry* 33:330–337.

92. Bullock, P., and P.J. Gregory (Eds.) 1991. *Soils in the Urban Environment*. Oxford, UK: Blackwell Scientific Publications. 174 pp. http://books.google.com/books/about/Soils_in_the_urban_environment.html?id=VbnMK_DZbmQC

93. Burdett, A.N., and P.A.F. Martin. 1982. Chemical root pruning of coniferous seedlings. *HortScience* 17:622–624.

94. Burger, D.W., G.W. Forister, and P.A. Kiehl. 1996. Height, caliper growth, and biomass response of ten shade tree species to treeshelters. *Journal of Arboriculture* 22:161–166.

95. Burger, D.W., G.W. Forister, and R. Gross. 1997. Short and long-term effects of tree shelters on the root and stem growth of ornamental trees. *Journal of Arboriculture* 23:49–56.

96. Burger, D.W., and T.E. Prager. 2008. Deep-rooted trees for urban environments: selection and propagation. *Arboriculture & Urban Forestry* 34:184–190.

97. Burger, D.W., P. Svihra, and R. Harris. 1992. Treeshelter use in producing container grown trees. *HortScience* 27:30–32.

98. Byrnes, R.L. 1976. Effects of soil amendments in variable ratios and irrigation levels on soil conditions and the establishment and growth of *Pittosporum tobira*. M.Sc. thesis, University of Florida, Gainesville, Florida.

99. Castle, W.S. 1983. Antitranspirant and root and canopy pruning effects on mechanically transplanted eight-year-old Murcott citrus trees. *Journal of American Society of Horticultural Science* 108:981–985.

100. Cathey, H.M. 1997. American Horticultural Society Plant Heat Zone Map. Alexandria, Virginia: American Horticultural Society. Accessed April 1, 2012 <http://www.ahs.org/publications/heat_zone_map.htm#1>.

101. Chen, T.H.H., P. Murakami, P. Lombard, and L.H. Fuchigami. 1991. Desiccation tolerance in bare-rooted apple trees prior to transplanting. *Journal of Environmental Horticulture* 9:13–17.

102. Chen, Y., S. Day, and P.E. Wiseman. [Internet, n.d.]. Soil Rehabilitation Experiment Site at Kentland Farm, Virginia Tech Center for Sustainable

Urban Landscapes, Virginia Tech. Accessed April 1, 2012 <http://urbanforestry.frec.vt.edu/SRES/Resources/SRESKentland3.pdf>.

103. Chong, C., G.P. Lumis, R.A. Cline, and H.J. Reissmann. 1987. Growth and chemical composition of *Populus deltoides* x *nigra* grown in field-grown fabric containers. *Journal of Environmental Horticulture* 5:45–48.

104. Clark, J.R., and R.K. Kjelgren 1989. Conceptual and management considerations for the dvelopment of urban tree plantings. *Journal of Arboriculture* 15:229–236.

105. ———. 1990. Water as a limiting factor in the development of urban trees. *Journal of Arboriculture* 16:203–208.

106. Cleary, B., and R. Tinus. 1980. Preservation of nursery stock quality through packaging storage, transport and planting. *New Zealand Journal of Forest Science* 10:295–296.

107. Clemens, J., and S.P. Radford. 1986. Establishment trials of ornamental trees and shrubs in coastal New South Wales. *Arboricultural Journal* 10:117–123.

108. Close, R.E., J.J. Kielbaso, P.V. Nguyen, and R.E. Schutski. 1996. Urban vs. natural sugar maple growth: II. Water relations. *Journal of Arboriculture* 22:187–192.

109. Close, R.E., P.V. Nguyen, and J.J. Kielbaso. 1996. Urban vs. natural sugar maple growth: I. Stress symptoms and phenology in relation to site characteristics. *Journal of Arboriculture* 22:144–150.

110. Cochard, H., and M.T. Tyree. 1990. Xylem dysfunction in *Quercus*: vessel sizes, tyloses, cavitation and seasonal changes in embolism. *Tree Physiology* 6:393–407.

111. Cock, J.H. 1982. Cassava: a basic energy source in the tropics. *Science* 218:755–762.

112. Cogger, C., R. Hummel, J. Hart, and A. Bary. 2008. Soil and redosier dogwood response to incorporated and surface-applied compost. *HortScience* 43:2143–2150.38.

113. Cohen, L. 1987. How do you move a large tree? *Landscape Contractor* (September):8–9.

114. Cole, J.C., and D.L. Hensley. 1994. Field-grown fabric containers do not affect transplant survival or establishment of green ash. *Journal of Arboriculture* 20:120–123.

115. Cool, R.A. 1976. Tree spade vs. bare root planting. *Journal of Arboriculture* 2:92–95.

116. Corkidi, L., E.B. Allen, D. Merhaut, M.F. Allen, J. Downer, J. Bohn, and M. Evans. 2005. Effectiveness of commercial mycorrhizal inoculants on the growth of *Liquidambar styraciflua* in plant nursery conditions. *Journal of Environmental Horticulture* 23:72–76.

117. Corley, W.L. 1984. Soil amendments at planting. *Journal of Environmental Horticulture* 2:27–30.

118. Costello, L.R., and K.S. Jones. 2003. *Reducing Infrastructure Damage by Tree Roots: A Compendium of Strategies*. Cohasset, California: WCISA. 119 pp.

119. Costello, L., and J.L. Paul. 1975. Moisture relations in transplanted container plants. *HortScience* 10:371–372.

120. Costello, L.R., C.L. Elmore, and S. Steinmaus. 1997. Tree root response to circling root barriers. *Journal of Arboriculture* 23:211–218.

121. Costello, L.R., K.S. Jones, and D.D. McCreary. 2005. Irrigation effects on the growth of newly planted oaks (*Quercus* spp.). *Journal of Arboriculture* 31:83–88.

122. Costello, L.R., A. Peters, and G.A. Giusti. 1996. An evaluation of treeshelter effects on plant survival and growth in a Mediterranean climate. *Journal of Arboriculture* 22:1–9.

123. Costonis, A.C. 1995. Factors affecting the survival of transplanted sabal palms. *Journal of Arboriculture* 21:98–102.

124. Couenberg, E.A.M. 1993. Amsterdam tree soil. In G. Watson and D. Neely (Eds.). *The Landscape Below Ground*, pp. 24–33. Savoy, Illinois: International Society of Arboriculture.

125. ———. 2009. A preliminary study evaluating oxygen status beneath different surface-hardening materials for park use. In G.W. Watson and Dx. Neely (Eds.). *The Landscape Below Ground III*, pp. 189–202. Champaign, Illinois: International Society of Arboriculture.

126. Coutts, M.P., and J.J. Philipson. 1976. The influence of mineral nutrition on the root development of trees. I. The growth of Sitka spruce with divided root systems. *Journal of Experimental Botany* 27:1102–1111.

127. Craul, P.J. 1992. *Urban Soil in Landscape Design*. New York: John Wiley & Sons, Inc. 396 pp.

128. Cutler, D.F., P.E. Gasson, and M.C. Farmer. 1990. The wind blown tree survey: analysis of results. *Arboricultural Journal* 14:265–286.

129. Cutler, D.F., and I.B.K. Richardson. 1989. *Tree Roots and Buildings*. Harlow, Essex, England: Longman Scientific & Technical. 71 pp.

130. D'Amato, N.E., T.D. Sydnor, M. Knee, R. Hunt, and B. Bishop. 2002. Which comes first, the root or the crack? *Journal of Arboriculture* 28:277–282.

131. D'Amato, N.E., T.D., Sydnor, R. Hunt, and B. Bishop. 2002. Root growth beneath sidewalks near trees of four genera. *Journal of Arboriculture* 28:283–290.

132. Dana, M.N., and S.C. Blessing. 1994. Post-transplant root growth and water relations of *Thuja occidentalis* from field and containers. In G.W. Watson and D. Neely (Eds.). *The Landscape Below Ground*, pp. 88–114. Savoy, Illinois: International Society of Arboriculture.

133. Davenport, D.C., P.E. Martin, and R.M. Hagan. 1972. Antitranspirants for conservation of leaf water potential of transplanted citrus trees. *HortScience* 7:511–512.

134. Davet, P. 2004. *Microbial Ecology of the Soil and Plant Growth*. Enfield, New Hampshire: *Science Publishers*. 604 pp.

135. Davidson, H., R. Mecklenburg, and C. Peterson. 1988. *Nursery Management*. Englewood Cliffs, New Jersey: Prentice Hall. 413 pp.

136. Davies, R.J. 1987. Trees and weeds: weed control for successful establishment. Forestry Commission Bulletin 2. London: HMSO. 36 pp.

137. Davis, D.D., L.J. Kuhns, K. Akina, and T.L. Harpster. 2004. Artillery fungus sporulation on 27 different mulches—a field study. *Journal of Environmental Horticulture* 22:117–123.

138. Davis, D.D., L.J. Kuhns, and T.L. Harpster. 2005. Use of mushroom compost to suppress artillery fungi. *Journal of Environmental Horticulture* 23:212–215.

139. Davis, T.D., N. Sankhla, R.H. Walser, and A. Upadhyaya. 1985. Promotion of adventitious root formation on cuttings by paclobutrazol. *HortScience* 20:883–885.

140. Day, S.D., and R.L. Amateis. 2011. Predicting canopy and trunk cross-sectional area of silver linden (*Tilia tomentosa*) in confined planting cutouts. *Urban Forestry & Urban Greening* 10:317–322.

141. Day, S.D., N.L. Bassuk, and H. Van Es. 1995. Effects of four compaction remediation methods for landscape trees on soil aeration, mechanical impedance and tree establishment. *Journal of Environmental Horticulture*. 13:64–71.

142. Day, S.D., and S.B. Dickinson (Eds.). 2008. *Managing Stormwater for Urban Sustainability Using Trees and Structural Soils*. Virginia Polytechnic Institute and State University, Blacksburg, Virginia. 63 pp.

143. Day, S.D., and J.R. Harris. 2007. Fertilization of red maple (*Acer rubrum*) and littleleaf linden (*Tilia cordata*) trees at recommended rates does not aid in tree establishment. *Arboriculture & Urban Forestry* 33:113–121.

144. ———. 2008. Growth, survival, and root system morphology of deeply planted *Corylus colurna* 7 years after transplanting and the effects of root collar excavation. *Urban Forestry & Urban Greening* 7:119–128.

145. Day, S.D., J.R. Seiler, and N. Persaud. 2000. A comparison of root growth dynamics of silver maple and flowering dogwood in compacted soil at different soil water contents. *Tree Physiology* 20:257–263.

146. DeGaetano, A.T. 2000. Specification of soil volume and irrigation frequency for urban tree containers using climate data. *Journal of Arboriculture* 26:142–150.

147. Derr, J.F., and B.L. Appleton. 1989. Weed control with landscape fabrics. *Journal of Environmental Horticulture* 7:129–133.

148. Devitt, D. A., R. L. Morris, and D. S. Neuman. 2003. Impact of water treatment on foliar damage of landscape trees sprinkle irrigated with reuse water. *Journal of Environmental Horticulture* 21:82–88.

149. Dierauf, T.A., and R.L. Marler. 1969. Clay dipped vs. bare rooted seedling survival. *Tree Planters' Notes* 20:5–8.

150. Dierich, A., G. Johnson, and S. Peterson. 2012. The Community Gravel Bed Guide. University of Minnesota, Department of Forestry, St. Paul, Minnesota. Accessed April 1, 2012 <www.trees.umn.edu>.

151. Dixon, R.K., and P.S. Johnson. 1992. Synthesis of ectomycorrhizae on Northern red oak seedlings in a Michigan nursery. *Journal of Arboriculture* 18:266–272.

152. Dobson, M.C. 1991. De-icing salt damage to trees and shrubs. Forestry Commission Bulletin 101. London, UK: HMSO. 64 pp.

153. Downer, J., and J. Hodel. 2001. The effects of mulching on establishment of *Syagrus romanzoffiana* (Cham.) Becc., *Washingtonia robusta* H. Wendl. and *Archontophoenix cunninghamiana* (H. Wendl.) H. Wendl. & Drude in the landscape. *Scientia Horticulturae* 87:85–92.

154. Drilias, M.J., J.E. Kuntz, and G.L. Worf. 1982. Collar rot and basal canker of sugar maple. *Journal of Arboriculture* 8:29–33.

155. Duryea, M.L., J.B. Huffman, R.J. English, and W. Osbrink. 1999. Will subterranean termites consume landscape mulches. *Journal of Arboriculture* 25:143–150.

156. Eckstein, R., and E.F. Gilman. 2008. Evaluation of landscape tree stabilization system. *Arboriculture & Urban Forestry* 34:216–211.

157. Ellyard, R.K. 1984. Effect of root pruning at time of planting on subsequent root development of two species of eucalyptus. *Journal of Arboriculture* 10:241–216.

158. Englert, J.M., L.H. Fuchigami, and T.H.H. Chen. 1993. Effects of storage temperatures and duration on the performances of bare-root deciduous hardwood trees. *Journal of Arboriculture* 19:106–112.

159. Englert, J.M., K. Warren, L.H. Fuchigami, and T.H.H. Chen. 1993. Antidesiccant compounds improve the survival of bare-root deciduous nursery trees. *Journal of the American Society for Horticultural Science* 118:228–235.

160. Evans, P., and J. Klett. 1984. The effects of dormant pruning treatments on leaf, shoot and root production from bare-root *Malus sargentii*. *Journal of Arboriculture* 10:298–302.

161. ———. 1985. The effects of dormant branch thinning on total leaf, shoot, and root production from bare-root *Prunus cerasifera* 'Newportii.' *Journal of Arboriculture* 11:149–151.

162. Fare, D.C. 2006. Should potting depth be a concern with container-grown trees? In *Proceedings of Trees and Planting: Getting the Roots Right*, pp. 25–29. Lisle, Illinois. Accessed April 1, 2012 <http://www.mortonarb.org/deeptree-roots/pdf/GRR_Proceedings.pdf#TOC>.

163. Fare, D.C., C.H. Gilliam, and H.G. Ponder. 1985. Root distribution of two field-grown Ilex. *HortScience* 20:1129–1130.

164. Feret, P.O., R.E. Kreh, and C. Mulligan. 1985. Effects of air drying on survival, height and root growth potential of loblolly pine seedlings. *Southern Journal of Applied Forestry* 9:125–128.

165. Ferrini, F., A. Fini, P. Frangi, and G. Amoroso. 2008. Mulching of ornamental trees: effects on growth and physiology. *Arboriculture & Urban Forestry* 34:157–162.

166. Ferrini, F., A. Giuntoli, F.P. Nicese, S. Pellegrini, and N. Vignozzi. 2005. Effect of fertilization and backfill amendments on soil characteristics, growth, and leaf gas exchange of English oak (*Quercus robur* L.). *Journal of Arboriculture* 31:182–190.

167. Ferrini, F., and F.P. Nicese. 2002. Response of English oak (*Quercus robur*) trees to biostimulants application in the urban environment. *Journal of Arboriculture* 28:70–75.

168. Ferrini, F., F.P. Nicese, S. Mancuso, and A. Giuntoli. 2000. Effect of nursery production method and planting techniques on tree establishment in urban sites: preliminary results. *Journal of Arboriculture* 26:281–283.

169. Feucht, J.R. 1986. Wire baskets can be slow killers of trees. *American Nurseryman* 163:156–159.

170. Fidanza, M.A., and D.D. Davis. 2009. Recycled mushroom compost suppresses bird's nest fungi in landscape mulch. *Journal of Environmental Horticulture* 27:238–240.

171. Fini, A., and F. Ferrini. 2011. Effects of mulching with compost on growth and physiology of *Acer campestre* L. and *Carpinus betulus* L. *Advances in Horticultural Sciences* 25:232-238.

172. Fini A., F. Ferrini, P. Frangi, and G. Amoroso. 2007. Growth and physiology of field-grown *Acer pseudoplatanus* L. trees as influenced by irrigation and fertilization. *Proceedings of SNA Research Conference* 52:51–58.

173. Fini, A., F. Ferrini, P. Frangi, G. Amoroso, and R. Piatti. 2009. Withholding irrigation during the establishment phase affected growth and physiology of Norway maple (*Acer platanoides*) and Linden (*Tilia* spp.). *Arboriculture & Urban Forestry* 35:241–251.

174. Fini, A., P. Frangi. G. Amoroso, R. Piatti, M. Faoro, C. Bellasio, and F. Ferrini. 2011. Effect of controlled inoculation with specific mycorrhizal fungi from the urban environment on growth and physiology of containerized shade tree species growing under different water regimes. *Mycorrhiza* 21:703–719.

175. Flemer, W. III. 1967. Is bare-root transplanting a dying art? *American Nurseryman* 126(1):24–25, 185–193.

176. Flott, J., B. Appleton, and R. Baker. 2009. Bare rooting: a planting and transplanting technique. *Arborist News* 18(6):35–39.

177. Foshee, W.G., III, W.D. Goff, M.G. Patterson, K.M. Tilt, W.A. Dozier, Jr., L.S. Tucker, and J.S. Bannon. 1999. Organic mulches affect soil and leaf nutrient levels of young pecan trees. *Journal of Arboriculture* 25:81–84.

178. Fostad, O., and P.A. Pedersen. 1997. Vitality, variation, and causes of decline of trees in Oslo center (Norway). *Journal of Arboriculture* 23:155–165.

179. Foster, R.S., and J. Blaine. 1978. Urban tree survival: trees in the sidewalk. *Journal of Arboriculture* 4:14–17.

180. Foth, H.D. 1990. *Fundamentals of Soil Science* (8th Ed.). New York: John Wiley & Sons. 360 pp.

181. Fox, L., and T. Montague. 2009. Influence of irrigation regime on growth of select field-grown tree species in a semi-arid climate. *Journal of Environmental Horticulture* 27:134–138.

182. Fraedrich, S.W., and D.L. Ham. 1982. Woodchip mulching around maples: effect on tree growth and soil characteristics. *Journal of Arboriculture* 8:85–89.

183. Francis, J.K., B.R. Parresol, and J.M. de Patino. 1996. Probability of damage to sidewalks and curbs by street trees in the tropics. *Journal of Arboriculture* 22:193–197.

184. Fraser, G.A., and G.C. Percival. 2003. The influence of biostimulants on growth and vitality of three urban tree species following transplanting. *Arboricultural Journal* 27:43–57.

185. Fretz, T.A. 1971. Influence of physical conditions on summer temperatures in nursery containers. *HortScience* 6:400–401.

186. Gamstetter, D. 1998. Designing the right place for the right tree. *Arborist News* 7(June):9–12.

187. Gardner-Young, J.W. 1981. A new method of planting trees and shrubs. *Arboriculture Journal* 5:45–48.

188. Garriou, D., S. Girard, J-M. Guehl, and B. Généré. 2000. Effect of desiccation during cold storage on planting stock quality and field performance in forest species. *Annals of Forest Science* 57:101–111.

189. Geng, M.C. 1989. A provenance test of white elm (*Ulmus pumila*) L. in China. *Silvae Genetica* 38:37–44.

190. Gerhold, H.D. 1999. Species differ in responses to tree shelters. *Journal of Arboriculture* 25:76–80.

191. Gerhold, H.D., and A.D. Johnson. 2003. Root dimensions of landscape tree cultivars. *Journal of Arboriculture* 29:322–325.

192. Giblin, C., J. Gillman, D. Hanson, G.R. Johnson, and P. Weicherding. 2005. The effects of soil depth on the long-term health and frequency of storm damage to trees in the upper Midwest, pp 33–39. In *Proceedings of Trees and Planting: Getting the Roots Right*. Lisle, Illinois. Accessed April 1, 2012 <http://www.mortonarb.org/deeptreeroots/pdf/GRR_Proceedings.pdf#TOC>.

193. Giblin, C.P., G.R. Johnson, J.H. Gillman, D.L. Hanson, and P.J. Weicherding. 2009. Stability and growth in pot-in-pot production: Is deeper better for containerized trees? In G. Watson et al. (Eds.). *The Landscape Below Ground* III, pp. 145–150. Savoy, Illinois: International Society of Arboriculture. 403 pp.

194. ———. 2011. The effects of planting depth on windthrow, stability, and growth for four tree species in containers. *Arboriculture & Urban Forestry* 37:247–253.

195. Gilbertson, P., and A.D. Bradshaw. 1985. The survival of newly planted trees in inner cities. *Arboricultural Journal* 14:287–309.

196. ———. 1990. The survival of newly planted trees in inner cities. *Arboricultural Journal* 14:287-309.

197. Gilbertson, P., A.D. Kendle, and A.D. Bradshaw. 1987. Root growth and the problems of trees in urban and industrial areas. In D. Patch (Ed.). *Advances in Practical Arboriculture*. Forestry Commission Bulletin 65, pp. 59–66. London, UK: HMSO.

198. Gilman, E.F. 1988. Tree root spread in relation to branch dripline and harvestable root ball. *HortScience* 23:351–353.

199. ———. 1989. Effects of injected and surface fertility on hibiscus growth in bare ground, mulch and turf. *Proceedings of the Annual Meeting of the Florida State Horticultural Society* 102:144–145.

200. ———. 1994. Establishing trees in the landscape. In G.W. Watson and D. Neely (Eds.). *The Landscape Below Ground*, pp. 69–77. Savoy, Illinois: International Society of Arboriculture.

201. ———. 1996. Root barriers affect root distribution. *Journal of Arboriculture* 22:151–154.

202. ———. 2001. Effect of nursery production method, irrigation, and inoculation with mycorrhizae-forming fungi on establishment of *Quercus virginiana*. *Journal of Arboriculture* 27:30–39.

203. ———. 2004. Effects of amendments, soil additives, and irrigation on tree survival and growth. *Journal of Arboriculture* 30:301–310.

204. ———. 2006. Deflecting roots near sidewalks. *Arboriculture & Urban Forestry* 32:18–22.

205. ———. 2012. *An Illustrated Guide to Pruning* (3rd Ed.). Albany, New York: Delmar, Cengage Learning. 476 pp.

206. Gilman, E.F., and P. Anderson. 2006. Root pruning and transplant success for Cathedral Oak® live oaks. *Journal of Environmental Horticulture* 24:13–17.

207. Gilman, E.F., and R.C. Beeson, Jr. 1996a. Production method affects tree establishment in the landscape. *Journal of Environmental Horticulture* 14:81–87.

208. ———. 1996b. Nursery production method affects root growth. *Journal of Environmental Horticulture* 14:88–91.

209. Gilman, E.F., R.C. Beeson Jr., and R.J. Black. 1992. Comparing root balls on laurel oak transplanted from the wild with those of nursery and container grown trees. *Journal of Arboriculture* 18:124–129.

210. Gilman, E.F., R.C. Beeson, and D. Meador. 2012. Impact of mulch on water loss from a container substrate and native soil. *Arboriculture & Urban Forestry* 2012 38:18–23.

211. Gilman, E.F., R.J. Black, and B. Dehgan. 1998. Irrigation volume and frequency and tree size affect establishment rate. *Journal of Arboriculture* 24:1–9.

212. Gilman, E.F., and J. Grabosky. 2004. Mulch and planting depth affect live oak (*Quercus virginiana* Mill.) establishment. *Journal of Arboriculture* 30:311–317.

213. ———. 2011. *Quercus virginiana* root attributes and lateral stability after planting at different depths. *Urban Forestry & Urban Greening* 10:3–9.

214. Gilman, E.F., J. Grabosky, A. Stodola, and M. D. Marshall. 2003. Irrigation and container type impact red maple (*Acer rubrum* L.) 5 years after landscape planting. *Journal of Arboriculture* 29:231–236.

215. Gilman, E.F., and C. Harchick. 2008. Planting depth in containers affects root form and tree quality. *Journal of Environmental Horticulture* 26:129–134.

216. Gilman, E.F., C. Harchick, and M. Paz. 2010a. Effect of container type on root form and growth of red maple. *Journal of Environmental Horticulture* 28:1–7.

217. ———. 2010b. Planting depth affects root form of three shade tree cultivars in containers. *Arboriculture & Urban Forestry* 36:132–139.

218. ———. 2010c. Root ball shaving improves root systems on seven species in containers. *Journal of Environmental Horticulture* 28:13–18.

219. Gilman, E.F., C. Harchick, and C. Wiese. 2009. Pruning roots affects tree quality in container-grown oaks. *Journal of Environmental Horticulture* 27:7–11.

220. Gilman, E.F., G.W. Knox, C.A. Neal, and U. Yadav. 1994. Microirrigation affects growth and root distribution of trees in fabric containers. *HortTechnology* 4:43–45.

221. Gilman, E.F., and S.J. Lilly. 2008. *Best Management Practices: Tree Pruning.* Champaign, Illinois: International Society of Arboriculture. 35 pp.

222. Gilman, E.F., and F.J. Masters. 2010. Effect of tree size, root pruning, and production method on root growth and lateral stability of *Quercus virginiana*. *Arboriculture & Urban Forestry* 36: 281–291.

223. Gilman, E.F., A. Stodola, and M.D. Marshall. 2002. Root pruning but not irrigation in the nursery affects live oak root balls and digging survival. *Journal of Environmental Horticulture* 20:122–126.

224. Gilman, E.F., C.L. Wiese, M. Paz, A.L. Shober, S.M. Scheiber, K.A. Moore, and M. Brennan. 2009. Effects of irrigation volume and frequency on shrub establishment in Florida. *Journal of Environmental Horticulture* 27:149–154.

225. Gilman, E.F., and T.H. Yeager. 1987. Root pruning *Quercus virginiana* to promote a compact root system. *Proceedings of the Southern Nursery Association Research Conference.* 32:340–342.

226. Gilman, E.F., T.H. Yeager, and D. Kent. 2000. Fertilizer rate and type impacts magnolia and oak growth in sandy landscape soil. *Journal of Arboriculture* 26:177–182.

227. Gilman, E.F., T.H. Yeager, and D. Weigle. 1996. Fertilizer, irrigation and root ball slicing affects Burford holly growth after planting. *Journal of Environmental Horticulture* 14:105–110.

228. Good, G.L., and T.E. Corell. 1982. Field trials indicate the benefits and limits of fall planting. *American Nurseryman* 156:31–34.

229. Goodwin, C., and G. Lumis. 1992. Embedded wire in tree roots: Implications for tree growth and root function. *Journal of Arboriculture* 18:115–123.

230. Gossard, A.C. 1942. Root and shoot production by young pecan trees treated with indole-butyric acid at the time of transplanting. *Proceedings of the American Society of Horticultural Science* 41:161–166.

231. Grabosky, J., and N. Bassuk. 1996. Testing of structural urban tree soil materials for use under pavement to increase street tree rooting volumes. *Journal of Arboriculture* 22:255–263.

232. ———. 2008. Sixth- and tenth-year growth measurements for three tree species in a load-bearing stone-soil blend under pavement and a tree lawn in Brooklyn, New York, U.S. *Arboriculture & Urban Forestry* 34:265–266.

233. Grabosky, J. N. Bassuk, L. Irwin, and H. Van Es. 2001. Shoot and root growth of three tree species in sidewalks. *Journal of Environmental Horticulture* 19:206–211.

234. Grabosky, J., N. Bassuk, and B.Z. Marranca. 2002. Preliminary findings from measuring street tree shoot growth in two skeletal soil installations compared to tree lawn plantings. *Journal of Arboriculture* 28:106–108.

235. Grabosky, J., and E. Gilman. 2004. Measurement and prediction of tree growth reduction from tree planting space design in established parking lots. *Journal of Arboriculture* 30:154–164.

236. Grabosky, J., E. Haffner, and N. Bassuk. 2009. Plant available moisture in stone-soil media for use under pavement while allowing urban tree root growth. *Arboriculture & Urban Forestry* 35:271–278.

237. Graves, W.R. 1991. Growth and iron content of three legume tree species at high root-zone temperature. *Journal of Arboriculture* 17:313–317.

238. ———. 1994. Urban soil temperatures and their potential impact on tree growth. *Journal of Arboriculture* 20:24–27.

239. ———. 1998. Consequences of high soil temperatures. In D. Neely and G.W. Watson (Eds.). *The Landscape Below Ground II*, pp. 27–35. Champaign, Illinois: International Society of Arboriculture.

240. Graves, W.R., and A.S. Aiello. 1997. High root-zone temperature causes similar changes in water relations and growth of silver maples from 33° and 44°N latitude. *Journal of American Society of Horticultural Science* 122(2):195–199.

241. Graves, W.R., and M.N. Dana. 1987. Root-zone temperature monitored at urban sites. *HortScience* 22:613–614.

242. Graves, W.R., M.N. Dana, and R.J. Joly. 1989a. Root-zone temperature affects water status and growth of red maple. *Journal of American Society of Horticultural Science* 114:406–410.

243. ———. 1989b. Influence of root-zone temperature on growth of *Ailanthus altissima* (Mill.) Swingle. *Journal of Environmental Horticulture* 7:79–82.

244. Graves, W.R., and R. St. Hilaire. 2000. Variation in leaves and roots of sugar maple and its allies: a key to improve performance of trees in the landscape?

In *Proceedings of the 11th Metropolitan Tree Improvement Alliance (METRIA) Conference.* Gresham, Oregon. Accessed April 16, 2012 <http://www.ces. ncsu.edu/fletcher/programs/nursery/metria/metria11/graves/index.html>.

245. Graves, W.R., and L.C. Wilkins. 1991. Growth of honey locust seedlings during high root-zone temperature and osmotic stress. *HortScience* 26:1312–1315.

246. Green, T.L., and G.W. Watson. 1989. Effects of turfgrass and mulch on the establishment and growth of bare-root sugar maples. *Journal of Arboriculture* 15:268–272.

247. Halcomb, M., and A. Fulcher. 2004. Sweating Nursery Stock to Break Dormancy. Accessed April 1, 2012 <http://www.ca.uky.edu/HLA/Dunwell/ lnrsweat.html>.

248. Halverson, H.G., and G.M. Heisler. 1981. Soil temperatures under urban trees and asphalt. USDA Forest Service Research Paper NE-481.

249. Hamilton, D.F., M.E.C. Graca, and S.D. Verkade. 1981. Critical effects of fertility on root and shoot growth of selected landscape plants. *Journal of Arboriculture* 7:281–290.

250. Hanslin, H.M. 2011. Short-term effects of alternative de-icing chemicals on tree sapling performance. *Urban Forestry & Urban Greening* 10:53–59.

251. Hanslin, H.M., A. Sæbø, and O. Bergersen. 2005. Estimation of oxygen concentration in the soil gas phase beneath compost mulch by means of a simple method. *Urban Forestry & Urban Greening* 4:37–40.

252. Hanson, A-M., J.R. Harris, R. Wright, and A. Niemera. 2004. Water content of a pine-bark growing substrate in a dry mineral soil. *HortScience* 39:591–594.

253. Harris, J.R., and N.L. Bassuk. 1994. Seasonal effects on transplantability of scarlet oak, green ash, Turkish hazelnut and tree lilac. *Journal of Arboriculture* 20:310–316.

254. ———. 1995. Effects of defoliation and antitranspiration on transplant response of scarlet oak, green ash and Turkish hazelnut. *Journal of Arboriculture* 21:33–36.

255. Harris, J.R., N.L. Bassuk, and T.H. Whitlow. 1994. A window into belowground growth of landscape trees: implications for transplanting success. *HortTechnology* 4:368–371.

256. Harris, J.R., N.L. Bassuk, R.W. Zobel, and T.H. Whitlow. 1995. Root and shoot growth periodicity of green ash, scarlet oak, Turkish hazelnut, and tree lilac. *Journal of American Society of Horticultural Science* 120:211–216.

257. Harris, J.R., and S.D. Day. 2010. Planting depth at onset of container production and subsequent rootball remediation at transplanting of pin oak and littleleaf Linden. *HortScience* 45:1793–1797.

258. Harris, J.R., S.D. Day, and B. Kane. 2008. Nitrogen fertilization during planting and establishment of the urban forest: a collection of five studies. *Urban Forestry & Urban Greening* 7:195–206.

259. Harris, J.R., and J. Fanelli. 1999. Root and shoot growth periodicity of pot-in-pot red and sugar maple. *Journal of Environmental Horticulture* 17:80–83.

260. Harris, J.R., J.K. Fanelli, A.X. Niemiera, and R.D. Wright. 2001. Root pruning pin oak liners affects growth and root morphology. *HortTechnology* 11:49–52.

261. Harris, J.R., J. Fanelli, and P. Thrift. 2002. Transplant timing affects early root system regeneration of sugar maple and northern red oak. *HortScience* 37:984–987.

262. Harris, J.R., and E.F. Gilman. 1993. Production method affects growth and post-transplant establishment of East Palatka holly. *Journal of the American Society of Horticultural Science* 118:194–200.

263. ———. 1991. Production system affects growth and root regeneration of leyland cypress, laurel oak and slash pine. *Journal of Arboriculture* 17:64–69.

264. Harris, J.R., P. Knight, and J. Fanelli. 1996. Fall transplanting improves establishment of balled and burlapped fringe tree (*Chionanthus virginicus* L.). *HortScience* 31:1143–1145.

265. ———. 1998. Effect of root severance on growth of field-grown sugar maple. *HortScience* 33:21–23.

266. Harris, J.R., A.X. Niemiera, R.D. Wright, and C.H. Parkerson. 1996. Chemically controlling root escape in pot-in-pot production of river birch and Yoshino cherry. *HortTechnology* 6:30–34.

267. Harris, J.R., R. Smith, and J. Fanelli. 2001. Transplant timing affects first-season root growth of Turkish hazelnut (*Corlus colurna* L.). *HortScience* 36:805–807.

268. Harris, R.W. 1992. Root-shoot ratios. *Journal of Arboriculture* 18:39–41.

269. Harris, R.W., J.R. Clark, N.P. Matheny. 2004. *Arboriculture: Integrated Management of Landscape Trees, Shrubs and Vines*. Upper Saddle River, New Jersey: Prentice Hall. 578 pp.

270. Harris, R.W., A.T. Leiser, and W.B. Davis. 1978. Staking landscape trees. Leaflet No. 2576. University of California–Davis, Division of Agricultural Sciences. 13 pp.

271. Harris, R.W., J.L. Paul, and A.T. Leiser. 1977. Fertilizing woody plants. Leaflet No. 2958 of University of California–Davis, Cooperative Extension. 23 pp.

272. Hart, J.H., and G.K. Dennis. 1978. Effect of tree wrap on the incidence of frost cracks in Norway maple. *Journal of Arboriculture* 4:226–227.

273. Hauer, R.J., M.C. Hruska, and J.O. Dawson. 1994. Trees and ice storms: the development of ice storm-resistant urban tree populations. Special Publication 94-1, Department of Forestry, University of Illinois at Urbana-Champaign. Urbana, Illinois. 12 pp.

274. Havis, J.R. 1976. Root hardiness of woody ornamentals. *HortScience* 11:385–386.

275. Headley, D.B., and N. Bassuk. 1991. Effect of time of application of sodium chloride in the dormant season on selected tree seedlings. *Journal of Environmental Horticulture* 9:130–136.

276. Heisler, G.M., R.E. Schutzki, R.P. Zisa, H.G. Halverson, and B.A. Hamilton. 1982. Effect of planting procedures on initial growth of *Acer rubum* L. and *Fraxinus pennsylvanicum* L. in a parking lot. USDA Forest Service Northeastern Forest Experiment Station Research Paper NE-513. 7 pp.

277. Henning, F.P., T.J. Smalley, O.M. Lindstrom, Jr., and J.M. Ruter. 2010. Effect of fall fertilization on freeze resistance of deciduous versus evergreen azaleas. *Journal of Environmental Horticulture* 28:235–239.

278. Hensley, D.L. 1993. Harvest method has no influence on growth of transplanted green ash. *Journal of Arboriculture* 19:379–382.

279. Hensley, D.L., and C.F. Fackler. 1984. Do water-holding compounds help in transplanting? *American Nurseryman*. 159:93.

280. Hensley, D.L., R.E. McNiel, and R. Sundheim. 1988. Management influences on growth of a transplanted *Magnolia grandiflora*. *Journal of Arboriculture* 14:204–207.

281. Hewitt, A., and G. Watson. 2009. Bare root liner production can alter tree root architecture. *Journal of Environmental Horticulture* 27:99–104.

from the archives of the International Society of Arboriculture

282. Hild, A.L., and D.L. Morgan. 1993. Mulch effects on crown growth of five southwestern shrub species. *Journal of Environmental Horticulture* 11:41–43.

283. Hillel, D. 1998. *Environmental Soil Physics*. New York: Academic Press. 771 pp.

284. Himelick, E.B. 1981. *Tree and Shrub Transplanting Manual*. Urbana, Illinois: International Society of Arboriculture. 78 pp.

285. Himelick, E.B., and G.W. Watson. 1990. Reduction of oak chlorosis with wood chip mulch treatments. *Journal of Arboriculture* 16:275–278.

286. Hodel, D.R. 2009. Planting and transplanting palms. *Arborist News* 18(2):36–38.

287. Hodel, D.R., A.J. Downer, and D.R. Pittenger. 1998. Palm root regeneration. In D. Neely and G. Watson (Eds.). *The Landscape Below Ground II*, pp. 46–50. Champaign, Illinois: International Society of Arboriculture.

288. ———. 2005. Palm root growth and implications for transplanting. *Journal of Arboriculture* 31:171–181.

289. ———. 2006. Effect of leaf removal and tie-up on transplanted large Mexican fan palms (*Washingtonia robusta*). *Palms* 50:76–81.

290. ———. 2009. Transplanting palms. *HortTechnology* 19:686–689.

291. Hodel, D.R, A.J. Downer, D.R. Pittenger, and P.J. Beaudoin. 2006. Effect of amended backfill soils when planting five species of palms. *HortTechnology* 16:457–460.

292. Hodel, D.R., D.R. Pittenger, A.J. Downer, and W.E. Richie. 2003. Effect of leaf removal and tie up on juvenile transplanted Canary Island date palms (*Phoenix canariensis*) and queen palms (*Syagrus romanzoffiana*). *Palms* 47:177–184.

293. Hodge, S.J. 1990. Organic soil amendments for tree establishment. *Arboricultural Research Note* 86-90-ARB. DOE Arboriculture Advisory and Information Service. Farnham, Surrey, United Kingdom. 4 pp.

294. ———. 1991. Urban Trees—A Survey of Street Trees in England, 1991. Forestry Commission Bulletin 99. HMSO London.

295. ———. 1995. The effect of seven organic amendments on planting pit soil and tree performance. *Arboricultural Journal* 19:245–266.

296. Hodge, S.J., and R. Boswell. 1993. A study of the relationship between site conditions and urban tree growth. *Journal of Arboriculture* 19:358–367.

297. Hoitink, H.A.J., A.G. Stone, and D.Y. Han. 1997. Suppression of plant diseases by composts. *HortScience* 32:184–187.

298. Hoitink, H.A.J., D.M. VanDoren Jr., and A.F. Schmitthenner. 1977. Suppression of *Phytophthora cinnamomi* in a composted hardwood bark potting medium. *Phytopathology* 67:561–565.

299. Holmes, F.W. 1984. Effects of maples of prolonged exposure by artificial girdling roots. *Journal of Arboriculture* 10:40–44.

300. Hook, D.D., C.L. Brown, and R.H. Wetmore. 1972. Aeration in trees. *Botanical Gazette* 133:443–454.

301. Horsley, S.B. 1971. Root tip injury and development of the paper birch root system. Forest Science 17:341–348.

302. Horsley, S.B., and B.F. Wilson. 1971. Development of the woody portion of the root system of *Betula papyrifera*. *American Journal of Botany* 58:141–147.

303. Hummel, R.L. 1990. Water relations of container-grown woody and herbaceous plants following antitranspirant sprays. *HortScience* 25:772–775.

304. Hummel, R.L., and C.R. Johnson. 1985. Amended backfills: their cost and effect on transplant growth and survival. *Journal of Environmental Horticulture* 3:76–79.

305. ———. 1986. Influence of pruning at transplant time on growth and establishment of *Liquidambar styraciflua* L., sweet gum. *Journal of Environmental Horticulture* 4:83–86.

306. Hunt, B., A.D. Bradsaw, and T.J. Walmsley. 1991. The importance of soil physical conditions for urban tree growth. In S.J. Hodge (Ed.). *Research for Practical Arboriculture. Forestry Commission Bulletin* 97, pp. 51–62. London, UK: HMSO.

307. Hutchings, R.R., D. Sinnett, A.J. Peace, and A.J. Moffat. 2006. The effect of woodland growth on a containment landfill site in Hertfordshire, UK. *Urban Forestry & Urban Greening* 5:169–176.

308. Hvass, N. 1994. Roots. *Arborist News* 3(6):9–11.

309. Iakovoglou, V., J. Thompson, and L. Burras. 2002. Characteristics of trees according to community population level and by land use in the U.S. Midwest. *Journal of Arboriculture* 28:59–69.

310. Iakovoglou, V., J. Thompson, L. Burras, and R. Kipper. 2001. Factors related to tree growth across urban-rural gradients in the Midwest, USA. *Urban Ecosystems* 5:71–85.

311. Iles, J.K., and M.S. Dosmann. 1999. Effect of organic and mineral mulches on soil properties and growth of Fairview Flame® red maple trees. *Journal of Arboriculture* 25:163–167.

312. Ingram, D.L. 1981. Characterization of temperature fluctuations and woody plant growth in white poly bags and conventional black containers. *HortScience* 16:762–763.

313. Ingram, D.L., and W. Burbage. 1985. Effects of irrigation regime, antitranspirants, and a water absorbing polymer on the survival and establishment of transplanted live oaks. *Proceedings of the Florida State Horticultural Society* 98:85–87.

314. Ingram, D.L., and H. van de Werken. 1978. Effects of container media and backfill composition on the establishment of container-grown plants in the landscape. *HortScience* 13:583–584.

315. Ingram, D.L., U. Yadav, and C.A. Neal. 1987. Do fabric containers restrict root growth in the deep south? *American Nurseryman* 166(5Sept.):91–96.

316. Irish, E.E. 1976. Transplanting large trees. *Journal of Arboriculture* 2:173–175.

317. Jacobs, D.F., R. Rose, D.L. Haase, and P.O. Alzugaray. 2004. Fertilization at planting impairs root system development and drought avoidance of Douglas-fir (*Pseudotsuga menziesii*) seedlings. *Annual Forest Science* 61:643–651.

318. Jacobs, K., B. Rao, B. Jeffers, and D. Danielson. 2000. The effect of Biobarrier® on mycorrhizae in oak and sweetgum. *Journal of Arboriculture* 26:92–96.

319. Jacobs, K.A. 2005. The potential of mulch to transmit three tree pathogens. *Journal of Arboriculture* 31:235–242.

320. Jerecki, M., D. Williams, and G. Kling. 2006. The effect of planting depth on tree performance in the nursery. In *Proceedings of Trees and Planting: Getting the Roots Right*, pp. 11–16. Lisle, Illinois. Accessed April 1, 2012 <http://www.mortonarb.org/deeptreeroots/pdf/GRR_Proceedings.pdf#TOC>.

321. Jim, C.Y. 1997. Roadside trees in urban Hong Kong: part II species composition. *Arboricultural Journal* 20:279–298.

322. Johnson, P.S., S.L. Novinger, and W.G. Mares. 1984. Root, shoot, and leaf area growth potentials of northern red oak planting stock. *Forest Science* 30:1017–1026.

323. Jones, R.H., A.H. Chappelka, and D.H. West. 1996. Use of plastic shelters for low-cost establishment of street trees. *Southern Journal of Applied Forestry* 20:85–89.

324. Jutras, P., S.O. Prasher, and G.R. Mehuys. 2010. Appraisal of key abiotic parameters affecting street tree growth. *Arboriculture & Urban Forestry* 36:1–10.

325. K.J. Labrosse, R.C. Corry, and Y. Zheng. 2011. Effects of tree stabilization systems on tree health and implications for planting specifications. *Arboriculture & Urban Forestry* 2011. 37:219–225.

326. Kaufman, M.R. 1968. Water relations of pine seedlings in relation to root and shoot growth. *Plant Physiology* 43:281–288.

327. Kawase, M. 1981. Anatomical and morphological adaptation of plants to waterlogging. *HortScience* 16:30–34.

328. Keever, G.S., and G.S. Cobb. 1984. Container and production bed mulch effects on media temperatures and growth of Hershey's red azalea. *HortScience* 19:439–441.

329. Kelly, R.J., and B.C. Moser. 1983. Root regeneration of *Liriodendron tulipifera* in response to auxin, stem pruning and environmental conditions. *Journal of American Society of Horticultural Science* 108:1085–1090.

330. Kelsey, P., and R. Hootman. 1990. Soil resource evaluation for a group of sidewalk street tree planters. *Journal of Arboriculture* 16:113–117.

331. ———. 1992. De-icing salt dispersion and effects on vegetation along highways. In F.M. D'Itri (Ed.). *Chemical De-icers and the Environment*, pp. 253–281. Ann Arbor, Michigan: Lewis Publishers.

332. Kelting, M., J.R. Harris, and J. Fanelli. 1998. Humate-based biostimulants affect early post-transplant root growth and sapflow of balled and burlapped red maple. *HortScience* 33:342–344.

333. Kelting, M., J.R. Harris, J. Fanelli, and B. Appleton. 1998. Biostimulants and soil amendments affect two-year posttransplant growth of red maple and Washington hawthorn. *HortScience* 33:819–822.

334. Kendle, A.D., P. Gilbertson, and A.D. Bradshaw. 1988. The influence of stock source on transplant performance. *Arboriculture Journal* 12:257–272.

335. Kielbaso, J.J., and J.H. Hart. 1996. Comparison of commercial compounds to promote wound closure on Michigan hardwoods. Abstract, American Phytopathology Society Conference. Indianapolis, Indiana.

336. Kjelgren, R. 1994. Growth and water relations of Kentucky coffee tree in protective shelters during establishment. *HortScience* 29:777–780.

337. Kjelgren, R., and B. Cleveland. 1994. Growth and water relations of Kentucky coffee tree and silver maple following transplanting. *Journal of Environmental Horticulture* 12:96–99.

338. Kjelgren, R., B. Cleveland, and M. Foutch. 1994. Establishment of white oak seedling with three post-plant handling methods on deep tilled minesoil during reclamation. *Journal of Environmental Horticulture* 12:100–103.

339. Kjelgren, R., and L. Rupp. 1997. Shelters affect tree seedling establishment under grass competition. *Journal of Arboriculture* 23:131–135.

340. Knight, P.R., J.R. Harris, and J.K Fanelli. 2000. Root severance at harvest increases embolism and decreases sap flow of field-grown *Acer rubrum* L. *HortScience* 35:833–836.

341. Knox, G.W. 1989. Water use and average growth index of five species of container grown woody landscape plants. *Journal of Environmental Horticulture* 7:136–139.

342. Koeser, A., and J.R. Stewart. 2009. Effects of transplanting on the growth and survival of nursery stock. In G. Watson et al. (Eds.). *The Landscape Below Ground III*, pp. 222–229. Savoy, Illinois: International Society of Arboriculture.

343. Kopinga, J. 1985. Research on street tree planting practices in the Netherlands. In L.J. Kuhns and J.C. Patterson (Eds.). *METRIA:5 Proceedings*, pp. 72–84. University Park, Pennsylvania: Pennsylvania State University.

344. ———. 1994. Aspects of the damage to asphalt road pavings caused by tree roots. In G. Watson and D. Neely (Eds.). *The Landscape Below Ground*, pp. 165–178. Savoy, Illinois: International Society of Arboriculture.

345. Kormanik, P.P., R.C. Schultz, and W.C. Bryan. 1982. The influence of vesic-ular-arbuscular mycorrhizae on the growth and development of eight hard-wood species. *Forest Science* 28:531–539.

346. Koski, R., and W.R. Jacobi. 2004. Tree pathogen survival in chipped wood mulch. *Journal of Arboriculture* 30:165–171.

347. Kozlowski, T.T. 1982. Water supply and tree growth. Part II. *Flooding. Forestry Abstracts* 43:145–161.

348. Kozlowski, T.T., and W.J. Davies. 1975. Control of water balance in trans-planted trees. *Journal of Arboriculture* 1:1–10.

349. Kristoffersen, P. 1999. Growing trees in road foundation materials. *Arboricul-tural Journal* 23:57–76.

350. Kristoffersen, P., O. Buhler, S.U. Larsen, and T.B. Randrup. 2010. Growth of newly established *Tilia platyphyllos* 'Rubra' roadside trees in response to weed control and pruning. *Arboriculture & Urban Forestry* 36:35–40.

351. Kuhns, M.R. 1997. Penetration of treated and untreated burlap by roots of balled-and-burlapped Norway maples. *Journal of Arboriculture* 23:1–6.

352. Kuzovkina, Y.A., M. Knee, and M.F. Quigley. 2004. Effects of soil compaction and flooding on the growth of 12 willow (*Salix* L.) species. *Journal of Environ-mental Horticulture* 22:155–160.

353. Lambers, H., F.S. Chapin, III, and T.L. Pons. 1998. *Plant Physiological Ecology.* New York: Springer-Verlag. 604 pp.

354. Larcher W. 1975. Physiological Plant Ecology. Berlin and New York: Springer-Verlag.

355. Larson, M.M. 1984. Seasonal planting, root regeneration and water deficits of Austrian pine and arborvitae. *Journal of Environmental Horticulture* 2:33–38.

356. Larson, M.M., and F.W. Whitmore. 1970. Moisture stress affects root regen-eration and early growth of red oak seedlings. *Forest Science* 16:495–498

357. Lathrop, J.K., and R.A. Mecklenburg. 1971. Root regeneration and root dormancy in *Taxus* spp. *Journal of American Society of Horticultural Science* 96:111–114.

358. Lauderdale, D.M., C.H. Gilliam, D.J. Eakes, G.J. Keever, and A.H. Chappelka. 1995. Tree transplant size influences post-transplant growth, gas exchange, and leaf water potential of 'October Glory' red maple. *Journal of Environmental Horticulture* 13:178–181.

359. Lesser, L.M. 2001. Hardscape damage by tree roots. *Journal of Arboriculture* 27:272–276.

360. Lindsey, P., and J. Lichter. (Eds.). 1994. Designing and Establishing Successful Woody Landscapes—A Technical Resource Manual. Department of Environ-mental Horticulture, University of California–Davis. 400 pp.

361. Lindsey, P., and N. Bassuk. 1991. Specifying soil volumes to meet the water needs of mature urban street trees and trees in containers. *Journal of Arbori-culture* 17:141–149.

362. Litzow, M., and H. Pellett. 1982. Establishment rates for different bareroot grades of trees. *Journal of Arboriculture* 8:264–266.

363. ———. 1983. Materials for potential use in sunscald prevention. *Journal of Arboriculture* 9:35–38.

364. Loh, F.C.W., J.C. Grabosky, and N.L. Bassuk. 2003. Growth response of *Ficus benjamina* to limited soil volume and soil dilution in a skeletal soils container study. *Urban Forestry & Urban Greening* 2:53–62.

365. Loper, S., A.L. Shober, C. Wiese, G. C. Denny, C. D. Stanley, and E.F. Gilman. 2010. Organic soil amendment and tillage affect soil quality and plant performance in simulated residential landscapes. *HortScience* 45:1522–1528.

366. Lumis, G.P. 1982. Stimulating root regeneration of landscape-size red oak with auxin root sprays. *Journal of Arboriculture* 8:325–326.

367. ———. 1990. Wire baskets: A further look. *American Nurseryman* 172:128–131.

368. Lumis, G.P., and S.A. Struger. 1988. Root tissue development around wire-basket transplant containers. *HortScience* 23:401.

369. Lyr, H., and G. Hoffmann. 1967. Growth rates and growth periodicity of tree roots. In J.A. Romberger and P. Mikola (Eds.). *International Review of Forestry Research*, Volume 2, pp. 181–236. New York: Academic Press.

370. Magley, S.B., and D.K. Struve. 1983. Effects of three transplant methods on survival, growth and root regeneration of caliper pin oaks. *Journal of Environmental Horticulture* 1:59–62.

371. Magussen, S. 1986. Effects of root-coating with polymer WaterLock on survival and growth of drought-stressed bareroot seedlings of white spruce (*Picea glauca* (Moench) Voss) and red pine (*Pinus resinosa* Ait.). *Tree Planters' Notes* 37:15–19.

372. Maleike, R., and R.L. Hummel. 1992. Planting landscape plants. *Arboricultural Journal* 16:217–226.

373. Marschner, H., and V. Römheld. 1996. Root-induced changes in the availability of micronutrients in the rhizosphere. In Y. Waisel, A. Eshel, and U. Kafkafi (Eds.). *Plant Roots: The Hidden Half*, pp. 557–580. New York: Marcel Dekker, Inc.

374. Marshall, M.D., and E.F. Gilman. 1998. Effects of nursery container type on root growth and landscape establishment of *Acer rubrum* L. *Journal of Environmental Horticulture* 16:55–59.

375. ———. 2007. Production method and irrigation affect root morphology of live oak. *Journal of Environmental Horticulture* 15:84–87.

376. Martin, C.A., and S. Bhattacharya. 1995. Effects of cupric hydroxide-treated containers on growth of four southwestern desert landscape trees. *Journal of Arboriculture* 21:235–238.

377. Martin, C.A., and D.L. Ingram. 1991. Root growth of southern magnolia following exposure to high root zone temperatures. *HortScience* 26:370–371.

378. ———. 1993. Container dimension affects rooting medium temperature patterns. *HortScience* 28:18–19.

379. Martínez-Trinidad, T., W.T. Watson, and R.K. Book. 2011. Impact of paclobutrazol on root-pruned live oak. *HortTechnology* 21:46–50.

380. Martínez-Trinidad, T., W.T. Watson, M.A. Arnold, and L. Lombardini. 2009. Investigations of exogenous applications of carbohydrates on the growth and vitality of live oaks. *Urban Forestry & Urban Greening* 8:41–48.

381. Mattheck, C., and H. Breloer. 1994. *The Body Language of Trees: A Handbook for Failure Analysis.* London, England: HMSO. 240 pp.

382. Maupin, C., and D.K. Struve. 1997. Red oak transplanted to different bulk density soils have similar water use characteristics. *Journal of Arboriculture* 23:233–238.

383. McClure, S. 1991. Fatal flaws (overlooking critical practices for planting B & B material may prove deadly). *American Nurseryman* 174(8):58–61.

384. McCracken, I.J. 1978. Carbon dioxide uptake of pine seedlings after cold storage. *Forest Science* 24:17–25.

385. McDonald, S.E., R.W. Tinus, and C.P.P. Reid. 1984. Modification of ponderosa pine root systems in containers. *Journal of Environmental Horticulture* 2:1–5.

386. McDougall, D.N., and R.A. Blanchette. 1996. Polyethylene plastic wrap for tree wounds: a promoter of wound closure on fresh wounds. *Journal of Arboriculture* 22:206–210.

387. McKay, H.M. 1999. Overwinter physiology and the practical implications for handling of bare-rooted silver birch seedlings. Forestry Commission Information Note 20. Edinburgh, Scotland: Forestry Commission. 6 pp.

388. McKay H.M., and J.L. Morgan. 2001. The physiological basis for the establishment of bare-root larch seedlings. *Forest Ecology and Management* 142:1–18.

389. McMillin, J.D., and M.R. Wagner. 1995. Effects of water stress on biomass partitioning of Ponderosa pine seedlings during primary root growth and shoot growth periods. *Forest Science* 41:594–610.

390. McPherson, E.G. 2000. Expenditures associated with conflicts between street tree root growth and hardscape in California, United States. *Journal of Arboriculture* 26:289–297.

391. McPherson, E.G., J.R. Simpson, P.J. Peper, and Q. Xiao. 1999. Tree guidelines for San Joaquin Valley communities. Local Government Commissions, Sacramento, California. 64 pp.

392. Meskimen, G. 1970. Comparing grass competition for eucalyptus planted in turf. *Tree Planters' Notes* 21:3–5.

393. Messenger, S.M. 1984. Treatment of chlorotic oaks and red maples by soil acidification. *Journal of Arboriculture* 10:122–128.

394. Milbocker, D.C. 1991. Low-profile containers for nursery-grown trees. *HortScience* 26:261–263.

395. Miller, A.N., P.B. Lombard, M.N. Westwood, and R.L. Stebbins. 1990. Tree and fruit growth of 'Napoleon' cherry in response to rootstock and planting method. *HortScience* 25:176–178.

396. Montague, T., C. McKenny, M. Maurer, and B. Winn. 2007. Influence of irrigation volume and mulch on establishment of select shrub species. *Arboriculture & Urban Forestry* 33:202–209.

397. Montague, T., R. Kjelgren, and L. Rupp. 1998. Surface energy balance affects gas exchange of three shrub species. *Journal of Arboriculture* 24:254–262.

398. Morgenroth, J. 2008. A review of root barrier research. *Arboriculture & Urban Forestry* 34:84–88.

399. Morgenroth, J., and G.D. Buchan. 2009. Soil moisture and aeration beneath pervious and impervious pavements. *Arboriculture & Urban Forestry* 35:135–141.

400. Muller, R.N., and C. Bornstein. 2010. Maintaining the diversity of California's municipal forests. *Arboriculture & Urban Forestry* 36:18–27.

401. Murakami, P., T.H.H. Chen, and L.H. Fuchigami. 1990. Desiccation tolerance of deciduous plants during postharvest handling. *Journal of Environmental Horticulture* 8:22–25.

402. Myers, M.K., and H.C. Harrison. 1988. Evaluation of container plantings in an urban environment. *Journal of Arboriculture* 14:293–297.

403. Nambiar, E.K.S. 1980. Root configuration and root regeneration in *Pinus radiata* seedlings. *New Zealand Journal of Forestry Science* 10:249–63.

404. NAPPFAST 2012. NAPPFAST Global Plant Hardiness Zone based on CFSR base data. August 2012. North Carolina State University APHIS Plant Pest Forecasting System, <http://www.nappfast.org>.

The Davey Tree Expert Company

405. National Invasive Species Council (NISC). 2011. Invasive Species Definition Clarification and Guidance White Paper. National Invasive Species Information Center. Beltsville, Maryland. Accessed April 1, 2012 <http://www.invasivespeciesinfo.gov/docs/council/isacdef.pdf>.

406. National Research Council (U.S.). Committee on the Comparative Costs of Rock Salt and Calcium Magnesium Acetate (CMA) for Deicing. 1991. Highway deicing: comparing salt and calcium magnesium acetate. Transportation Research Board Special Report 235. National Research Council. Washington, D.C.

407. Neal, C. 2009. Nursery container types affect root zone temperatures, survival, and growth of overwinter plants. In G. Watson, L. Costello, B. Scharenbroch, and E. Gilman (Eds.). *The Landscape Below Ground III*, pp. 121–125. Champaign, Illinois: International Society of Arboriculture.

408. Neely, D. 1984. Grass competition for nitrogen around landscape trees. *Journal of Environmental Horticulture* 2:86–88.

409. Neely, D., and E.B. Himelick. 1987. Fertilizing and watering trees. Illinois Natural History Survey Circular 56. Third revision. 24 pp.

410. Neely, D., E.B. Himelick, and W.R. Crowley, Jr. 1970. Fertilization of Established Trees: A Report of Field Studies. Illinois Natural History Survey Bulletin No. 30:235–266.

411. Nelms, L.R., and L.A. Spomer. 1983. Water retention of container soils transplanted into ground beds. *HortScience* 18:863–866.

412. Neuman, D.S. 1993. Shoot responses to root stress—a resource gathering point of view. *Journal of Arboriculture* 19:118–124.

413. Newman, C.J. 1982. English techniques in large tree transplanting. *Journal of Arboriculture* 8:90–93.

414. Nicoll, B.C., and A. Armstrong. 1997. Street tree root architecture and pavement damage. Arboriculture Research and Information Note 138/97/SILN Arboricultural Advisory and Information Service. Farnham, Surrey, England.

415. ———. 1998. Development of Prunus root systems in a city street: pavement damage and root architecture. *Arboricultural Journal* 22:259–270.

416. Nicolosi, R.T. 1981. Influence of backfill and soil density on root growth of urban plants, pp. 48–51. New Horizons. Washington, DC: Horticultural Research Institute.

417. Norges standardiseringsforbund. 2000. The Norwegian Standard for Nursery Stock 4402 (3rd Ed.). Nursery stock—Deciduous trees (in Norwegian). Oslo.

418. Nowak, D.J., M. Kuroda, and D.E. Crane. 2004. Tree mortality rates and tree population projections in Baltimore, Maryland, USA. *Urban Forestry & Urban Greening* 2:139–147.

419. Nowak, D.J., R.E. Hoehn III, D.E. Crane, J.C. Stevens, C.L. Fisher. 2010. Assessing urban forest effects and values, Chicago's urban forest. Resource Bulletin NRS-37. Newtown Square, Pennsylvania: U.S. Department of Agriculture, Forest Service, Northern Research Station. 27 pp.

420. NRCS Soil Quality Institute. 2000. Urban soil compaction. United States Department of Agriculture Natural Resources Conservation Service Soil Quality—Urban Technical Note No. 2. Accessed May 7, 2012 <http://soils.usda.gov/sqi/management/files/sq_utn_2.pdf>.

421. O'Callaghan, D.P.O. 1989. Transplanting a mature cutleaf basswood in Preston, England. *Journal of Arboriculture* 15:V.

422. ———. 2005. Transplanting mature trees—lessons from case histories. *Arboricultural Journal* 29:19–41.

423. Oddiraju, V.G., C.A. Beyl, and P.A. Barker. 1996. Root growth of seedlings and microcuttings of western black cherry grown in compacted soil. *HortScience* 31:453–457.

424. Östberg, J., M. Martinsson, Ö. Stål, and A-M. Fransson. 2012. Risk of root intrusion by tree and shrub species in sewer pipes in Swedish urban areas. *Urban Forestry & Urban Greening* 11:65–71.

425. Owen, N.P., C.S. Sadof, and M.J. Raupp. 1991. The effect of plastic tree wrap on borer incidence in dogwood. *Journal of Arboriculture* 17:29–31.

426. Patterson, J.C. 1976. Soil compaction and its effects upon urban vegetation. *Better Trees for Metropolitan Landscapes Symposium Proceedings*. USDA Forest Service General Technical Report NE-22.

427. Pauleit, S., N. Jones, G. Garcia-Martin, J.L. Garcia-Valdecantos, L.M. Rivière, L. Vidal-Beaudet, M. Bodson, and T.B. Randrup. 2002. Tree establishment practice in towns and cities—results from a European survey. *Urban Forestry & Urban Greening* 1:83–96.

428. Pellett, H. 1971. Effect of soil amendments on growth of landscape plants. *American Nurseryman* 134(10):12, 103–106.

429. ———. 1981. Soil temperature effects on urban plants, pp. 34–36. New Horizons. Washington, DC: Horticultural Research Institute.

430. Pellett, H., R. Hummel, and L. Mainquist. 1980. Relationship of fall watering practice to winter injury of conifers. *Journal of Arboriculture* 6:146–149.

431. Peper, P.J., and S. Mori. 1999. Root barrier and extension casing effects on Chinese hackberry. *Journal of Arboriculture* 25:1–7.

432. Percival, G.C. 2004. Sugar feeding enhances root vigor of young trees following containerization. *Journal of Arboriculture* 30:357–364.

433. Percival, G.C., and S. Barnes. 2004. Auxins and water-retaining polymer root dips affect survival and growth of newly transplanted bare-rooted European beech and silver birch. *Journal of Environmental Horticulture* 22:183–188.

434. ———. 2007. The influence of carbohydrates, nitrogen fertilisers and water-retaining polymer root dips on survival and growth of newly transplanted bare-rooted silver birch (*Betula pendula* Roth.) and European Beech (*Fagus sylvatica* L.). *Arboricultural Journal* 30:223–244.

435. Percival, G.C., and G.A. Fraser. 2005. Use of sugars to improve root growth and increase transplant success of birch (*Betula pendula* Roth.). *Journal of Arboriculture* 31:66–78.

436. Percival, G.C., E. Gklavakis, and K. Noviss. 2009. Influence of pure mulches on survival, growth and vitality of containerized and field planted trees. *Journal of Environmental Horticulture* 27:200–206.

437. Percival G.C., I.P. Keary, and K. Marshall. 2006. The use of film-forming polymers to control Guignardia leaf blotch and powdery mildew on *Aesculus hippocastanum* L. and *Quercus robur* L. *Arboriculture & Urban Forestry* 32:100–107.

438. Perry, E., and G.W. Hickman. 1992. Growth response of newly planted valley oak trees to supplemental fertilizers. *Journal of Environmental Horticulture* 10:242–244.

439. Pezeshki, S.R. 1991. Root responses of flood-tolerant and flood-sensitive tree species to soil redox conditions. *Trees* 5:180–186.

440. Pham, C.H., H.G. Halverson, and G.M. Heisler. 1978. Red maple (*Acer rubrum* L.) growth and foliar nutrient responses to soil fertility level and water regime. USDA Forest Service Research Paper NE-412. 7 pp.

441. Pittenger, D., and D. Hodel. 2009. Six-year evaluation of circular root barriers on two tree species. *Arboriculture & Urban Forestry* 35:41–46.

442. Ponder, Jr., F. 1997. Survival and growth of hardwood seedlings following preplanting root treatments and treeshelters. In S.G. Pallardy, R.A. Cecich, H.E. Garrett, and P.E. Johnson (Eds.). *Proceedings of The 11th Central Hardwood Forest Conference*, General Technical Report NC-188, pp. 332–340. St. Paul, Minnesota: U.S. Department of Agriculture, Forest Service, North Central Forest Experiment Station.

443. ———. 2000. Survival and growth of planted hardwoods in harvested openings with first-order lateral root differences, root-dipping, and tree shelters. *Northern Journal of Applied Forestry* 17:45–50.

444. Ponder, H.G., and A.L. Kenworthy. 1976. Trickle irrigation of shade trees growing in the nursery: II. Influence on root distribution. *Journal of the American Society of Horticultural Science* 101:104–107.

445. Ponder, H.G., C.H. Gilliam, E. Wilkinson, J. Eason, and C.E. Evans. 1984. Influence of trickle irrigation and nitrogen rates to *Acer rubrum* L. *Journal of Environmental Horticulture* 2:40–43.

446. Potter, J.J. 1988. Treeshelters improve survival and increase early growth rates. *Journal of Forestry* 86:39–41

447. Potter, M.J. 1991. Treeshelters. Forestry Commission Handbook 7. London, UK: HMSO. 48 pp.

448. Prager, C.M., and G.P. Lumis. 1983. IBA and some IBA-synergist increases of root regeneration of landscape-sized trees. *Journal of Arboriculture* 9:117–123.

449. Preaus, K.B., and C.E. Whitcomb. 1980. Transplanting landscape trees. *Journal of Arboriculture* 6:221–223.

450. Privett, D.W., and R.L. Hummel. 1992. Root and shoot growth of 'Coral Beauty' cotoneaster and leyland cypress produced in porous and nonporous containers. *Journal of Environmental Horticulture* 10:133–136.

451. Rae, W.A. 1969. Large tree moving by frozen root balls. *Trees* 29(Jan–Feb):8–9.

452. ———. 1976. Tree transplanting. *Journal of Arboriculture* 2:133–135.

453. Rahardjo, H., F.R. Harnas, E.C. Leong, P.Y. Tan, Y.K. Fong, and E.K. Sim. 2009. Tree stability in an improved soil to withstand wind loading. *Urban Forestry & Urban Greening* 8:237–247.

454. Rahman, M.A., J.G. Smith, P. Stringer, and A.R. Ennos. 2011. Effect of rooting conditions on the growth and cooling ability of *Pyrus calleryana*. *Urban Forestry & Urban Greening* 10:185–192.

455. Randrup, T. 2000. Occurrence of tree roots in Danish municipal sewer systems. *Arboricultural Journal* 24:283–306.

456. Randrup, T.B., E.G. McPherson, and L.R. Costello. 2003. A review of tree root conflicts with sidewalks, curbs, and roads. *Urban Ecosystems* 5:209–225.

457. Ranney, T.G., N.L. Bassuk, and T.H. Whitlow. 1989. Effect of transplanting practices on growth and water relations of 'Colt' cherry trees during reestablishment. *Journal of Environmental Horticulture* 7:41–45.

458. Rathjens, R.G., T.D. Sydnor, and D.S. Gardner. 2007. A survey of the depth of the main lateral roots of nursery trees in Ohio before and after harvest. *Journal of Environmental Horticulture* 25:187–190.

459. Reichwein, S. 2002. Baumwurzeln unter Verkehrsflächen: Untersuchungen zu Schäden an Verkehrsflächen durch Baumwurzeln und Ansätze zur Schadensbehebung und Schadensvermeidung. Heft 66, Beiträge zur raumlichen Planung. [Tree roots under sidewalks. Doctoral dissertation.] Fachbereich Landschaftsarchitektur und Umweltentwicklung, Universität Hanover, Hanover Germany.

460. Reiger, R., and C. Whitcomb. 1984. A root control system for growing and transplanting trees. *Arboricultural Journal* 9:33–38.

461. Richardson-Calfee, L.E., and J.R. Harris. 2005. A review of the effects of transplant timing on landscape establishment of field-grown deciduous trees in temperate climates. *HortTechnology* 15:132–135.

462. Richardson-Calfee, L.E., J.R. Harris, and J.K. Fanelli. 2004. Seasonal effects of transplanting on northern red oak and willow oak. *Journal of Environmental Horticulture* 22:75–79.

463. ———. 2007. Posttransplant root and shoot growth periodicity of sugar maple. *Journal of American Society of Horticultural Science* 132:147–157.

464. ———. 2008. Root and shoot growth response of balled-and-burlapped and pot-in-pot sugar maple to transplanting at five phenological growth stages. *Journal of Environmental Horticulture* 26:171–176.

465. Richardson-Calfee, L.E., J.R. Harris, R.H. Jones, and J.K. Fanelli. 2010. Patterns of root production and mortality during transplant establishment of landscape-sized sugar maple. *Journal of American Society of Horticultural Science* 135:203–211.

466. Riikonen, A., L. Lindén, M. Pulkkinen, and E. Nikinmaa. 2011. Post-transplant crown allometry and shoot growth of two species of street trees. *Urban Forestry & Urban Greening* 10:87–94.

467. Ritchie, G.A., and J.R. Dunlap. 1980. Root growth potential: its development and expression in forest tree seedlings. *New Zealand Journal of Forest Science* 10:218–248.

468. Roberts, B.R. 2006. Compost-containing substrates and their effect on posttransplant growth of containerized tree seedlings. *Arboriculture & Urban Forestry* 32:289–296.

469. Roberts, D.R. 1993. How pot-in-pot systems save time, money. *Nursery Manager* 9(6):46, 48, 50.

470. Rohsler, M. 1982. Root hardiness ratings of woody nursery plants. *Tennessee Nursery Digest* 4(5): 5-7.

471. Rolf, K. 1991. Soil improvement and increased growth response from subsoil cultivation. *Journal of Arboriculture* 17:200–204.

472. Rolf, K., and Ö. Stål. 1994. Tree roots in sewer systems in Malmo, Sweden. *Journal of Arboriculture* 20:329–335

473. Roloff, A., S. Korn, and S. Gillner. 2009. The climate-species-matrix to select tree species for urban habitats considering climate change. *Urban Forestry & Urban Greening* 8:295–308.

474. Roman, L.A., and F.N. Scatena. 2011. Street tree survival rates: meta-analysis of previous studies and application to a field survey in Philadelphia, PA, USA. *Urban Forestry & Urban Greening* 10:269-274.

475. Rook, D.A. 1973. Conditioning radiata pine seedlings to transplanting by restricted watering. New Zealand Journal of Forest Science 3:54–69.

476. Roppolo, D.J., Jr., and R.W. Miller. 2001. Factors predisposing urban trees to sunscald. *Journal of Arboriculture* 27:246–254.

477. Ruter, J.M. 1993. Growth and landscape performance of three landscape plants produced in conventional and pot-in-pot production systems. *Journal of Environmental Horticulture* 11:124–127.

478. ———. 1994. Growth responses of four vigorous-rooted tree species in cupric hydroxide-treated containers. *HortScience* 29:1089.

479. Sæbø, A., T. Benedikz, and T.B. Randrup. 2003. Selection of trees for urban forestry in the Nordic countries. *Urban Forestry & Urban Greening* 2:101–114.

480. Sammons, J.D., and D.K. Struve. 2004. Effect of Bioplex™ on transplant success of non-dormant red oak (*Quercus rubra* L.). *Journal of Environmental Horticulture* 22:197–201.

481. Santamour, Jr., F.S. 1979. Root hardiness of green ash seedlings from different provenances. *Journal of Arboriculture* 5:276–279.

482. ———. 1990. Trees for urban planting: diversity, uniformity and common sense. In *Proceedings of The 7th Conference of Metropolitan Tree Improvement Alliance (METRIA)*, pp. 57–65. The Morton Arboretum, Lisle, Illinois.

483. Santamouris, M. 2001. Heat-island effect. In M. Santamouris (Ed.). *Energy and Climate in the Urban Built Environment*, Volume 1, pp. 48–68. London, UK: James & James, Ltd.

484. Sarvaš, M. 2003. Effect of desiccation on the root system of Norway spruce (*Picea abies* [L.] Karst.) seedlings and a possibility of using hydrogel Stocksorb® for its protection. *Journal of Forest Science* 49:531–536.

485. Scharenbroch, B.C. 2009. A meta-analysis of studies published in *Arboriculture & Urban Forestry* relating to organic materials and impacts on soil, tree, and environmental properties. *Arboriculture & Urban Forestry* 35:221–231.

486. Scharenbroch, B.C., W. Treasurer, M. Catania, and V. Brand. 2011. Laboratory assays on the effects of aerated compost tea and fertilization on biochemical properties and denitrification in A silt loam and Bt clay loam soils. *Arboriculture & Urban Forestry* 37:269–277.

487. Scheiber, S.M., E.F. Gilman, M. Paz, and K.A. Moore. 2007. Irrigation affects landscape establishment of Burford holly, Pittosporum, and sweet Viburnum. *HortScience* 42:344–348.

488. Scheyer, J.M., and K.W. Hipple. 2005. Urban Soil Primer. United States Department of Agriculture, Natural Resources Conservation Service, National Soil Survey Center, Lincoln, Nebraska. Accessed April 1, 2012 <http://soils.usda.gov/use/urban/primer.html>.

489. Schluckebier, J.G., and C.A. Martin. 1997. Effects of above-ground pot-in-pot (PIP) placement and humic acid extract on growth of crape myrtle. *Journal of Environmental Horticulture* 15(1):41–44.

490. Schnelle, M.A., and J.E. Klett. 1992. The effects of cold storage and dormant pruning on growth of radiant crabapple. *Journal of Arboriculture* 18:136–144.

491. Schoeneweiss, D.F. 1978. The influence of stress on diseases of nursery and landscape plants. *Journal of Arboriculture* 4:217–225.

492. ———. 1981. Infectious diseases of trees associated with water and freezing stress. *Journal of Arboriculture* 7:13–18.

493. Schroeder, H.W., J.F. Dwyer, and J. Flannigan. 2009. Big trees in the urban forest: an endangered resource worth sustaining. *Arborist News* 18(2):60–62.

494. Schuch, U.K., and D.R. Pittenger. 1996. Root and shoot growth of eucalyptus in response to container configuration and copper carbonate. *HortScience* 31:165.

495. Schulte, J.R., and C.E. Whitcomb. 1975. Effects of soil amendments and fertilizer levels on the establishment of silver maple. *Journal of Arboriculture* 1:192–195.

496. Scott, T.K. 1972. Auxins and roots. Annual Review of *Plant Physiology* 23:235–258.

497. Shaw, D.C. 1980. Moving large trees. *Journal of Arboriculture* 6:51–52.

498. Shigo, A.L. 1993. *100 Tree Myths*. Durham, New Hampshire: Shigo and Trees Associates. 80 pp.

499. Shober, A.L., S. Davis, M.D. Dukes, G.C. Denny, S.P. Brown, and S. Vyapari. 2009. Performance of Florida landscape plants when irrigated by ET-based controllers and time-based methods. *Journal of Environmental Horticulture* 27:251–256.

500. Shober, A.L., K.A. Moore, C. Wiese, S.M. Scheiber, E.F. Gilman, M. Paz, M.M. Brennan, and S. Vyapari. 2009. Posttransplant irrigation frequency affects growth of container-grown sweet viburnum in three hardiness zones. *Hort-Science* 44:1683–1687.

501. Shoup, S., R. Reavis, and C. Whitcomb. 1981. Effects of pruning and fertilizers on establishment of bareroot deciduous trees. *Journal of Arboriculture* 7:155–157.

502. Sibley, J.L., J.M. Ruter, and D.J. Eakes. 1999. Growth periodicity for container-grown red and Freeman maple cultivars in AHS Head-Zone 8. *Journal of Environmental Horticulture* 17:141–146.

503. Sinclair, W.A., H.H. Lyon, and W.T. Johnson. 1987. *Diseases of Trees and Shrubs*. Ithaca, New York: Cornell University Press. 575 pp.

504. Singer, C.K., and C.A. Martin. 2008. Effect of landscape mulches on desert landscape microclimates. *Arboriculture & Urban Forestry* 34:230–237.

505. ———. 2009. Effect of landscape mulches and drip irrigation on transplant establishment and growth of three North American desert native plants. *Journal of Environmental Horticulture* 27:166–170.

506. Sivyer, D., J.R. Harris, N. Persaud, and B. Appleton. 1997. Evaluation of a pan evaporation model for estimating post-planting street tree irrigation requirements. *Journal of Arboriculture* 23:250–256.

507. Sjöman, H., and A.B. Nielsen. 2010. Selecting trees for urban paved sites in Scandinavia—a review of information on stress tolerance and its relation to the requirements of tree planters. *Urban Forestry & Urban Greening* 9:281–293.

508. Sjöman, H., J. Östberg, and O. Bühler. 2012. Diversity and distribution of the urban tree population in ten major Nordic cities. *Urban Forestry & Urban Greening* 11:31–39.

509. Skinner, D.N. 1986. Planting success rates—standard trees. *Arboricultural Research Note* 66:86 DoE Arboricultural Advisory and Information Service, Farnham, Surrey.

510. Sloan, J.P. 1994. The use of root dips on North American conifer seedlings: a review of the literature. *Tree Planters' Notes* 45:26–31.

511. Smalley, T.J., and C.B. Wood. 1995. Effect of backfill amendment on growth of red maple. *Journal of Arboriculture* 21:247–249.

512. Smiley, E.T. 2005. Root growth near vertical root barriers. *Journal of Arboriculture* 31:150–152.

513. ———. 2008. Comparison of methods to reduce sidewalk damage from tree roots. *Arboriculture & Urban Forestry* 34:179–183.

514. Smiley, E.T., L. Calfee, B.R. Fraedrich, and E.J. Smiley. 2006. Comparison of structural and noncompacted soils for trees surrounded by pavement. *Arboriculture & Urban Forestry* 34:164–169.

515. Smiley, E.T., A. Key, and C. Greco. 2000. Root barriers and windthrow potential. *Journal of Arboriculture* 26:213–217.

516. Smiley, E.T., E. LeBrun, and E. Gilbert. 2003. Evaluation of extraction force for wooden guy anchors. *Journal of Arboriculture* 29:295–297.

517. Smiley, E.T, S.J. Lilly, and P. Kelsey. 2002. *Best Management Practices: Tree and Shrub Fertilization.* Champaign, Illinois: International Society of Arboriculture. 34 pp.

518. Smiley, E.T., and A.M. Shirazi. 2003. Fall fertilization and cold hardiness in landscape trees. *Arboriculture & Urban Forestry* 29:342–346.

519. Smiley, E.T., L. Wilkinson, and B.R. Fraedrich. 2009. Root growth near vertical root barriers after seven years. *Arboriculture & Urban Forestry* 35:23–26.

520. Smith, K., P. May, and R. White. 2010. Above and belowground growth of *Corymbia maculata* in a constructed soil: the effect of profile design and organic amendment. *Arboriculture & Urban Forestry* 36:11–17.

521. Soil and Water Conservation Society (SWCS). 2000. Soil Biology Primer. (Rev. ed.). Ankeny, Iowa: Soil and Water Conservation Society. Accessed April 1, 2012 <http://soils.usda.gov/sqi/concepts/soil_biology/biology.html>.

522. Soil Climate Analysis Network (SCAN). [Internet, n.d.]. USDA National Resource and Conservation Service. Accessed April 1, 2012 <http://www.wcc.nrcs.usda.gov/scan/>.

523. Solfjeld, I., and O.B. Hansen. 2004. Post-transplant growth of five deciduous Nordic tree species as affected by transplanting date and root pruning. *Urban Forestry & Urban Greening* 2:129–137.

524. Solfjeld, I., and P.A. Pedersen. 2006. Growth of *Betula pendula* Roth. The first season after transplanting at two phenological stages. *Urban Forestry & Urban Greening* 5:101–106.

525. Spomer, L.A. 1980. Container soil water relations: production, maintenance, and transplanting. *Journal of Arboriculture* 6:315–320.

526. ———. 1983. Physical amendment of landscape soils. *Journal of Environmental Horticulture.* 1:77–80.

527. Starbuck, C., D.K. Struve, and H. Mathers. 2005. Bare root and ball-and-burlapped red oak and green ash can be summer transplanted using the Missouri gravel bed system. *HortTechnology* 15:122–127.

528. Stone, E.C., and J.L. Jenkinson. 1970. Influence of soil water on root growth capacity of ponderosa pine transplants. *Forest Science* 16:230–239.

Charles F. Irish

529. Struve, D.K. 1990. Root regeneration in transplanted deciduous nursery stock. *HortScience* 25:266–270.

530. ———. 1993. Effect of copper-treated containers on transplant survival and regrowth of four tree species. *Journal of Environmental Horticulture* 11:196–199.

531. Struve, D.K., and F.A. Blazich. 1982. Comparison of three methods of auxin application on rooting of eastern white pine stem cuttings. *Forest Science* 28:337–344.

532. Struve, D.K., L. Burchfield, and C. Maupin. 2000. Survival and growth of transplanted large- and small-caliper red oaks. *Journal of Arboriculture* 26:162–169.

533. Struve, D.K., and R.J. Joly 1992. Transplanted red oak seedlings mediate transplant shock by reducing leaf surface area and altering carbon allocation. *Canadian Journal of Forest Research* 22:1441–1448.

534. Struve, D.K., R.D. Kelly, and B.C. Moser. 1983. Promotion of root regeneration of difficult-to-transplant species. *Proceedings of the International Plant Propagators Society* 33:433–439.

535. Struve, D.K., and B.C. Moser. 1984a. Root system and root regeneration characteristics of pin and scarlet oak. *HortScience* 19:123–125.

536. ———. 1984b. Auxin effects on root regeneration of scarlet oak seedlings. *Journal of American Society of Horticultural Science* 109:91–95.

537. ———. 1985. Soil temperature effects on root regeneration of scarlet oak seedlings. Research Circular—Ohio Agricultural Research and Development Center 2841:12–14.

538. Struve, D.K., and W.T. Rhodus. 1988. Phenyl indole-3-thiobutyrate increases growth of transplanted 1-0 red oak. *Canadian Journal of Forest Research* 18:131–134.

539. Struve, D.K., T.D. Sydnor, and R. Rideout. 1989. Root system configuration affects transplanting of honeylocust and English oak. *Journal of Arboriculture* 15:129–134.

540. Studer, E.J., P.L. Steponkus, G.L. Good, and S.C. Weist. 1978. Root hardiness of container-grown ornamentals. *HortScience* 13:172–174.

541. Sutton, R.F., and R.W. Tinus. 1983. Root and Root System Terminology. Forest Science Monographs 24. 137 pp.

542. Svihra, P., D. Burger, and D. Ellis. 1999. Effects of 3 trunk support systems on growth of young Pyrus calleryana trees. *Journal of Arboriculture* 25:319–324.

543. Svihra, P., D. Burger, and R. Harris. 1996. Treeshelter effect on root development of redwood trees. *Journal of Arboriculture* 22:174–179.

544. Switzer, G.L. 1960. Exposure and planting depth effects on loblolly pine planting stock on poorly drained sites. *Journal of Forestry* 58:390–391.

545. Sydnor, T.D., D. Gamstetter, J. Nichols, B. Bishop, J. Favorite, C. Blazer, and L. Turpin. 2000. Trees are not the root of sidewalk problems. *Journal of Arboriculture* 26:20–29.

546. Sydnor, T.D., S. Subburayalu, and M. Bumgardner. 2010. Contrasting Ohio nursery stock availability with community planting needs. *Arboriculture & Urban Forestry* 36:47–54.

547. Taylor, G., and W.J. Davies. 1990. Root growth of *Fagus sylvatica*: impact of air quality and drought at a site in southern Britain. *New Phytology* 116:457–464.

548. Taylor, H.M., and H.R. Gardner. 1963. Penetration of cotton seedling taproots as influenced by bulk density, moisture content, and strength of soil. *Soil Science* 96:153–156.

549. Thien, S.J. 1979. A flow diagram for teaching texture by feel analysis. *Journal of Agronomic Education* 8:54–55.

550. Thomas, D.S. 2008. Hydrogel applied to the root plug of subtropical eucalypt seedlings halves transplant death following planting. *Forest Ecology and Management* 255:1305–1314.

551. Timonen, S., and P. Kauppinen. 2008. Mycorrhizal colonisation patterns of *Tilia* trees in street, nursery and forest habitats in southern Finland. *Urban Forestry & Urban Greening* 7:265–276.

552. Tinus, R.W. 1996. Root growth potential as an indicator of drought stress history. *Tree Physiology* 16:795–799.

553. Todhunter, M.N., and W.F. Beineke. 1979. Effect of fescue on black walnut growth. *Tree Planters' Notes* 30:20–23

554. Toliver, J.R., R.C. Sparks, and T. Hansbrough. 1980. Effects of top and lateral pruning on survival and early growth—three bottomland hardwood tree species. *Tree Planters' Notes* 31:13–15.

555. Tomlinson, P.B. 1990. *The Structural Biology of Palms*. Oxford, UK: Oxford University Press.

556. Travers, D.M., and C.R. Ireland. 1993. A comparative study of the responses of three amenity tree species to differing water supply during establishment. *Acta Horticulturae* 335:277–295.

557. Tryon, P.R., and F.S. Chapin III. 1983. Temperature control over root growth and root biomass in taiga forest trees. *Canadian Journal of Forest Research* 13:827–833.

558. Urban, J. 1992. Bringing order to the technical dysfunction within the urban forest. *Journal of Arboriculture* 18:85–90.

559. ———. 2008. *Up by Roots: Healthy Soils and Trees in the Built Environment*. Champaign, Illinois: International Society of Arboriculture. 479 pp.

560. USDA Plant Hardiness Zone Map. 1990. USDA Miscellaneous Publication No. 1475. Accessed December 3, 2012 <http://planthardiness.ars.usda.gov/PHZMWeb/Images/USZoneMap.jpg/>.

561. ———. 2012. Agricultural Research Service, U.S. Department of Agriculture. Accessed April 1, 2012 <http://planthardiness.ars.usda.gov/>.

562. van de Werken, H. 1981. Fertilization and other factors enhancing the growth rate of young shade trees. *Journal of Arboriculture* 7:33–37.

563. ———. 1982. Effects of four root barrier fabrics on penetration and self pruning of roots. *Proceedings of the Southern Nursery Association Research Conference* 27:292–293.

564. ———. 1984. Fertilization practices as they influence the growth rate of young shade trees. *Journal of Environmental Horticulture* 2:64–69.

565. Vanstone, D.E., and W.G. Ronald. 1981. Comparison of bare-root versus tree spade transplanting of boulevard trees. *Journal of Arboriculture* 7:271–274.

566. Viswanathan, B., A. Volder, W.T. Watson, and J.A. Aitkenhead-Peterson. 2011. Impervious and pervious pavements increase soil CO_2 concentrations

and reduce root production of American sweetgum (*Liquidambar styraciflua*). *Urban Forestry & Urban Greening* 10:133–139.

567. Volder, A., T. Watson, and B. Viswanathan. 2009. Potential use of pervious concrete for maintaining existing mature trees during and after urban development. *Urban Forestry & Urban Greening* 8:249–256.

568. von der Heide-Spravka, K.G., and G.W. Watson. 1990. Directional variation in growth of trees. *Journal of Arboriculture* 16:169–173.

569. Wagar, J.A. 1985. Reducing surface rooting of trees with control planters and wells. *Journal of Arboriculture* 11:165–171.

570. Wagar, J.A., and P.A. Barker. 1993. Effectiveness of three barrier materials for stopping regenerating roots of established trees. *Journal of Arboriculture* 19:332–338.

571. Wagar, J.A., and A.L. Franklin. 1994. Sidewalk effects on soil moisture and temperature. *Journal of Arboriculture* 20:237–238.

572. Walmsley, T.J., B. Hunt, and A.D. Bradshaw. 1991. Root growth, water stress and tree establishment. In S.J. Hodge (Ed.). *Research for Practical Arboriculture. Forestry Commission Bulletin* 97, pp. 38–43. London, UK: HMSO.

573. Walters, D.T., and A.R. Gilmore. 1976. Allelopathic effects of fescue on growth of sweetgum. *Journal of Chemical Ecology* 2:469–479.

574. Ware, G. 1994. Tough trees for tough situations. *Journal of Arboriculture* 20:98–103.

575. Wargo, P.M. 1975. Estimating starch content in roots of deciduous trees—a visual technique. USDA Forest Service Research Paper NE-313. 9 pp.

576. Watson, G. 1985. Tree size affects root regeneration and top growth after transplanting. *Journal of Arboriculture* 11:37–40.

577. ———. 2004. Effect of transplanting and Paclobutrazol on root growth of 'green column' black maple and 'summit' green ash. *Journal of Environmental of Horticulture* 22(4):209–212.

578. ———. 2006. Establishing a relationship between soil aeration and fine root development of seven tree species using the steel rod technique. *Arboricultural Journal* 29:161–172.

579. ———. 2008. Discoloration and decay in severed tree roots. *Arboriculture & Urban Forestry* 34:260–264.

580. ———. 2009. Desiccation tolerance of green ash and sugar maple fine roots. *Journal of Environmental Horticulture* 27:229–233.

581. Watson, G.W. 1986. Cultural practices can influence root development for better transplanting success. *Journal of Environmental Horticulture* 4:32–34.

582. ———. 1987a. Are auxins practical for B&B tress? *American Nurseryman* 166:183–184.

583. ———. 1987b. The relationship of root growth and tree vigour following transplanting. *Arboricultural Journal* 11:97–104.

584. ———. 1988. Organic mulch and grass competition influence tree root development. *Journal of Arboriculture* 14:200–203.

585. ———. 1992. Tree and shrub fertilization. *Grounds Maintenance* 27(1):43–46.

586. ———. 1994. Root growth response to fertilizers. *Journal of Arboriculture* 20:4–8.

587. Watson, G.W., and S. Clark. 1993. Regeneration of girdling roots after removal. *Journal of Arboriculture* 19:278–280.

588. Watson, G.W., S. Clark, and K. Johnson. 1990. Formation of girdling roots. *Journal of Arboriculture* 16:197–202.

589. Watson, G.W., and A.M. Hewitt. 2006. Deep roots of landscape trees. Accessed April 1, 2012 <http://www.mortonarb.org/deeptreeroots/>.

590. ———. 2012. The influence of root depth on performance of street trees. *Arboriculture & Urban Forestry* 38:13–17.

591. Watson, G.W., and E.B. Himelick. 1982a. Root distribution of nursery trees and its relationship to transplanting success. *Journal of Arboriculture* 8:225–229.

592. ———. 1982b. Seasonal variation in root regeneration of transplanted trees. *Journal of Arboriculture* 8:305–310.

593. ———. 2005. *Best Management Practices: Tree Planting*. Champaign, Illinois: International Society of Arboriculture. 41 pp.

594. Watson, G.W., E.B. Himelick, and E.T. Smiley. 1986. Twig growth of eight species of shade trees following transplanting. *Journal of Arboriculture* 12:241–245.

595. Watson, G.W., and G. Kupkowski. 1991. Soil moisture uptake by green ash trees after transplanting. *Journal of Environmental Horticulture* 9:227–230.

596. Watson, G.W., G. Kupkowski, and K.G. von der Heide-Spravka. 1992. The effect of backfill soil texture and planting hole shape on root regeneration of transplanted green ash. *Journal of Arboriculture* 18:130–135.

597. ———. 1993. Influence of backfill soil amendments on establishment of container-grown shrubs. *HortTechnology* 3:188–189.

598. Watson, G.W., and T.D. Sydnor. 1987. The effect of root pruning on the root system of nursery trees. *Journal of Arboriculture* 13:126–130.

599. Webb, D.P. 1977. Root regeneration and bud dormancy of sugar maple, silver maple and white ash seedlings: effects of chilling. *Forest Science* 23:474–483.

600. Webb, R. 1995. Moving mature banyan trees in Hong Kong. *Arboricultural Journal* 19:339–347.

601. Weicherding, P.J., C.P. Giblin, J.H. Gillman, D.L. Hanson, and G.R. Johnson. 2007. Mechanical root-disruption practices and their effect on circling roots of pot-bound *Tilia cordata* Mill. and *Salix alba* L. 'Niobe.' *Arboriculture & Urban Forestry* 33:43–47.

602. Welker, W.V., and D.M. Glenn. 1985. The relationship of sod proximity to the growth and nutrient composition of newly planted peach trees. *HortScience* 20:417–418.

603. Weller, F. 1966. Horizontal distribution of absorbing roots and the utilization of fertilizers in apple orchards. *Erwobstbobstbau* 8:181–184.

604. Wells, C., K. Townsend, J. Caldwell, D. Ham, E.T. Smiley, and M. Sherwood. 2006. Effects of planting depth on landscape tree survival and girdling root formation. *Arboriculture & Urban Forestry* 32:305–311.

605. Wells, C.A., D. Whigham, and H. Lieuth. 1972. Investigation of mineral nutrient cycling in an upland piedmont forest. *Journal of the Elisha Mitchell Scientific Society* 88:66–78.

606. Werner, L.P., and L.G. Jull. 2009. Fertilizer uptake, partitioning, and recovery in container-grown common hackberry (*Celtis occidentalis*) trees. *Arboriculture & Urban Forestry* 35:252–262.

607. Werner, L.W. 2000. Nitrogen relations of ornamental trees in urban soils: a first look. M.Sc. thesis. University of Wisconsin–Stevens Point, Stevens Point, Wisconsin, U.S. 99 pp.

608. West, D.H., A.H. Chappelka, K.M. Tilt, H.G. Ponder, and J.D. Williams. 1999. Effect of tree shelters on survival, growth, and woody quality of 11 tree species commonly planted in the southern United States. *Journal of Arboriculture* 25:69–75.

609. Whitcomb, C.E. 1975. Effects of soil amendments on growth of silver maple trees in the landscape. *SNA Nursery Research Conference Proceedings* 20:49–50.

610. ———. 1980. Effects of black plastic and mulches on growth and survival of landscape plants. *Journal of Arboriculture* 6:10–12.

611. ———. 1981. Response of woody landscape plants to Bermuda grass competition and fertility. *Journal of Arboriculture* 7:191–194.

612. ———. 1985. Innovations and the nursery industry. *Journal of Environmental Horticulture* 3:33–38.

613. ———. 1987. *Establishment and Maintenance of Landscape Plants*. Stillwater, Oklahoma: Lacebark Publications. 618 pp.

614. Whitlow, T., and N. Bassuk. 1987. Trees in difficult sites. *Journal of Arboriculture* 13:10–17.

615. ———. 1988. Ecophysiology of urban trees and their management—the North American experience. *HortScience* 23:542–546.

616. Whitlow, T.H., N.L. Bassuk, and D.L. Reichert. 1992. A 3-year study of water relations of urban street trees. *Journal of Applied Ecology* 29:436–450.

617. Wiese C.L., A.L. Shober, E.F. Gilman, M. Paz, K.A. Moore, S.M. Scheiber, M.M. Brennan, and S. Vyapari. 2009. Effects of irrigation frequency during establishment on growth of *Ilex cornuta* 'Burfordii Nana' and *Pittosporum tobira* 'Variegata.' *HortScience* 44:1438–1443.

618. Wilde, S.A. 1958. *Forest Soils*. New York: Ronald Press. 537 pp.

619. Williams, J.D., H.G. Ponder, and C.H. Gilliam. 1987. Response of *Cornus florida* to moisture stress. *Journal of Arboriculture* 13:98–101.

620. Williamson, J.G., D.C. Coston, and J.A. Cornell. 1992. Root restriction affects shoot development of peach in a high-density orchard. *Journal of American Society for Horticultural Science* 117:362–367.

621. Williston, H.L. 1967. Clay slurry root dip impairs survival of loblolly pine seedlings in Mississippi. *Tree Planters' Notes* 18:28–30.

622. Winkelmann, M., and A.D. Kendle. 1996. The effect of hydrophilic polyacrylamide gels on establishment of woody plants under droughted and saline conditions. *Arboricultural Journal* 20:387–404.

623. Wiseman, P.E., K.H. Colvin, and C.E. Wells. 2009. Performance of mycorrhizal products marketed for woody landscape plants. *Journal of Environmental Horticulture* 27:41–50.

624. Wiseman, P.E., and C.E. Wells. 2005. Soil inoculum potential and arbuscular mycorrhizal colonization of *Acer rubrum* in forested and developed landscapes. *Journal of Arboriculture* 31:296–302.

625. ———. 2009. Arbuscular mycorrhizal inoculation affects root development of Acer and Magnolia species. *Journal of Environmental Horticulture* 27:70–79.

626. Witherspoon, W.R., and G.P. Lumis. 1986. Root regeneration of *Tilia cordata* cultivars after transplanting in response to root exposure and soil moisture levels. *Journal of Arboriculture* 12:165–168.

627. Witmer, R.K., H.D. Gerhold, and E.R. Ulrich. 1997. Tree shelters accelerate slow-growing species in nurseries. *Journal of Arboriculture* 23:40–48.

628. Wong, T.L., R.W. Harris, and R.E. Fissell. 1971. Influence of high soil temperatures on five woody-plant species. *Journal of American Society of Horticultural Science* 96:80–82.

629. Wong, T.W., J.E.G. Good, and M.P. Denne. 1988. Tree root damage to pavements and kerbs in the city of Manchester. *Arboricultural Journal* 12:17–34.

630. Wood, C.B., T.J. Smalley, M. Rieger, and D.E. Radcliffe. 1994. Growth and drought tolerance of *Viburnum plicatum* var. *tomentosum* 'Mariesii' in pine bark-amended soil. *Journal of American Society for Horticulture Science* 119:687–692.

631. Wright, A.N., S.L. Warren, and F.A. Blazich. 2007. Effect of root-zone temperature on survival, growth, and root morphology of *Kalmia latifolia* and *Ilex crenata* 'Compacta.' *Journal of Environmental Horticulture* 25:73–77

632. Wright, A.N., S.L. Warren, F. Blazich, J.R. Harris, and R.D. Wright. 2005. Initial plant size and landscape exposure affect establishment of transplanted *Kalmia latifolia* 'Olympic Wedding.' *Journal of Environmental Horticulture* 23:91–96.

633. Wright, R.A., R.W. Wein, and B.P. Dancik. 1992. Population differentiation in seedling root size between adjacent stands of jack pine. *Forest Science* 38:777–785.

634. Wright, R.D., and E.B. Hale. 1983. Growth of three shade tree genera as influenced by irrigation and nitrogen rates. *Journal of Environmental Horticulture* 1:5–6.

635. Wrigley, M.P., and G.S. Smith. 1978. Staking and pruning effects on trunk and root development of four ornamental trees. *New Zealand Journal of Experimental Agriculture* 6:309–311.

636. Yeager, T.H., and R.D. Wright. 1981. Influence of nitrogen and phosphorous on shoot:root ratio of *Ilex crenata* Thumb. Helleri. *HortScience* 16:564–565.

637. Young K., and K.R.W. Hammett. 1980. Temperature patterns in exposed black polyethylene plant containers. *Agricultural Meteorology* 21:165–172.

638. Zahreddine, H.G., D.K. Struve, and M. Quigley. 2004. Growing Pinus nigra seedlings in a Spinout™-treated containers reduces root malformation and increases growth after transplanting. *Journal of Environmental Horticulture* 22:176–182.

639. Zainudin, S.R., K. Awang, and A.H. bin Mohd. Hanif. 2003. Effects of combined nutrient and water stress on the growth of *Hopea odorata* Roxb. and *Mimusops elengi* Linn. seedlings. *Journal of Arboriculture* 29:79–83.

Appendix A
Digging a Tree Bare Root

▷ Start by marking of the location where a circular trench will be dug. Three times the diameter of a standard root ball—36 inches (91 cm) diameter per caliper inch—is preferred.

◁ The trench should be deep enough to be below the level of spreading roots.

▷ Remove the soil from the roots by working inward from the trench. The soil should be loosened and carefully combed out of the roots toward the trench. A narrow-tined spading fork is a serviceable tool for this operation.

◁ Roots should be protected from exposure as much as possible. As portions of the root system are exposed, be prepared to protect them from drying out.

◁ Once soil was removed from half the roots of this tree, they were covered with a shallow layer of loose soil to protect them. Wet burlap or a tarp could also be used.

▷ Once the shallow lateral roots have been worked free of soil, work should proceed from opposite sides of the ball so that the tree can be tilted to get at the deeper oblique roots and soil. The plant should not be forced over because the bark near the base of the trunk may loosen and slip or some of the roots may split or break.

◁ Anchor, tap, or sinker roots may need to be cut with a sharp spade. If practical, a partial ball or at least some soil clinging to the roots should be left.

▷ The majority of the root system can be moved with the tree and will improve chances of successful transplanting.

Appendix B
Drum Lacing a Root Ball

Drum lacing is the standard method for wrapping root balls that are not dug by machine and placed in a wire basket. It takes considerable experience to be able to wrap a large root ball securely enough to provide good support.

◁ After the root ball is dug and shaped, wrapping starts by draping lengths of burlap across the top and down the sides.

▷ Multiple layers are added in opposite directions.

◁ A continuous piece is then wrapped around the sides. The upper edge is secured with small nails weaved between the fibers. The burlap is folded and fastened with nails to draw it tight wherever needed.

▷ To drum lace the sides, twine is drawn up under a loop at the bottom of the root ball and temporarily held in place at the top by nails.

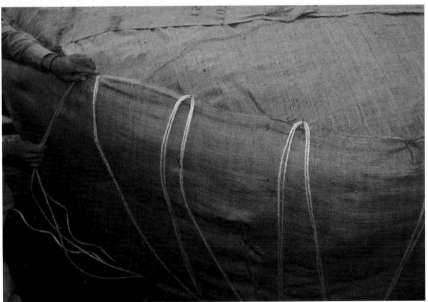

◁ Twine is then threaded through the vertical loops and tightened.

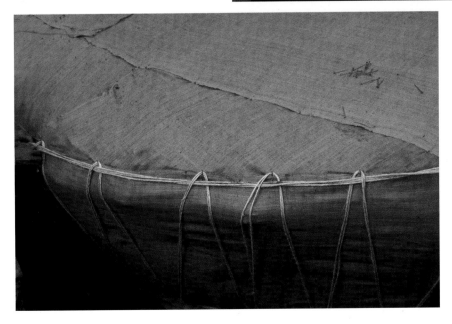

◁ To top lace the ball, twine is systematically weaved across the top of the root ball in a rotating pattern.

▷ Tension is increased on these toplacing ropes by weaving another rope around the top in a circular pattern.

◁ Wire mesh, often referred to as hogwire, is placed around the perimeter to further stabilize the root ball.

◁ It is tightened snug to the root ball by systematically twisting with a hook.

△ The finished product is a very secure package that will hold together as the tree is lifted by it.

Appendix C
Moving a Large Tree

Moving large trees requires special procedures. A method has been developed that creates a solid platform under the soil ball that can be used to lift the tree. Variations on the method described here have been used in many countries.

◁ A 17-inch (43 cm) dbh Accolade™ elm (*Ulmus japonica × wilsoniana* 'Morton') needed to be moved as part of a construction project. The move could not take place until midsummer, but the root ball was dug in the spring, while the tree was still dormant. Some concrete was removed first to provide better access.

▷ The root ball was wrapped in burlap, twine, and metal wire to provide support during the move (see Appendix B for a description of the process).

◁ The root ball was left in place, but covered in mulch and watered regularly to keep it from drying out.

△ When the project had reached the point where the tree could be moved, the process of building a lifting platform under it began. Metal well casing pipes are driven horizontally under the root ball. This requires digging a long, shallow pit adjacent to the tree.

(inset) A pneumatic ramming tool, sometimes called a "mole," was used to drive the pipes.

◁ Pipes are driven successively to create the platform.

▷ Lumber is placed over the top of the root ball to protect it as chains are used to anchor the root ball to the platform underneath it in preparation for the crane lift.

◁ The crane lifts the tree by the platform and the root ball breaks free. The closely spaced pipes have created separation between the root ball and the soil beneath. On most species, there will be few large roots beneath the root ball anchoring the tree, and most will have already been severed by the pipes.

◁ The tree was being moved to a new location on the same site, and it is easily accomplished with this method. The tree can be moved in midsummer with no more stress than normal for a transplanted tree because it was dug while dormant. There is no distubance of the root ball with this method, as there can be when the root ball is lifted and tipped with a chain harness.

▷ The pipes are not removed. They will help to stabilize the root ball on the new site. They will not interfere with root regeneration at that depth.

◁ Even very large trees can be transplanted with this method, but these larger trees will require many years of proper maintenance to re-establish.

Appendix D
Moving Larger Trees Bare Root

The introduction of air excavation tools that can excavate soil efficiently without harming roots has revived the 100-year-old practice of transplanting large trees bare root (Figure 4-6). The advantage is that more roots can be moved with the tree, though greater care must be taken to protect them from desiccation once they are exposed.

◁ The first step is to mark the area that will be excavated. A radius equal to 12 times the diameter of the trunk is typically the minimum. This is more than twice the diameter of a standard root ball.

All photos in Appendix D courtesy Mark Hoenigman

▷ Air excavation tools are very effective at removing the soil without harming the roots.

◁ As when using conventional tools to dig trees bare root, it is best to start by digging a trench at the perimeter for the loose soil to fall into. The loose soil will have to be excavated periodically.

▷ Once the shallow spreading lateral roots are excavated, equipment may be needed to tip these larger trees to excavate farther beneath them.

◁ Some soil will remain at the center of the root system, which can be left to support the weight of the tree when it is placed in the planting hole.

◁ The bare root trees have to be lifted by the trunk and branches.

▷ The trunk must be well padded, and wide straps must be used to lift the trees. Attachment points must distribute the weight evenly.

◁ On larger trees, a crane may be needed to lift the tree.

▷ Once in the new location, it is important to backfill with quality soil and fill all the air pockets in between the roots using the air tool, followed by soaking with water.

◁ Trees can be successfully moved bare root in-leaf, but protecting the roots from drying out in hot weather can be challenging.

Index

Graphs, tables, and charts are indicated by *italic* type. Photographs, illustrations, and maps are indicated by **boldface** type.